DATE DUE

2-10-10		
11-17-11		
		Demco

The Art of
Huckleberry Finn

SRA Science Research Associates, Inc., 259 East Erie Street, Chicago, Illinois 60611
A Subsidiary of IBM   Distributors

THE ART OF

Huckleberry Finn

SECOND EDITION

TEXT • SOURCES • CRITICISM

Selected and Edited by

DISCARDED

HAMLIN HILL *University of Chicago*

WALTER BLAIR *University of Chicago*

Chandler Publishing Company

124 SPEAR STREET

SAN FRANCISCO, CALIFORNIA 94105

CONTENTS

Introduction

THE COMPOSITION OF
HUCKLEBERRY FINN
STUDYING SOURCES
EVALUATING CRITICISM
BIBLIOGRAPHY
A NOTE ON THE TEXTS

THE COMPOSITION OF
HUCKLEBERRY FINN

SAMUEL LANGHORNE CLEMENS began writing and traveling while he was in his teens, and kept up both "occupations" as a reporter in the Far West, the Sandwich Islands, and Europe and the Near East until the late 1860's. Soon after his marriage in 1870 Mark Twain (as he had signed himself since 1863) settled down to do more "serious" literary work than that of a reporter, though continuing to utilize the remembrances of his earlier days in travel books (*The Innocents Abroad,* 1869, and *Roughing It,* 1872), newspaper and magazine articles and a collaborative novel (*The Gilded Age,* 1873). In 1874, returning for the first time in a sustained literary work to the scenes, settings, characters, and incidents of his boyhood in Hannibal, Missouri, he began work on *The Adventures of Tom Sawyer.* In a way, *Tom* was the first mining of appropriated youthful memories that included "Old Times on the Mississippi" and *Adventures of Huckleberry Finn* as the most important yields.

During the summer of 1876, while proofs for *Tom* were still coming to him, Mark Twain began the manuscript of what was to become *Huck.* That summer, he wrote through Chapter XVI of the book, except for the *Walter Scott* episode in Chapter XII and Chapters XIII and XIV. Apparently he was carried on into the second book by the impetus of the first. In subject matter, characterization, and tone, the opening chapters of the new book sound more appropriate to *Tom Sawyer* than they do to the middle section of *Huck Finn.*

Somewhere along the way, though, Twain conceived a distinct idea for the second book, and the indication is that he had done so even before he completed *Tom Sawyer* in the summer of 1875. He and William Dean Howells, editor of the *Atlantic Monthly,* conducted a debate about *Tom Sawyer* that centered in the idea of having the boy "drift into manhood." Ultimately Twain decided not to carry Tom "beyond boyhood" but to create another "boy of twelve & run him on through life." In 1874, he had written an outline note in the manuscript of *Tom Sawyer* that has significant overtones: "1, Boyhood & Youth; 2 y & early manh; 3 the Battle of Life in many lands; 4 (age 37 to 40,) return & meet grown babies & toothless old drivelers who were the grandees of his boyhood. The Adored Unknown a faded old maid & full of rasping, puritanical vinegar piety." Three things stand out in this: the main character was to grow to maturity, to be carried "on through life"; he was to travel "in many lands" while he matured; and when he ultimately returned home he was to become disillusioned. Though Huck does not grow up physically in the book and does not travel in many lands, on a long journey he does mature morally, and does reach the point of revolting against the mores of antebellum slaveholding society. The note, though inchoate, sounds as though it is exploring themes and structures which were to become *Huckleberry Finn*. From the beginning of his work on *Tom Sawyer*, therefore, Twain quite possibly had in mind some of the things his novel would do.

Twain composed the 1876 chapters in the comparative seclusion of Quarry Farm in Elmira, New York, an isolated spot in which Theodore and Susan Crane had built him an odd eight-sided study. Here he wrote about 400 pages during a month or so. Relatively undisturbed, then, enjoying a string of best-sellers, his wife in better health than usual, and already basking in the national limelight (no small matter to him), Twain ground out portions of the book which if not completely idyllic at least reflected to some extent the serenity of their author's situation. As little more than a continuation of *Tom*, the first few chapters of the book fail to utilize the preliminary but abandoned *Tom Sawyer* outline, and *Huckleberry Finn* begins with its protagonist little more than the straight man for Tom the rigid rule-follower. But even in this overflow from the earlier volume, there are foreshadowings of some of the most important matter of later parts of the novel. Huck's pragmatic common sense—in conflict with Tom's romanticism, with Widow Douglas's rosy idealism, and with Miss Watson's stern authoritarianism—suggests his character, his methods of combatting force, and his desire to test by practical application the impressive but thin veneer of the culture in which he is living; all of these suggestions will be found repeated on more serious levels further along in the novel.

A basic tendency of Huck's is to act independently and to gauge his relations with others according to the "best way to get along." From the first, his getting along when he can and "lighting out" when he can't are recurrent patterns. Pap Finn, in his tirade against the government and the free Negro, reflects the irrational biases of the Southerner, just as his greed for Huck's share of the treasure foreshadows the avaricious traits of the characters to be encountered later. So although it is quite true that the structure of the novel is to shift and that the tone will change several times, themes which will have significance are introduced in the St. Petersburg chapters written in 1876.

After the high jinks with Tom, as most critics have noted, the basic concern of the section is one of escape down the Mississippi River. As Huck and Jim, two outsiders allied by fear and self-interest, make their way down toward Cairo and freedom from slavery and people who try to "sivilize" Huck, the river not only controls the movement of the two but also determines the idyllic tone, the emotional security, and the most important action. In the 1876 chapters Huck and Jim are important for their relationship to each other; their only contact with the shore is the short encounter with the two slave hunters. This companionship through isolation which the river imposes makes the Mississippi something like a major character. It delivers up a canoe for Huck's initial escape and a raft for Huck's and Jim's downstream trip, guides the two runaways downriver, and providentially offers money and Barlow knives; it provides the fog that sends Jim and Huck past Cairo, and therefore makes necessary Huck's initial verdict concerning slave society, in the scene of the storm that separates Jim and Huck and leads to Huck's perception, after he tricks Jim, that a Negro is a human being worthy of respect. The river in the 1876 chapters, then, is more than a passive setting for an escape on a raft; as Huck comes to understand Jim during the part of their journey when they are sealed off from society, the Mississippi operates as a controlling force.

When Twain put the manuscript aside in 1876, he had used a large share of his memories of the Upper Mississippi and Hannibal. His characters' plan to sail up the Ohio toward free states threatened to carry the story into waters unfamiliar to the author. Also, if the theme of liberation was to be kept, the urge to continue down the Mississippi—the part of the river Twain knew from his piloting years—would give an implausible turn to the action.

For three years Twain left his manuscript; then in 1879-1880 he returned to it to write the Grangerford-Shepherdson feud chapters (XVII and XVIII). Since here Huck and Jim are separated, away from the river, and in a static setting, these chapters postponed this important decision. But these nevertheless are vital chapters. In them, Twain's relatively genial assault on the South of the earliest portion is replaced by a fiercer one. At the Grangerfords', the façade of material gaudiness, sentimentality, and religion is shown covering a brutal, bloodthirsty society. The completely lost origins of the feud, the descriptions of the Grangerfords' house, the account of Emmeline's sentimental creations, the church service with two feuding families listening to a sermon on brotherly love with their guns in easy reach: these are a forceful literary indictment.

Between 1876 and 1882, some disrupting things happened to the mind of Sam Clemens to make the rest of Mark Twain's book differ from the first part. A series of abortive or unsuccessful literary projects and a disheartening trip to Europe increased his cantankerousness. Reading Carlyle, Dickens, Baring-Gould, and others on the French Revolution increased his dissatisfaction with the "damned human race," which he vented in works on "Universal Suffrage," "The Great Revolution in Pitcairn," and *The Prince and the Pauper.* Suspicions aroused by associates in business dealings made him certain that he was being cheated right and left. His reading in W. E. H. Lecky's *History of European Morals,* which he had discovered some years earlier, led him toward a deterministic philosophy and a predilection for brooding over the value of a conscience. In Presidential election campaigning during 1879, the Republicans (Clemens among them) made much of the alliance of the Democratic Party with the South—the part of the country where, so political propaganda alleged, duels, murders, lynchings, feuds, and brutality to Negroes were everyday happenings. His work on an anthology, eventually to be published as *Mark Twain's Library of Humor* (1888), refamiliarized him with an impressive number of old Southwestern humorists. A trip on the Mississippi in 1882 did more than just revive memories of his youth; it also provided him with ammunition for an attack on the South, material dealing with feuds, duels, and mob rule, some of which he deleted from *Life on the Mississippi* at its publisher's suggestion. In different ways these experiences had effects on the Mark Twain who returned to his manuscript and on the portions of *Huck Finn* he had still to write.

In 1879 or 1880, part way through the feud chapters, Twain paused to take stock of his manuscript, surveying the story so far and projecting it into the future in the jottings that have become known as the "A Notes"* of *Huckleberry Finn.* Some of the pages refer back to manuscript already written, and some contain ideas Twain would use later. Others, which eventually he discarded, suggest he may have thought about keeping Huck and Jim in the vicinity of the Grangerfords, winding up with a murder trial with all the trimmings for a grand finale. (Notations about the village school and fire suggest a stay of some length and others might be interpreted as hinting at the trial.) Even before he finished writing the notes, though, he had hit upon ideas for *Richard III* and the Royal Nonesuch, the circus scene, two tramp printers who fleece the river-town folks, and the identity of one of his tramps

---

* The working notes are reproduced in Bernard DeVoto's "Noon and the Dark— *Huckleberry Finn,*" pp. 45-104 of *Mark Twain at Work* (1942).

—"the King." One note, wherein he tells himself to resurrect the old raft for continued use, reveals that he had made up his mind to continue the downstream drift of Huck and Jim.

When he returned to the book itself again—some time between late 1880 and early 1883—Twain put into action those two "tramp printers," the Duke and the Dauphin. They solved many problems: by appropriating the raft through sheer force, they kept it going on a river Twain himself knew; their shenanigans ashore allowed for continued exploitation of the orneriness of Southern whites; the pair also allowed the author to keep on writing basically anecdotal, episodic material rather than straining to keep his story sustained in one setting and with one cast of characters, often a dangerous thing for him to do. Apparently in this burst of energy, between 1880 and the summer of 1883, he wrote Chapters XIX, XX, and at least part of XXI.

The segment of material on Bricksville—Boggs and Sherburn, the attempted lynching, the circus, the Royal Nonesuch—not only embodies a wealth of source materials; it also continues the raft-shore dichotomy begun in the Grangerford-Shepherdson chapters, in which the serenity and security of the raft contrast with the violence and lawlessness of the shore. More important, Huck, having found that Jim is a fine human being, now in a series of adventures along the Arkansas shore gets a chance to re-evaluate the society that insists Jim is merely property. Having had a chance to learn the truth about the Negro, Huck is now given the opportunity on zig-zags between shore and raft to observe the Southern white: a creature characterized by Mark Twain, in the Bricksville segment alone, as sadistic, lazy, stupid, gullible—an unthinking, conforming part of a herd.

The "C Notes" to the book, which Twain wrote some time between the Bricksville chapters and the completion of his manuscript, are centered almost entirely around the plans for the "evasion," the burlesque rescue of Jim from Uncle Silas. Only one of the notes—"Jim cries, to think of his wife & 2 ch[n]" —echoes the Jim of the upper-river chapters, and accounts probably for the insertion of Jim's memories about his deaf daughter in Chapter XXIII. By exploiting the character of the river-townsmen, the whole section builds up to Huck's two vital verdicts: "Human beings *can* be awful cruel to one another," and "All right, then, I'll *go* to hell."

Both of these decisions occur *before* the ten final chapters that drag out Jim's rescue to tedious length. Does *Huck Finn* really end, as Ernest Hemingway once suggested, when Jim is stolen from Huck? The problem has engaged many students of the novel for quite some time, and every once in a while somebody offers a new justification for the last chapters. People have suggested that the burlesque evasion returns to the mood of Hannibal-St. Petersburg, that it returns Huck to anonymity when Tom Sawyer takes front-stage center, that it burlesques "authorities" of the variety that have caused the South's decay, that it amplifies a theme of Huck's search for a family which runs through the novel; but the very fact that this insistence is necessary suggests an uneasiness which the ending causes. Having struggled with his conscience and reached an independent, nonconforming opinion, Huck gives up his freedom to follow Tom's lead in an elaborately absurd scheme to free Jim which, whatever alibis can be offered for it, reduces both Huck and Jim in stature.

In the summer and autumn of 1883, Twain also wrote most of Chapter XII and Chapters XIII and XIV following his suggestion (in Note C-4) to have the pair back on the raft find some books about royalty. Thus the *Walter Scott* episode (one of the rare instances when "shore people" intrude on the river in the first fifteen chapters) and the discussion about Solomon and the French language were crammed into their places in 1883, and the novel was complete.

In spite of its fantastically chaotic composition, halts and flurries when Twain allowed his "tank" of inspiration to fill up, drain, and fill up again, *Huckleberry Finn,* like all literature, has to be evaluated as a complete work of art. Critics therefore pose and try to answer the question, "Did Twain manage to write a unified novel in spite of the conditions under which it was written? Does *Huck Finn* hold together?" A few critics are convinced that Twain failed, because the tone and characterization of the last fifth of the novel are inconsistent. Others suggest that the presence of the river, the indictment of Southern society, the pattern of death and rebirth, the gradual moral awakening of the hero, or the juxtaposition of comic and tragic variations on the same theme operate to give the book a unity that transcends even its burlesque conclusion.

STUDYING SOURCES

No AUTHOR writes in a vacuum. External influences of all kinds shape his finished literary works. At the simplest level, it is possible to distinguish two kinds of influences, *literary sources* and *biographical sources,* which work upon almost any author.

Watching productions of William Shakespeare's great play, *Othello,* and reading the drama in print, for example, scholars were led to wonder where the author had picked up ideas for his characters and his plot. The scholars suspected that Shakespeare's reading had played an important role since they knew it had done so when he wrote other dramas. Looking at books available to the playwright, they came upon a collection of Italian tales by Giraldi (surnamed Cinthio), *The Hecatommithi* (1565). The characters in this crude narrative, its plot, and even some of the language were much like those of *Othello;* and moreover scholars noticed in the same collection a story which the dramatist retold in another play. So they decided that Giraldi was a "literary source" for *Othello.* Contrasting the source with the play, scholars learned a great deal about the way Shakespeare worked, and they were tremendously impressed with the artistry which the comparison revealed. Reworking story into drama, he accelerated the action, knit the plot more tightly, modified the characters so that they became far more interesting and their actions more believable, and gave them speeches to utter which increased tension and emotional impact. Thus, as Professor Oscar J. Campbell says, Shakespeare "transformed" a "farrago of blood and horror . . . into a drama of terrifying power yet of complete plausibility." "Such a transmutation of base metal into gold," says Professor Hardin Craig, "is hardly to be found in the study of literary history."

The literary source, then, is material consciously or unconsciously "borrowed" from another author. "Source hunting," as it is sometimes derogatorily called, is frequently looked on as a sort of stepdaughter among critical techniques. Critics with other disciplines insist that source hunting really provides nothing in the way of insight into the creative process; it simply proves, or tends to prove, they claim, that an author read a book or a short story by another author and that at some later date he relied upon something from the earlier author. So, say some critics, source study tells us only what a given author's reading interests might have included at a given period, and while it may be interesting biographically or historically it is not really more than a curious adjunct to the study of literature as art.

This criticism is all too often justified. Too often source study is merely identification, and as such it stops short of its full possibilities. When an author's reading provides valuable thematic explanations, as Twain's reading W. E. H. Lecky does for *Huckleberry Finn,* even identification is valuable. But far more important to the student of literature is a study of sources which provide a means of seeing the creative talent in operation. The actual borrowing of material is far less important than the modification of it. In other words, whether the author is writing *Huck* or *Othello,* how he manipulates his material justifies much closer scrutiny than where he got it. The folklorist should seek analogies; the student of literature should explore the differences. And because there is a concrete source to which to refer, this particular method of analysis can be one of the most rewarding. As many critics have confessed, analysis of works of art entails intelligent and sensitive guesses. Barring some sort of external proof that an author was deliberately working with a theory, an idea, or an aim in mind, the critic has ultimately to admit one of two things: either he is mind-reading and attempting to persuade you that his interpretation of an author's intention is correct (because he is an "authority" on that author, because circumstantial evidence or internal evidence supports his theory, because the author did something similar in another book) or he admits that what the author himself did or was trying to do is irrelevant, and that the work of art operates on its readers completely independent of what the author had in mind. But when the student or critic has before him an analogue in black and white, he can examine closely the author's selectivity and invention; he can ask himself a series of questions that will help reconstruct a picture of the author at work.

In a somewhat similar fashion to Shakespeare's use of *The Hecatommithi,* Herman Melville used his own personal experiences in his novel *Redburn.* In June, 1839, young Melville set sail aboard the *St. Lawrence* for Liverpool. He wandered around Liverpool on Sundays and afternoons for the six weeks the *St. Lawrence* was docked and returned to the United States in late September. Ten years later, Melville decided to write a book utilizing his biographical experiences on the *St. Lawrence;* he called it "a plain, straightforward, amusing narrative of personal experience." Scholars examining factual documents have discovered that though Melville based much of his novel on actual experience, he transmuted fact and biography to serve his fictional purposes, so that, as Newton Arvin says, the book "abounds in *subjective* realism." The narrator (like the narrator in "Old Times on the Mississippi") was made younger and more naïve at the beginning of the story than the real Melville was, so that he seems to mature throughout the story. The villainous Jackson is shown falling from the yardarm and receiving the punishment he deserves, rather than (as his prototype did) leaving the ship unharmed at the end of the voyage. Melville added social, economic, and humanitarian themes to the novel (notably by adding a hold full of steerage passengers). In sum, then, though a thread of factual reminiscence prompted the events in *Redburn,* and the *St. Lawrence* trip is therefore a "biographical source," it is fact transformed by the creative process.

Again, when Melville uses his own sea experiences in *Redburn,* or any author uses biographical material, it is the transmutation of biography into fiction that should occupy the student's attention. The "source"—the bases in fact—in this area may be discovered in a newspaper story, an autobiographical reminiscence, a scholarly reconstruction of an actual incident, or (as in the case of the Owsley-Smarr murder that Twain converted into the Boggs-Sherburn episode in *Huckleberry Finn*) a legal deposition. Although it may well be, as Twain said, the "most valuable capital . . . usable in the building of novels," the biographical source is also often difficult to use in an evaluation of the skill of the author because the historical material is sketchy and because precisely how much of it is faithfully recorded and how much is invented is usually hard to determine. Nevertheless, in so far as the student can reconstruct the biographical material, he may profitably compare it with the finished literary product by asking almost the same questions that he might pose about a literary source.

Why, for example, has the author chosen to include this and exclude that character, conversation, or incident from the source? Has he altered the style or the tone of a literary source? What in his version is not in the source but new? Is the newer version better than the original in the context? And most important of all, what function do these changes serve, and are they successful? When the student asks and answers these questions, he is in effect watching the writer create, seeing him choose, select, and adapt material to serve his purposes.

In a source study, therefore, the student should take three steps, which provide as well a formula or an outline which often may be useful for the presentation of material:

First is a consideration of evidence that the author had the experience or read the work that is being offered as a source. If some event in the author's life seems a likely source, the student has to check the records of the event with great care. If a literary source is involved, the student needs to realize that an author is not likely to use a source available only in a language he could not read, or published after his own version, or written by an author whom he refused to read. (A theory that Henry James's *The Bostonians* influenced *Huckleberry Finn,* say, would be demolished by the fact that this novel appeared after *Huck* and by Sam Clemens's remark that he would rather be damned to John Bunyan's heaven than read James.) The best proof of an author's awareness of a literary source is his own mention of the work in a letter, conversation, or some other record, or his proven ownership of a personally annotated copy of the source work. This ideal is frequently impossible to reach. There are cases of strong probability, however, that are almost as satisfactory. If the source was the work of a close friend or of a writer whom the author enjoyed reading, if it was a work of the sort that the author often read (the native American humor that Clemens knew and liked, for example), if it appeared in a magazine or a newspaper the author read fairly consistently, these are a few ways of suggesting the probability of contact. Whatever the proof of reliance is, the student of sources should consider carefully whether there is convincing evidence to support the identification.

The second step (or the first if the student cannot find exterior evidence of indebtedness) is a close examination of the two records or works in question. Two literary works under comparison may be so remarkably similar that the earlier must presumably be a source for the later one. In cases like this, internal evidence—similarity of phrasing, proper names, place names, incidents, settings, tone—may help to verify a source. In other instances, a fiction writer may be indebted to a source not for plots or characters but for concepts—as Mark Twain was to Lecky's writings. Again the student must study the parallels between the works and make sure that they are valid. The form of a source and an adaptation may be similar enough to be compared through the use of direct quotations from both, or ideally, through parallel texts. Identical phraseology, similar formulas in plot development, analogous structural techniques are important enough points of comparison and contrast to deserve close consideration and quotation rather than paraphrasing. This step not only provides reinforcing evidence for the identification; it also illustrates graphically the transmutation that a source is undergoing when a later author makes use of it.

Third, the student should study carefully the differences between the event or the literary source and the passage in which the author draws upon it, should try to answer the important questions mentioned earlier. At this critical stage of a source study, evaluation comes to the front. Since quirks in an author's mind, political or social or religious ideas or biases, the special contexts of the story he is writing, or simply a creative genius superior to that of the author of the source could all account for important modifications, having established the existence of a source the student must interpret the findings he has discovered. Now he must apply to the material the same criteria he would apply to a critical discussion. And he must so set forth his findings that ultimately he will persuade his readers that indeed his premises and his conclusions about the source and the adaptation are correct.

With Mark Twain, studying adaptations is especially rewarding. On many occasions he voiced his awareness of sources for his fiction. Once, for example, he insisted that "the most valuable capital, or culture, or education usable in the building of novels is personal experience," and about the same time he warned, "If you attempt to create a wholly imagined incident, adventure or situation, you will go astray and the artificiality will be detectable, but if you found on *fact* in your personal experience, it is an acorn, a root, and every created adornment that grows out of it, and spreads its foliage and blossoms to the sun will seem reality, not inventions." Later, he told an interviewer:

> I don't believe an author . . . ever lived, who created a character. It was always drawn from his recollection of some one he had known. Sometimes, like a composite photograph, an author's presentation of a character may possibly be from the blending of two or more real characters in his recollection. But even when he is making no attempt to draw his character from life . . . , he is yet unconsciously drawing from memory.

These quotations attest to the use of biographical sources.

Mark Twain also gave his approval explicitly to the use of literary sources: "There are few stories that have anything superlatively good in them except the *idea,*—& that is always bettered by transplanting." Throughout his own works he constantly adapted the material of others to his own purposes. An omnivorous literary appetite, an acute awareness of the unconscious humor in stodgy or sentimental works, a sulphurous indignation with pretension, pomposity, and injustice, and an ingenious facility for turning other books into skeletal frames for his own works all combined to make Twain in one sense one of the least independent of major authors. (The sense, we hasten to add, is one that makes Shakespeare one of the least independent, too.) Twain never wrote a work as completely indebted to its sources for meaning as, say, Joyce's *Ulysses* or Faulkner's *The Fable,* or used his sources to compound his own meaning as T. S. Eliot does. Scholars have nevertheless pointed out his indebtedness to a remarkably wide range of material: *Don Quixote, Le Morte d'Arthur,* "The Gold Bug," *A Tale of Two Cities,* and *The Vicar of Wakefield* are among the many literary works he assimilated; biographies of Joan of Arc and Shelley, travel books like William C. Prime's *Tent Life in the Holy Land,* Wright's history of *The Big Bonanza,* Carlyle, Lecky, even newspaper stories—all these and more he used as sources, padding, or ammunition. Frequently he identified his source, just stuffing it verbatim into his books when he wanted to supply his publisher with a bulky bundle of manuscript, but as the following selections indicate, in more revealing passages he also adapted and reworked materials.

There is so little disagreement that *Huckleberry Finn* is a great novel that at the present time the question critics are trying to answer is "why" rather than "whether." It is far from our intention to persuade any student that the greatness of the novel lies solely in the sources Twain chose to use or that once he has compared those sources with the book there is nothing else left to do with the novel. Indeed, with as complex a work as *Huck,* there are layers of meaning, structural patterns, literary techniques with which a study of sources will hardly acquaint the student. But the materials we have included here will provide you a thorough view of one aspect of our greatest humorist at work on his greatest achievement and persuade you, we hope, to explore *Huckleberry Finn* further.

EVALUATING CRITICISM

WE MENTIONED that there is a point, ideally, at which a source study becomes a critical essay because it interprets the findings that the comparison has revealed. Since criticism is persuasion, it might appear at first that when the student decides whether he is indeed persuaded he also decides whether the criticism is sound or not. But there are some things worth mentioning that can help students avoid a common fault among undergraduates first approaching critical studies—that of accepting indiscriminately every critical evaluation they run down. If he starts searching for criticism of a major text, the student will probably be overwhelmed, because he will find hundreds of essays about the book. The first problem he faces, then, is one of selection. Suppose he is to write a research paper on Mark Twain, and his instructor wants him to use materials in the library. It will be necessary for him to work his way through references to books, articles, possibly even newspapers; and he will discover an interminable list of materials. How can he, first of all, determine which of these are the best ones to go to the trouble of looking for?

Common sense can help. Titles of articles occasionally give clues to their contents and the number of pages tells the length of the article. So if he discovers a reference to an article two pages long titled "Mark Twain," it ought to be fairly obvious that the topic is too large and the length too short for more than a thumbnail biography and a general evaluation. (This deficiency incidentally, applies to encyclopedias, frequently the crutch of undergraduates writing research papers; they are almost always a waste of time.) He can, on the other hand, be pretty sure that a two-page article called "The Duke's Tooth-Powder Racket" (there is one, by Joseph Jones) treats an extremely limited topic from *Huckleberry Finn* at what is comparatively great length.

The name of the author of the article might help, either because the student encounters it frequently digging around in Mark Twain criticism or because his instructor suggests some of the reliable Mark Twain authorities. There is no law (sometimes unfortunately) preventing anyone from writing about a book; sometimes a fresh, perceptive interpretation will come from an unexpected source: T. S. Eliot's essay on *Huck* is an example. But sometimes the student will come across opinions, occasionally by people who are respected in some literary circles, that are worthless. To give an example, Ernest Hemingway once said, in evaluating T. S. Eliot, that if Eliot's body ground into powder and strewn over the grave of Joseph Conrad could bring Conrad back to life, Hemingway would leave on the next boat for England with a sausage-grinder for baggage. This facetious statement, though it tells us some things about Hemingway, is not of much value in enlightening the reader on Eliot. So the student can select his criticism by author, once he has become aware of some of the reputable ones.

Finally, the student can get some hints about the probable subject-matter from the magazine or journal in which the article appeared. *Papers of the Bibliographical Society of America* prints information about manufacturing, publishing, and selling books; *The Explicator,* as the name suggests, is interested in close interpretations of texts. *Modern Language Notes* or *Notes & Queries* publish short, specific, narrowly limited studies; *PMLA* is most frequently interested in longer, more generalized material. *American Literature, New England Quarterly,* and *American Quarterly* limit themselves to topics specifically in areas of American literature or history and American Studies. An awareness of the range of interest of the scholarly journals can guide the student toward essays in some and away from essays in others.

Suppose the student selects his references with care and good judgment winding up with a few critical articles from reputable journals and by presumably reputable scholars. Does he accept them all at face value? The answer, since the student can obviously find critical arguments diametrically opposed to one another, is that he does not.

It is perhaps necessary to mention that there are different general theories of criticism that the student might encounter in his research. Among various schools are psychological critics, social, economic, biographical, textual, and myth critics, and there are literary historians and historians of ideas, to name a few. Even more confusing to the beginning student, there are subdivisions among some of the various "schools" of criticism. Each of these different types of critics has a set of principles which he believes constitutes what literary criticism ought to do, and occasionally the distinctions are subtle and confusing. At the best, the undergraduate ought to look for clues to the general type of criticism an author is writing, even though it is probably not necessary for him to know all the tenets and theories of the many branches of criticism. He can notice, though, that a critic's choice of words, his methods of interpretation, or his conclusions center around one specific area, that, to cite a specific example, he appears to be writing about *Huckleberry Finn* as a social document involved with the moral degeneration of the South.

More important, any critic, even when he is not affiliated with one of the "schools," usually has a specific thesis he is trying to prove. He assembles facts and then offers his interpretation of them. So the student who works methodically with criticism needs to determine (1) what the thesis of the article is, (2) what the facts offered in proof of the thesis are, and (3) whether the interpretation is substantiated by the "proof." As long as the student is uncertain why an article or book was written, he is in no position to evaluate either its facts or its conjectures. Usually critics help by offering in the title or either at the beginning or at the end—or both—a statement of the problem that they are about to explore or that they have "solved." Even when the critics forget to help, the student can look for summarizing paragraphs and general statements that betray the author's aim. Once he knows what the critic is trying to prove, he can evaluate the evidence.

Fact is not always incontrovertible. Critics can amass quotations from a work under study and still play havoc with it. When the reader is as familiar with the book being scrutinized as we hope you will be with *Huckleberry Finn,* he can tell whether vital factual evidence is quoted in context or whether damning contradictory evidence has been quietly ignored. Does the critic, in other words, use his facts completely legitimately or does he manage to twist them, even slightly, to serve his purpose? Does he consider only part of the book rather than the whole of it, as some critics have done with *Huck?* The student needs to remember that the critic is often just one more hidden persuader, who tries psychologically to make theories sound like laws, conjecture sound like fact, and possibilities sound like certainties. The writer of a critical essay can insist that "obviously" or "conclusively" a fact proves something, when actually he is only hoping it will prove what he wants it to.

When the critic begins evaluating his own material he tries to convince his reader that *his* way of looking at his facts is the best (if not the only) way. The reader has to determine for himself if a critical judgment holds water or leaks, and he needs to exercise some critical acumen himself, because there are nearly always alternatives. For example: when Mark Twain was composing *Roughing It,* he wrote his brother Orion asking for information about their encounter with a desperado named Slade on their trip to Nevada. Orion's letter pointed out an intriguing fact. When Sam and Orion Clemens had breakfast with Slade, they did not know who he was and had heard none of the stories about him. But when Mark Twain came to write Chapter X of his manuscript he showed the breakfast occurring *after* the two travelers had heard countless tales of Slade's bloodthirstiness. Twain represented himself as terrified of the murderer who sat down beside him. Why change the historical facts? One critic might suggest that by exaggerating his own timidity and cowardice Twain was heightening the contrast between the Eastern tenderfoot and the hardened Westerner he would become in the course of the narrative. A psychological critic might suggest that Twain was representing the two sides of a schizophrenic personality: the untrammeled, uninhibited Westerner on the one hand, and the repressed, respectable "gentleman" he was forced to be on the other. A case could be made that Twain simply saw that the comic possibilities of the incident would be heightened by a respectable awe on the part of the traveler and juggled his facts accordingly. Whichever critic was the most persuasive, and whichever interpretation seemed the most logical, would be the "best" one.

The critical essays in this volume offer widely varied insights concerning Twain's novel. They are by critics with fascinatingly different attitudes toward the book, and their value for any alert reader lies not only in the aptness of what they have to say but also in the reliability of their techniques. And this the student must intelligently weigh for himself.

BIBLIOGRAPHY

INDISPENSABLE to any student working with Mark Twain are *Mark Twain's Letters* (1917), *Mark Twain's Notebook* (1935), Albert Bigelow Paine's *Mark Twain: A Biography* (1912), and *Mark Twain's Autobiography* (1921) and additional autobiographical reminiscences published under the title *Mark Twain in Eruption* (1940). Minnie Mae Brashear's *Mark Twain: Son of Missouri* (1934), Gladys Bellamy's *Mark Twain as Literary Artist* (1950), Bernard DeVoto's *Mark Twain's America* (1932), E. Hudson Long's *Mark Twain Handbook* (1957), and Dixon Wecter's *Sam Clemens of Hannibal* (1954) provide important background material; and Kenneth Andrews' *Nook Farm: Mark Twain's Hartford Circle* (1950) centers in the years of the writing of *Huckleberry Finn*. Bernard DeVoto's "Noon and the Dark—*Huckleberry Finn*," pp. 45-104 in *Mark Twain at Work* (1942), reproduces the working notes.

Studies of *Huckleberry Finn* include the following:

Auden, W. H. "Huck and Oliver," *Listener*, L (October 1, 1953), 540-541.

Baldanza, Frank. "The Structure of *Huckleberry Finn*," *American Literature*, XXVII (November, 1958), 347-355.

Blair, Walter. "The French Revolution and *Huckleberry Finn*," *Modern Philology*, LV (August, 1957), 21-35.

———— "When Was *Huckleberry Finn* Written?" *American Literature*, XXX (March, 1958), 1-25.

———— *Mark Twain & Huck Finn*. Berkeley, California, 1960.

Hunting, Robert. "Mark Twain's Arkansas Yahoos," *Modern Language Notes*, LXXIII (April, 1958), 264-268.

Lynn, Kenneth S. *Mark Twain and Southwestern Humor*. Boston, 1960.

Moore, Olin H. "Mark Twain and Don Quixote." *PMLA*, XXXVII (June, 1922), 324-346.

Rogers, Franklin. *Mark Twain's Burlesque Patterns*. Dallas, 1960.

Slater, Joseph. "Music at Colonel Grangerford's." *American Literature*, XXI (March, 1949), 108-116.

Smith, Henry Nash. "Introduction" to *Huckleberry Finn*. Boston, 1958.

Whiting, B. J. "Guyascutus, Royal Nonesuch, and Other Hoaxes." *Southern Folklore Quarterly*, VIII (December, 1944), 251-275.

A NOTE ON THE TEXTS

THE TEXT of *Huckleberry Finn* in this book is a facsimile of the first American edition, published by Charles L. Webster Co. on February 18, 1885. Accordingly, it includes all the typographical errors and the established bibliographical points of the first issue. Students who might be interested in the knotty problems of the bibliography of the book will want to note that the picture between frontispiece and title page is "tipped in," the title-page leaf and leaf 283-284 are pasted to stubs, page 13 lists an illustration on page 88 that actually appears on page 87, page 57, line 23, reads "with the was" instead of "with the saw," and on page 155 the second 5 of the pagination is a larger font type. Our facsimile page size is reduced about ten per cent from the original. "Mark Twain" has been deleted from the facsimile title-page because the Mark Twain Estate maintains the attitude that "Mark Twain" is a trade mark.

Facsimile texts of sources have been chosen whenever possible from an edition Clemens used or probably used. With Hooper's *Simon Suggs' Adventures,* for example, we have used not the first edition issued by Carey and Hart in 1845, but a Peterson imprint because in his *Library of Humor* Clemens acknowledged Peterson as the copyright holder. In many cases there was only a single edition published; in a few cases we have had to pick a contemporary edition that was at least a possibility. Because the exact date when Clemens first became acquainted with Dickens is uncertain, we have reproduced the edition of *A Tale of Two Cities* that was issued in London by Chapman and Hall in 1866 and sold in the United States by James R. Osgood. Clemens frequently bought books from Osgood, and may well have purchased a copy of Dickens's novel from him. Similarly, because Clemens might have used it and because the edition he used is not certain, we have reproduced pertinent pages from the first edition of Carlyle's *The French Revolution.* In the case of Lecky, the actual copy Clemens owned, with marginal notations in his handwriting, is extant at the Mark Twain Research Association, Perry, Missouri. We were denied permission to use it, but we have reproduced a text identical with the one he read and annotated.

ADVENTURES

OF

HUCKLEBERRY FINN.

HUCKLEBERRY FINN.

E.W. Kemble
-1884-

Mark Twain

FROM THE BUST BY KARL GERHARDT.

rinting Co.

Boston and New York.

ADVENTURES

OF

HUCKLEBERRY FINN

(TOM SAWYER'S COMRADE).

Scene: The Mississippi Valley.
Time: Forty to Fifty Years Ago.

WITH ONE HUNDRED AND SEVENTY-FOUR ILLUSTRATIONS.

NEW YORK:

CHARLES L. WEBSTER AND COMPANY.

1885.

PRESS OF J. J. LITTLE & CO.,
NOS. 10 TO 20 ASTOR PLACE, NEW YORK.

NOTICE.

Persons attempting to find a motive in this narrative will be prosecuted; persons attempting to find a moral in it will be banished; persons attempting to find a plot in it will be shot.

BY ORDER OF THE AUTHOR
Per G. G., CHIEF OF ORDNANCE.

EXPLANATORY.

N this book a number of dialects are used, to wit : the Missouri negro dia-
; the extremest form of the backwoods South-Western dialect ; the ordinary
ke-County" dialect ; and four modified varieties of this last. The shadings
not been done in a hap-hazard fashion, or by guess-work ; but pains-takingly,
with the trustworthy guidance and support of personal familiarity with these
ral forms of speech.

make this explanation for the reason that without it many readers would
ose that all these characters were trying to talk alike and not succeeding.

THE AUTHOR.

CONTENTS.

ILLUSTRATIONS.

The Adventures of Huckleberry Finn

Chapter I.

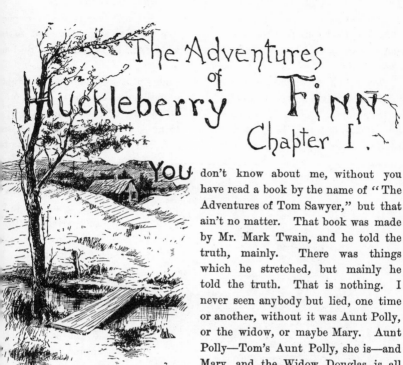

THE WIDOW'S.

YOU don't know about me, without you have read a book by the name of " The Adventures of Tom Sawyer," but that ain't no matter. That book was made by Mr. Mark Twain, and he told the truth, mainly. There was things which he stretched, but mainly he told the truth. That is nothing. I never seen anybody but lied, one time or another, without it was Aunt Polly, or the widow, or maybe Mary. Aunt Polly—Tom's Aunt Polly, she is—and Mary, and the Widow Douglas, is all told about in that book—which is mostly a true book ; with some stretchers, as I said before.

Now the way that the book winds is this : Tom and me found the money that the robbers hid in the cave, it made us rich. We got six thousand dollars apiece—all gold. It was an [awfu]l sight of money when it was piled up. Well, Judge Thatcher, he took it [and] put it out at interest, and it fetched us a dollar a day apiece, all the year [roun]d—more than a body could tell what to do with. The Widow Douglas, she [took] me for her son, and allowed she would sivilize me ; but it was rough living [in th]e house all the time, considering how dismal regular and decent the widow [was] in all her ways ; and so when I couldn't stand it no longer, I lit out. I got [into] my old rags, and my sugar-hogshead again, and was free and satisfied. But

Tom Sawyer, he hunted me up and said he was going to start a band of robb
and I might join if I would go back to the widow and be respectable.   So I w
back.

The widow she cried over me, and called me a poor lost lamb, and she ca
me a lot of other names, too, but she never meant no harm by it.   She put
in them new clothes again, and I couldn't do nothing but sweat and sweat,
feel all cramped up.   Well, then, the old thing commenced again.   The wi
rung a bell for supper, and you had to come to time.   When you got to the t

you couldn't go right to
ing, but you had to wait
the widow to tuck down
head and grumble a li
over   the   victuals, tho
there warn't really anyth
the matter with them.   T
is, nothing only everyth
was cooked by itself.   I
barrel of odds and ends i
different ; things get mi
up, and the juice kind
swaps around, and the thi
go better.

After supper she got
her book and learned
about Moses and the I
rushers ; and I was in a sw
to find out all about h

LEARNING ABOUT MOSES AND THE "BULRUSHERS."

but by-and-by she let it out that Moses had been dead a considerable long ti
so then I didn't care no more about him ; because I don't take no stock in d
people.

Pretty soon I wanted to smoke, and asked the widow to let me.   But
wouldn't.   She said it was a mean practice and wasn't clean, and I n
try to not do it any more.   That is just the way with some people.   T

down on a thing when they don't know nothing about it. Here she
s a bothering about Moses, which was no kin to her, and no use to any-
ly, being gone, you see, yet finding a power of fault with me for doing
hing that had some good in it. And she took snuff too; of course
t was all right, because she done it herself.

Her sister, Miss Watson, a tolerable slim old maid, with goggles on, had
t come to live with her, and took
set at me now, with a spelling-book.
e worked me middling hard for about
hour, and then the widow made her
e up. I couldn't stood it much longer.
en for an hour it was deadly dull,
l I was fidgety. Miss Watson would
, "Dont put your feet up there,
ckleberry;" and "dont scrunch up
e that, Huckleberry—set up straight;"
d pretty soon she would say, "Don't
p and stretch like that, Huckleberry—
y don't you try to behave?" Then
e told me all about the bad place,
d I said I wished I was there. She
t mad, then, but I didn't mean no
rm. All I wanted was to go some-
eres; all I wanted was a change, I
rn't particular. She said it was
cked to say what I said; said she

Miss Watson

uldn't say it for the whole world; *she* was going to live so as to go to
e good place. Well, I couldn't see no advantage in going where she
s going, so I made up my mind I wouldn't try for it. But I never said
, because it would only make trouble, and wouldn't do no good.

Now she had got a start, and she went on and told me all about the
od place. She said all a body would have to do there was to go around
l day long with a harp and sing, forever and ever. So I didn't think

much of it.   But I never said so.   I asked her if she reckoned T
Sawyer would go there, and, she said, not by a considerable sight.   I w
glad about that, because I wanted him and me to be together.

Miss Watson she kept pecking at me, and it got tiresome and loneson
By-and-by they fetched the niggers in and had prayers, and then everybo
was off to bed.   I went up to my room with a piece of candle and p
it on the table.   Then I set down in a chair by the window and tried
think of something cheerful, but it warn't no use.   I felt so lonesome
most wished I was dead.   The stars was shining, and the leaves rustled
the woods ever so mournful; and I heard an owl, away off, who-whooi
about somebody that was dead, and a whippowill and a dog crying abo
somebody that was going to die; and the wind was trying to whisper son
thing to me and I couldn't make out what it was, and so it made the co
shivers run over me.   Then away out in the woods I heard that kind of
sound that a ghost makes when it wants to tell about something that's on
mind and can't make itself understood, and so can't rest easy in its gra
and has to go about that way every night grieving.   I got so down-heart
and scared, I did wish I had some company.   Pretty soon a spider we
crawling up my shoulder, and I flipped it off and it lit in the candle; a
before I could budge it was all shriveled up.   I didn't need anybody to t
me that that was an awful bad sign and would fetch me some bad luck,
I was scared and most shook the clothes off of me.   I got up and turn
around in my tracks three times and crossed my breast every time; a
then I tied up a little lock of my hair with a thread to keep witch
away.   But I hadn't no confidence.   You do that when you've lost
horse-shoe that you've found, instead of nailing it up over the door, but
hadn't ever heard anybody say it was any way to keep off bad luck wh
you'd killed a spider.

I set down again, a shaking all over, and got out my pipe for a smok
for the house was all as still as death, now, and so the widow wouldr
know.   Well, after a long time I heard the clock away off in the tov
go boom — boom — boom — twelve licks — and all still again — stiller the
ever.   Pretty soon I heard a twig snap, down in the dark amongst tl

es—something was a stirring. I set still and listened. Directly I could
t barely hear a *"me-yow! me-yow!"* down there. That was good! Says I,
me-yow! me-yow!" as soft as I could, and then I put out the light and
ambled out of the window onto the shed. Then I slipped down to
ground and crawled in amongst the trees, and sure enough there was
m Sawyer waiting for me.

HUCK STEALING AWAY.

Chapter II

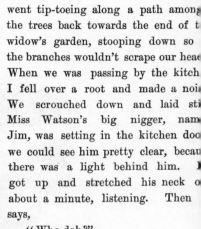

THEY TIP-TOED ALONG.

WE went tip-toeing along a path among
the trees back towards the end of t
widow's garden, stooping down so
the branches wouldn't scrape our head
When we was passing by the kitch
I fell over a root and made a nois
We scrouched down and laid sti
Miss Watson's big nigger, nam
Jim, was setting in the kitchen doo
we could see him pretty clear, becau
there was a light behind him.
got up and stretched his neck o
about a minute, listening. Then
says,

"Who dah?"

He listened some more; then
come tip-toeing down and sto
right between us; we could a touch
him, nearly. Well, likely it was mi
utes and minutes that there warn't
sound, and we all there so clo
together. There was a place on m
ankle that got to itching; but
dasn't scratch it; and then my ear begun to itch; and next my back, right b
tween my shoulders. Seemed like I'd die if I couldn't scratch. Well, I'
noticed that thing plenty of times since. If you are with the quality, or at
funeral, or trying to go to sleep when you ain't sleepy—if you are anywher

ere it won't do for you to scratch, why you will itch all over in upwards of a
ousand places. Pretty soon Jim says:

" Say—who is you? Whar is you? Dog my cats ef I didn' hear sumf'n. Well,
nows what I's gwyne to do. I's gwyne to set down here and listen tell I hears
agin."

So he set down on the ground betwixt me and Tom. He leaned his back up
ainst a tree, and stretched his legs out till one of them most touched one of
ne. My nose begun to itch. It itched till the tears come into my eyes. But
lasn't scratch. Then it begun to itch on the inside. Next I got to itching
derneath. I didn't know how I was going to set still. This miserableness
nt on as much as six or seven minutes; but it seemed a sight longer than that.
vas itching in eleven different places now. I reckoned I couldn't stand it
ore'n a minute longer, but I set my teeth hard and got ready to try. Just then
m begun to breathe heavy; next he begun to snore—and then I was pretty soon
mfortable again.

Tom he made a sign to me—kind of a little noise with his mouth—and we went
eeping away on our hands and knees. When we was ten foot off, Tom whis-
red to me and wanted to tie Jim to the tree for fun; but I said no ; he might
ke and make a disturbance, and then they'd find out I warn't in. Then Tom
d he hadn't got candles enough, and he would slip in the kitchen and get
me more. I didn't want him to try. I said Jim might wake up and come.
t Tom wanted to resk it; so we slid in there and got three candles, and Tom
d five cents on the table for pay. Then we got out, and I was in a sweat to
t away; but nothing would do Tom but he must crawl to where Jim was, on
s hands and knees, and play something on him. I waited, and it seemed a good
ile, everything was so still and lonesome.

As soon as Tom was back, we cut along the path, around the garden fence,
d by-and-by fetched up on the steep top of the hill the other side of the house.
m said he slipped Jim's hat off of his head and hung it on a limb right over
m, and Jim stirred a little, but he didn't wake. Afterwards Jim said the
tches bewitched him and put him in a trance, and rode him all over the State,
d then set him under the trees again and hung his hat on a limb to show who
ne it. And next time Jim told it he said they rode him down to New Orleans;

and after that, every time he told it he spread it more and more, till by-and
he said they rode him all over the world, and tired him most to death, and
back was all over saddle-boils. Jim was monstrous proud about it, and he got so
wouldn't hardly notice the other niggers. Niggers would come miles to hear J
tell about it, and he was more looked up to than any nigger in that count

JIM.

Strange niggers would stand with their mou
open and look him all over, same as if he w
a wonder. Niggers is always talking abo
witches in the dark by the kitchen fire; b
whenever one was talking and letting on
know all about such things, Jim would happ
in and say, "Hm! What you know 'bo
witches?" and that nigger was corked up a
had to take a back seat. Jim always kept th
five-center piece around his neck with a stri
and said it was a charm the devil give to h
with his own hands and told him he could c
anybody with it and fetch witches whenever
wanted to, just by saying something to it; b
he never told what it was he said to it. Nigg
would come from all around there and give J
anything they had, just for a sight of that fi
center piece; but they wouldn't touch it, b
cause the devil had had his hands on it. J
was most ruined, for a servant, because he g
so stuck up on account of having seen the devil and been rode by witches.

Well, when Tom and me got to the edge of the hill-top, we looked aw
down into the village and could see three or four lights twinkling, where the
was sick folks, may be; and the stars over us was sparkling ever so fine; a
down by the village was the river, a whole mile broad, and awful still and gran
We went down the hill and found Jo Harper, and Ben Rogers, and two or th
more of the boys, hid in the old tanyard. So we unhitched a skiff and pulled do
the river two mile and a half, to the big scar on the hillside, and went ashore.

We went to a clump of bushes, and Tom made everybody swear to keep the ~~~ret, and then showed them a hole in the hill, right in the thickest part of ~~ bushes. Then we lit the candles and crawled in on our hands and knees. ~~ went about two hundred yards, and then the cave opened up. Tom poked ~~ut amongst the passages and pretty soon ducked under a wall where you ~~uldn't a noticed that there was a hole. We went along a narrow place and ~~ into a kind of room, all damp and sweaty and cold, and there we stopped. ~~m says :

"Now we'll start this band of robbers and call it Tom Sawyer's Gang.

TOM SAWYER'S BAND OF ROBBERS.

~~erybody that wants to join has got to take an oath, and write his name in ~~od."

Everybody was willing. So Tom got out a sheet of paper that he had wrote ~~ oath on, and read it. It swore every boy to stick to the band, and never ~~l any of the secrets ; and if anybody done anything to any boy in the band, ~~ichever boy was ordered to kill that person and his family must do it, and he ~~ustn't eat and he mustn't sleep till he had killed them and hacked a cross in

their breasts, which was the sign of the band. And nobody that didn't belo
to the band could use that mark, and if he did he must be sued ; and if he do
it again he must be killed. And if anybody that belonged to the band told t
secrets, he must have his throat cut, and then have his carcass burnt up a
the ashes scattered all around, and his name blotted off of the list with blo
and never mentioned again by the gang, but have a curse put on it and be forg
forever.

Everybody said it was a real beautiful oath, and asked Tom if he got it o
of his own head. He said, some of it, but the rest was out of pirate books, a
robber books, and every gang that was high-toned had it.

Some thought it would be good to kill the *families* of boys that told t
secrets. Tom said it was a good idea, so he took a pencil and wrote it in. Th
Ben Rogers says :

" Here's Huck Finn, he hain't got no family—what you going to do 'bo
him ? "

" Well, hain't he got a father ? " says Tom Sawyer.

" Yes, he's got a father, but you can't never find him, these days. He us
to lay drunk with the hogs in the tanyard, but he hain't been seen in the
parts for a year or more."

They talked it over, and they was going to rule me out, because they sa
every boy must have a family or somebody to kill, or else it wouldn't be fa
and square for the others. Well, nobody could think of anything to do—eve
body was stumped, and set still. I was most ready to cry ; but all at once
thought of a way, and so I offered them Miss Watson—they could kill h
Everybody said :

" Oh, she'll do, she'll do. That's all right. Huck can come in."

Then they all stuck a pin in their fingers to get blood to sign with, and
made my mark on the paper.

" Now," says Ben Rogers, " what's the line of business of this Gang ? "

" Nothing only robbery and murder," Tom said.

" But who are we going to rob ? houses—or cattle—or—— "

" Stuff ! stealing cattle and such things ain't robbery, it's burglary," sa
Tom Sawyer. " We ain't burglars. That ain't no sort of style. We are hig

ymen.   We stop stages and carriages on the road, with masks on, and kill
people and take their watches and money."

"Must we always kill the people?"

"Oh, certainly.   It's best.   Some authorities think different, but mostly it's
sidered best to kill them.   Except some that you bring to the cave here and
p them till they're ransomed."

"Ransomed?   What's that?"

"I don't know.   But that's what they do.   I've seen it in books; and so of
rse that's what we've got to do."

"But how can we do it if we don't know what it is?"

"Why blame it all, we've *got* to do it.   Don't I tell you it's in the books?
you want to go to doing different from what's in the books, and get things
muddled up?"

"Oh, that's all very fine to *say*, Tom Sawyer, but how in the nation are these
lows going to be ransomed if we don't know how to do it to them? that's
thing *I* want to get at.   Now what do you *reckon* it is?"

"Well I don't know.   But per'aps if we keep them till they're ransomed, it
means that we keep them till they're dead."

"Now, that's something *like*.   That'll answer.   Why couldn't you said that
ore?   We'll keep them till they're ransomed to death—and a bothersome lot
y'll be, too, eating up everything and always trying to get loose."

"How you talk, Ben Rogers.   How can they get loose when there's a guard
r them, ready to shoot them down if they move a peg?"

"A guard.   Well, that *is* good.   So somebody's got to set up all night and
er get any sleep, just so as to watch them.   I think that's foolishness.   Why
't a body take a club and ransom them as soon as they get here?"

"Because it ain't in the books so—that's why.   Now Ben Rogers, do you
at to do things regular, or don't you?—that's the idea.   Don't you reckon
t the people that made the books knows what's the correct thing to do?
you reckon *you* can learn 'em anything?   Not by a good deal.   No, sir,
ll just go on and ransom them in the regular way."

"All right.   I don't mind; but I say it's a fool way, anyhow.   Say—do we
the women, too?"

"Well, Ben Rogers, if I was as ignorant as you I wouldn't let on. Kill women? No—nobody ever saw anything in the books like that. You fe them to the cave, and you're always as polite as pie to them ; and by-and-by t fall in love with you and never want to go home any more."

"Well, if that's the way, I'm agreed, but I don't take no stock in it. Mig soon we'll have the cave so cluttered up with women, and fellows waiting to ransomed, that there won't be no place for the robbers. But go ahead, I a got nothing to say."

Little Tommy Barnes was asleep, now, and when they waked him up he scared, and cried, and said he wanted to go home to his ma, and didn't w to be a robber any more.

So they all made fun of him, and called him cry-baby, and that made l mad, and he said he would go straight and tell all the secrets. But Tom g him five cents to keep quiet, and said we would all go home and meet n week and rob somebody and kill some people.

Ben Rogers said he couldn't get out much, only Sundays, and so he wan to begin next Sunday ; but all the boys said it would be wicked to do it Sunday, and that settled the thing. They agreed to get together and fix a da soon as they could, and then we elected Tom Sawyer first captain and Harper second captain of the Gang, and so started home.

I clumb up the shed and crept into my window just before day was breaki My new clothes was all greased up and clayey, and I was dog-tired.

HUCK CREEPS INTO HIS WINDOW.

Chapter III.

MISS WATSON'S LECTURE.

WELL, I got a good going-over in the morning, from old Miss Watson, on account of my clothes ; but the widow she didn't scold, but only cleaned off the grease and clay and looked so sorry that I thought I would behave a while if I could. Then Miss Watson she took me in the closet and prayed, but nothing come of it. She told me to pray every day, and whatever I asked for I would get it. But it warn't so. I tried it. Once I got a fish-line, but no hooks. It warn't any good to me without hooks. I tried for the hooks three or four times, but somehow I couldn't make it work. By-and-by, one day, I asked Miss Watson to try for me, but she said I was a fool. She never told me y, and I couldn't make it out no way.

I set down, one time, back in the woods, and had a long think about it. I s to myself, if a body can get anything they pray for, why don't Deacon nn get back the money he lost on pork ? Why can't the widow get back silver snuff-box that was stole ? Why can't Miss Watson fat up ? No, says myself, there ain't nothing in it. I went and told the widow about it, she said the thing a body could get by praying for it was "spiritual gifts." is was too many for me, but she told me what she meant—I must help er people, and do everything I could for other people, and look out for them the time, and never think about myself. This was including Miss Watson,

as I took it. I went out in the woods and turned it over in my mind a l
time, but I couldn't see no advantage about it—except for the other peopl
so at last I reckoned I wouldn't worry about it any more, but just let it
Sometimes the widow would take me one side and talk about Providence in a v
to make a body's mouth water; but maybe next day Miss Watson would t
hold and knock it all down again. I judged I could see that there was
Providences, and a poor chap would stand considerable show with the wido
Providence, but if Miss Watson's got him there warn't no help for him any m
I thought it all out, and reckoned I would belong to the widow's, if he wan
me, though I couldn't make out how he was agoing to be any better off t
than what he was before, seeing I was so ignorant and so kind of low-do
and ornery.

Pap he hadn't been seen for more than a year, and that was comfortable
me; I didn't want to see him no more. He used to always whale me when
was sober and could get his hands on me; though I used to take to the wo
most of the time when he was around. Well, about this time he was found
the river drowned, about twelve mile above town, so people said. They jud
it was him, anyway; said this drowned man was just his size, and was ragg
and had uncommon long hair—which was all like pap—but they couldn't m
nothing out of the face, because it had been in the water so long it warn't m
like a face at all. They said he was floating on his back in the water. T
took him and buried him on the bank. But I warn't comfortable long, beca
I happened to think of something. I knowed mighty well that a drownded m
don't float on his back, but on his face. So I knowed, then, that this wa
pap, but a woman dressed up in a man's clothes. So I was uncomfortable ag
I judged the old man would turn up again by-and-by, though I wished
wouldn't.

We played robber now and then about a month, and then I resign
All the boys did. We hadn't robbed nobody, we hadn't killed any peo
but only just pretended. We used to hop out of the woods and go cha
ing down on hog-drovers and women in carts taking garden stuff to mark
but we never hived any of them. Tom Sawyer called the hogs "ingot
and he called the turnips and stuff "julery" and we would go to the c

pow-wow over what we had done and how many people we had killed
marked. But I couldn't see no profit in it. One time Tom sent a boy
un about town with a blazing stick, which he called a slogan (which
the sign for the Gang to get together), and then he said he had got
et news by his spies that next day a whole parcel of Spanish
chants and rich A-rabs was going to camp in Cave Hollow with two
dred elephants, and six hundred camels, and over a thousand "sumter"
es, all loaded down with di'monds, and they didn't have only a guard of
: hundred soldiers, and so we would lay in ambuscade, as he called it,
kill the lot and scoop the things. He said we must slick up our

rds and guns, and get
ly. He never could go
r even a turnip-cart but
must have the swords and
s all scoured up for it;
gh they was only lath and
m-sticks, and you might
ur at them till you rotted
then they warn't worth a
thful of ashes more than
t they was before. I didn't
eve we could lick such a
vd of Spaniards and A-rabs,
I wanted to see the camels
elephants, so I was on hand
t day, Saturday, in the
uscade; and when we got
word, we rushed out of
woods and down the hill.
there warn't no Spaniards
A-rabs, and there warn't no
els nor no elephants. It

THE ROBBERS DISPERSED.

n't anything but a Sunday-school picnic, and only a primer-class at that. We busted it up, and chased the children up the hollow; but never got anything but some doughnuts and jam, though Ben Rogers a rag doll, and Jo Harper got a hymn-book and a tract; and then teacher charged in and made us drop everything and cut. I didn't see di'monds, and I told Tom Sawyer so. He said there was loads of th there, anyway; and he said there was A-rabs there, too, and elepha and things. I said, why couldn't we see them, then? He said if I war so ignorant, but had read a book called "Don Quixote," I would kn without asking. He said it was all done by enchantment. He said th was hundreds of soldiers there, and elephants and treasure, and so on, we had enemies which he called magicians, and they had turned the wh thing into an infant Sunday school, just out of spite. I said, all rig then the thing for us to do was to go for the magicians. Tom Sawyer s I was a numskull.

"Why," says he, "a magician could call up a lot of genies, and th would hash you up like nothing before you could say Jack Robinson. Th are as tall as a tree and as big around as a church."

"Well," I says, "s'pose we got some genies to help us—can't we the other crowd then?"

"How you going to get them?"

"I don't know. How do *they* get them?"

"Why they rub an old tin lamp or an iron ring, and then the genies cc tearing in, with the thunder and lightning a-ripping around and the sm a-rolling, and everything they're told to do they up and do it. They dc think nothing of pulling a shot tower up by the roots, and belting a Sund school superintendent over the head with it—or any other man."

"Who makes them tear around so?"

"Why, whoever rubs the lamp or the ring. They belong to whoe rubs the lamp or the ring, and they've got to do whatever he says. If tells them to build a palace forty miles long, out of di'monds, and fill full of chewing gum, or whatever you want, and fetch an emper daughter from China for you to marry, they've got to do it—and they got to do it before sun-up next morning, too. And more—they've got

tz that palace around over the country wherever you want it, you
derstand."

"Well," says I, "I think they are a pack of flatheads for not keeping
palace themselves 'stead of fooling them away like that. And what's
re—if I was one of them I would see a man in Jericho before I would

p my business and come
him for the rubbing of an
tin lamp."

"How you talk, Huck
n. Why, you'd *have* to
e when he rubbed it,
ther you wanted to or
."

"What, and I as high as
tree and as big as a
rch? All right, then; I
ld come; but I lay I'd
e that man climb the
hest tree there was in the
ntry."

"Shucks, it ain't no use
alk to you, Huck Finn.
don't seem to know
thing, somehow — perfect
-head."

RUBBING THE LAMP.

I thought all this over for two or three days, and then I reckoned I
ld see if there was anything in it. I got an old tin lamp and an iron
g and went out in the woods and rubbed and rubbed till I sweat like
Injun, calculating to build a palace and sell it; but it warn't no use,
e of the genies come. So then I judged that all that stuff was only
one of Tom Sawyer's lies. I reckoned he believed in the A-rabs and the
hants, but as for me I think different. It had all the marks of a
day school.

Chapter IV

WELL, three or four months run along, and it was well into the winter, now. I had been to school most all the time, and could spell, and read, and write just a little, and could say the multiplication table up to six times seven is thirty-five, and I don't reckon I could ever get any further than that if I was to live forever. I don't take no stock in mathematics, anyway.

! ! ! ! !

At first I hated the school, but by-and-by I got so I could stand it. Whenever I got uncommon tired I played hookey, and the hiding I got next day done me good and cheered me up. So the longer I went to school the easier it got to be. I was getting sort of used to the widow's ways, too, and they warn't so raspy on me. Living in a house, and sleep-ing in a bed, pulled on me pretty tight, mostly, but before the cold weather I used to slide out and sleep in the woods, sometimes, and so that was a rest to me. I liked the old ways best, but I was getting so I liked the new ones, too, a little. The widow said I was coming along slow but sure, and doing very satisfactory. She said she warn't ashamed of me.

)ne morning I happened to turn over the salt-cellar at breakfast. I reached
ome of it as quick as I could, to throw over my left shoulder and keep off
ad luck, but Miss Watson was in ahead of me, and crossed me off. She says,
,ke your hands away, Huckleberry—what a mess you are always making." The
w put in a good word for me, but that warn't going to keep off the bad luck,
owed that well enough. I started out, after breakfast, feeling worried and
y, and wondering where it was going to fall on me, and what it was going
. There is ways to keep off some kinds of bad luck, but this wasn't one of
kind; so I never tried to do anything, but just poked along low-spirited and
e watch-out.

went down the front garden and clumb over the stile, where you go through
igh board fence. There was an inch of new snow on the ground, and I seen
body's tracks. They had come up from the quarry and stood around the
a while, and then went on around the garden fence. It was funny they hadn't
in, after standing around so. I couldn't make it out. It was very curious,
how. I was going to follow around, but I stooped down to look at the tracks
I didn't notice anything at first, but next I did. There was a cross in the
boot-heel made with big nails, to keep off the devil.

was up in a second and shinning down the hill. I looked over my shoulder
y now and then, but I didn't see nobody. I was at Judge Thatcher's as quick
could get there. He said:

" Why, my boy, you are all out of breath. Did you come for your interest ?"

" No sir," I says ; " is there some for me?"

" Oh, yes, a half-yearly is in, last night. Over a hundred and fifty dollars.
e a fortune for you. You better let me invest it along with your six thou-
, because if you take it you'll spend it."

" No sir," I says, " I don't want to spend it. I don't want it at all—nor the
housand, nuther. I want you to take it; I want to give it to you—the six
sand and all."

Ie looked surprised. He couldn't seem to make it out. He says:

" Why, what can you mean, my boy ?"

says, "Don't you ask me no questions about it, please. You'll take
won't you?"

He says:

"Well I'm puzzled. Is something the matter?"

"Please take it," says I, "and don't ask me nothing—then I won't ⌷ to tell no lies."

JUDGE THATCHER SURPRISED.

He studied a while, then he says:

"Oho-o. I think I ⌷ You want to *sell* all y⌷ property to me—not giv⌷ That's the correct idea.'⌷

Then he wrote someth⌷ on a paper and read it o⌷ and says:

"There—you see it ⌷ 'for a consideration.' T⌷ means I have bought i⌷ you and paid you for ⌷ Here's a dollar for y⌷ Now, you sign it."

So I signed it, ⌷ left.

Miss Watson's nig⌷ Jim, had a hair-ball as big as your fist, which had been took out of ⌷ fourth stomach of an ox, and he used to do magic with it. He said t⌷ was a spirit inside of it, and it knowed everything. So I went to him that n⌷ and told him pap was here again, for I found his tracks in the snow. W⌷ I wanted to know, was, what he was going to do, and was he going to stay? Jim ⌷ out his hair-ball, and said something over it, and then he held it up and dropp⌷ on the floor. It fell pretty solid, and only rolled about an inch. Jim trie⌷ again, and then another time, and it acted just the same. Jim got·down on ⌷ knees and put his ear against it and listened. But it warn't no use; he sai⌷ wouldn't talk. He said sometimes it wouldn't talk without money. I told hi⌷

an old slick counterfeit quarter that warn't no good because the brass showed ugh the silver a little, and it wouldn't pass nohow, even if the brass didn't ᵥ, because it was so slick it felt greasy, and so that would tell on it every time. ᵉckoned I wouldn't say nothing about the dollar I got from the judge.) I d it was pretty bad money, but maybe the hair-ball would take it, because be it wouldn't know the difference. Jim smelt it, and bit it, and rubbed it, said he would manage so the hair-ball would think it was good. He said he ld split open a raw Irish potato and stick the quarter in between and keep it e all night, and next morning you couldn't see no brass, and it wouldn't feel sy no more, and so anybody in town would take it in a minute, let alone a -ball. Well, I knowed a potato would do that, before, but I had forgot it. Jim put the quarter under the hair-ball and got down and listened again.

s time he said the
-ball was all right.
said it would tell
whole fortune if I
ted it to. I says,
n. So the hair-ball
ed to Jim, and Jim
it to me. He says:
" Yo' ole father doan'
w, yit, what he's
ᵥyne to do. Some-
ᵉs he spec he'll go
ᵥ, en den agin he
 he'll stay. De bes'

JIM LISTENING.

is to res' easy en let de ole man take his own way. Dey's two angels hoverin' ᵢ' 'bout him. One uv 'em is white en shiny, en 'tother one is black. De ᵗe one gits him to go right, a little while, den de black one sail in en bust it ᵤp. A body can't tell, yit, which one gwyne to fetch him at de las'. But is all right. You gwyne to have considable trouble in yo' life, en considable Sometimes you gwyne to git hurt, en sometimes you gwyne to git sick; every time you's gwyne to git well agin. Dey's two gals flyin' 'bout you in yo' life. One uv 'em's light en 'tother one is dark. One is rich 'tother is po'. You's gwyne to marry de po' one fust en de rich one en-by. You wants to keep 'way fum de water as much as you kin, don't run no resk, 'kase it's down in de bills dat you's gwyne to git hu

When I lit my candle and went up to my room that night, there pap, his own self!

Chapter V

"PAP."

I HAD shut the door to. Then I turned around, and there he was. I used to be scared of him all the time, he tanned me so much. I reckoned I was scared now, too; but in a minute I see I was mistaken. That is, after the first jolt, as you may say, when my breath sort of hitched—he being so unexpected; but right away after, I see I warn't scared of him worth bothering about.

He was most fifty, and he looked it. His hair was long and tangled and greasy, and hung down, and you could see his eyes shining through like he was behind vines. It was all black, no gray; so was his long, mixed-up whiskers. There warn't no color in his face, where his face showed; it was white; not like another man's white, but a white to make a body sick, a white to make a body's flesh crawl—a tree-toad white, a fish-belly white. As for his clothes—just rags, that was all. He had one ankle resting on 'tother knee; the boot on that foot was busted, and two of his toes stuck through, and he worked them now and then. His hat was laying on the floor; an old black slouch with the top caved in, like a lid.

I stood a-looking at him; he set there a-looking at me, with his chair tilted back a little. I set the candle down. I noticed the window was

ap; so he had clumb in by the shed. He kept a-looking me all o
By-and-by he says:

"Starchy clothes—very. You think you're a good deal of a big-
don't you?"

"Maybe I am, maybe I ain't," I says.

"Don't you give me none o' your lip," says he. "You've put on
siderble many frills since I been away. I'll take you down a peg be
I get done with you. You're educated, too, they say; can read and wr
You think you're better'n your father, now, don't you, because he ca
I'll take it out of you. Who told you you might meddle with s
hifalut'n foolishness, hey?—who told you you could?"

"The widow. She told me."

"The widow, hey?—and who told the widow she could put in
shovel about a thing that ain't none of her business?"

"Nobody never told her."

"Well, I'll learn her how to meddle. And looky here—you drop
school, you hear? I'll learn people to bring up a boy to put on airs
his own father and let on to be better'n what *he* is. You lemme ca
you fooling around that school again, you hear? Your mother coul
read, and she couldn't write, nuther, before she died. None of the fa
couldn't, before *they* died. *I* can't; and here you're a-swelling your
up like this. I ain't the man to stand it—you hear? Say—lemme
you read."

I took up a book and begun something about General Washington and
wars. When I'd read about a half a minute, he fetched the book a whack w
his hand and knocked it across the house. He says:

"It's so. You can do it. I had my doubts when you told me. Now lo
here; you stop that putting on frills. I won't have it. I'll lay for you,
smarty; and if I catch you about that school I'll tan you good. First you kr
you'll get religion, too. I never see such a son."

He took up a little blue and yaller picture of some cows and a boy,
says:

"What's this?"

"It's something they give me for learning my lessons good."

He tore it up, and says—

"I'll give you something better—I'll give you a cowhide."

He set there a-mumbling and a-growling a minute, and then he says—

"*Ain't* you a sweet-scented dandy, though? A bed; and bedclothes; and ook'n-glass; and a piece carpet on the floor—and r own father got to sleep h the hogs in the tanyard. ever see such a son. I I'll take some o' these ls out o' you before I'm e with you. Why there 't no end to your airs— y say you're rich. Hey? ow's that?"

"They lie—that's how."

"Looky here—mind how talk to me; I'm a-stand-about all I can stand, —so don't gimme no sass. been in town two days,

HUCK AND HIS FATHER.

I hain't heard nothing but about you bein' rich. I heard about it away n the river, too. That's why I come. You git me that money to-morrow— ant it."

"I hain't got no money."

"It's a lie. Judge Thatcher's got it. You git it. I want it."

"I hain't got no money, I tell you. You ask Judge Thatcher; he'll tell you same."

"All right. I'll ask him; and I'll make him pungle, too, or I'll know the on why. Say—how much you got in your pocket? I want it."

"I hain't got only a dollar, and I want that to——"

"It don't make no difference what you want it for—you just shell it out."

He took it and bit it to see if it was good, and then he said he was g
down town to get some whisky ; said he hadn't had a drink all day.   Whe
had got out on the shed, he put his head in again, and cussed me for put
on frills and trying to be better than him ; and when I reckoned he was gone
come back and put his head in again, and told me to mind about that sch
because he was going to lay for me and lick me if I didn't drop that.

Next day he was drunk, and he went to Judge Thatcher's and bullyrag
him and tried to make him give up the money, but he couldn't, and then
swore he'd make the law force him.

The judge and the widow went to law to get the court to take me away f
him and let one of them be my guardian ; but it was a new judge that had
come, and he didn't know the old man ; so he said courts mustn't interfere
separate families if they could help it ; said he'd druther not take a child a
from its father.   So Judge Thatcher and the widow had to quit on
business.

That pleased the old man till he couldn't rest.   He said he'd cowhide me
I was black and blue if I didn't raise some money for him.   I borrowed t
dollars from Judge Thatcher, and pap took it and got drunk and went a-blow
around and cussing and whooping and carrying on ; and he kept it up
over town, with a tin pan, till most midnight ; then they jailed him,
next day they had him before court, and jailed him again for a week.   Bu
said *he* was satisfied ; said he was boss of his son, and he'd make it warm
him.

When he got out the new judge said he was agoing to make a man of l
So he took him to his own house, and dressed him up clean and nice, and
him to breakfast and dinner and supper with the family, and was just old pi
him, so to speak.   And after supper he talked to him about temperance and s
things till the old man cried, and said he'd been a fool, and fooled away his l
but now he was agoing to turn over a new leaf and be a man nobody wouldn'
ashamed of, and he hoped the judge would help him and not look down on l
The judge said he could hug him for them words ; so *he* cried, and his wife
cried again ; pap said he'd been a man that had always been misunderstood bef
and the judge said he believed it.   The old man said that what a man wa

was down, was sympathy; and the judge said it was so; so they cried
n. And when it was bedtime, the old man rose up and held out his
d, and says:

"Look at it gentlemen, and ladies all; take ahold of it; shake it. There's
and that was the hand of a hog; but it ain't so no more; it's the hand
 man that's started in on a new life, and 'll die before he'll go back. You
k them words—don't forget I said them. It's a clean hand now; shake
don't be afeard."

REFORMING THE DRUNKARD.

So they shook it, one after the other, all around, and cried. The judge's
 she kissed it. Then the old man he signed a pledge—made his mark. The
ge said it was the holiest time on record, or something like that. Then
 tucked the old man into a beautiful room, which was the spare room, and
he night sometime he got powerful thirsty and clumb out onto the porch-roof
slid down a stanchion and traded his new coat for a jug of forty-rod, and
nb back again and had a good old time; and towards daylight he crawled out
n, drunk as a fiddler, and rolled off the porch and broke his left arm in
places and was most froze to death when somebody found him after sun-up.

And when they come to look at that spare room, they had to take soundi
before they could navigate it.

The judge he felt kind of sore. He said he reckoned a body could refo
the ole man with a shot-gun, maybe, but he didn't know no other way.

FALLING FROM GRACE.

Chapter VI.

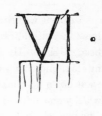

GETTING OUT OF THE WAY.

WELL, pretty soon the old man was up and around again, and then he went for Judge Thatcher in the courts to make him give up that money, and he went for me, too, for not stopping school. He catched me a couple of times and thrashed me, but I went to school just the same, and dodged him or out-run him most of the time. I didn't want to go to school much, before, but I reckoned I'd go now to spite pap. That law trial was a slow business; appeared like they warn't ever going to get started on it; so every now and then I'd borrow two or three dollars off of the judge for him, to keep from getting a cowhiding. Every time he got money he got drunk; and every time he got drunk he raised Cain around town; and every time he raised Cain he got jailed. He was just suited—this kind of thing was right in his line.

He got to hanging around the widow's too much, and so she told him at last, that if he didn't quit using around there she would make trouble for him. Well, wasn't he mad? He said he would show who was Huck Finn's boss. So he watched out for me one day in the spring, and catched me, and took me up the river about three mile, in a skiff, and crossed over to the Illinois shore where it was woody and there warn't no houses but an old log hut in a place where the timber was so thick you couldn't find it if you didn't know where it was.

He kept me with him all the time, and I never got a chance to run off.
lived in that old cabin, and he always locked the door and put the key under
head, nights.   He had a gun which he had stole, I reckon, and we fished
hunted, and that was what we lived on.   Every little while he locked me in
went down to the store, three miles, to the ferry, and traded fish and game
whisky and fetched it home and got drunk and had a good time, and licked
The widow she found out where I was, by-and-by, and she sent a man over to

SOLID COMFORT.

to get hold of me, but pap drove him off with the gun, and it warn't long a
that till I was used to being where I was, and liked it, all but the cowhide pa
It was kind of lazy and jolly, laying off comfortable all day, smoking
fishing, and no books nor study.   Two months or more run along, and
clothes got to be all rags and dirt, and I didn't see how I'd ever got to like it so
at the widow's, where you had to wash, and eat on a plate, and comb up, and g
bed and get up regular, and be forever bothering over a book and have old N
Watson pecking at you all the time.   I didn't want to go back no more.   I
stopped cussing, because the widow didn't like it ; but now I took to it again

se pap hadn't no objections. It was pretty good times up in the woods there, e it all around.

But by-and-by pap got too handy with his hick'ry, and I couldn't stand it. I was over welts. He got to going away so much, too, and locking me in. Once he ked me in and was gone three days. It was dreadful lonesome. I judged he got drowned and I wasn't ever going to get out any more. I was scared. I le up my mind I would fix up some way to leave there. I had tried to out of that cabin many a time, but I couldn't find no way. There warn't a dow to it big enought for a dog to get through. I couldn't get up the chimbly, as too narrow. The door was thick solid oak slabs. Pap was pretty careful to leave a knife or anything in the cabin when he was away ; I reckon I had ted the place over as much as a hundred times ; well, I was 'most all the time , because it was about the only way to put in the time. But this time I found ething at last ; I found an old rusty wood-saw without any handle ; it was in between a rafter and the clapboards of the roof. I greased it up and went vork. There was an old horse-blanket nailed against the logs at the far end he cabin behind the table, to keep the wind from blowing through the chinks putting the candle out. I got under the table and raised the blanket and t to work to saw a section of the big bottom log out, big enough to let me ough. Well, it was a good long job, but I was getting towards the end of it n I heard pap's gun in the woods. I got rid of the signs of my work, and opped the blanket and hid my saw, and pretty soon pap come in.

Pap warn't in a good humor—so he was his natural self. He said he was down own, and everything was going wrong. His lawyer said he reckoned he ld win his lawsuit and get the money, if they ever got started on the trial; then there was ways to put it off a long time, and Judge Thatcher knowed r to do it. And he said people allowed there'd be another trial to get me away n him and give me to the widow for my guardian, and they guessed it would , this time. This shook me up considerable, because I didn't want to go back to widow's any more and be so cramped up and sivilized, as they called it. Then old man got to cussing, and cussed everything and everybody he could think of, then cussed them all over again to make sure he hadn't skipped any, and r that he polished off with a kind of a general cuss all round, including a con-

siderable parcel of people which he didn't know the names of, and so called th
what's-his-name, when he got to them, and went right along with his cussing.

He said he would like to see the widow get me. He said he would wa
out, and if they tried to come any such game on him he knowed of a pl
six or seven mile off, to stow me in, where they might hunt till they drop
and they couldn't find me. That made me pretty uneasy again, but only
a minute ; I reckoned I wouldn't stay on hand till he got that chance.

The old man made me go to the skiff and fetch the things he ha
got. There was a fifty-pound sack of corn meal, and a side of bac
ammunition, and a four-gallon jug of whisky, and an old book and t
newspapers for wadding, besides some tow. I toted up a load, and w
back and set down on the bow of the skiff to rest. I thought it all ov

and I reckoned I would w
off with the gun and so
lines, and take to the wo
when I run away. I guess
I wouldn't stay in one pla
but just tramp right across
country, mostly night tim
and hunt and fish to keep ali
and so get so far away t
the old man nor the wid
couldn't ever find me any m
I judged I would saw out a
leave that night if pap
drunk enough, and I reckon
he would. I got so full of
I didn't notice how long
was staying, till the old m
hollered and asked me whet
I was asleep or drownded.

THINKING IT OVER.

I got the things all up to the cabin, and then it was about da
While I was cooking supper the old man took a swig or two and got

warmed up, and went to ripping again. He had been drunk over in
n, and laid in the gutter all night, and he was a sight to look at.
body would a thought he was Adam, he was just all mud. Whenever
liquor begun to work, he most always went for the govment. This
e he says :

" Call this a govment ! why, just look at it and see what it's like.
e's the law a-standing ready to take a man's son away from him—a
1's own son, which he has had all the trouble and all the anxiety and
the expense of raising. Yes, just as that man has got that son raised
ast, and ready to go to work and begin to do suthin' for *him* and give
a rest, the law up and goes for him. And they call *that* govment !
t ain't all, nuther. The law backs that old Judge Thatcher up and
s him to keep me out o' my property. Here's what the law does.
law takes a man worth six thousand dollars and upards, and jams him
an old trap of a cabin like this, and lets him go round in clothes
t ain't fitten for a hog. They call that govment ! A man can't get
rights in a govment like this. Sometimes I've a mighty notion to
leave the country for good and all. Yes, and I *told* 'em so ; I told old
tcher so to his face. Lots of 'em heard me, and can tell what I said.
s I, for two cents I'd leave the blamed country and never come anear
gin. Them's the very words. I says, look at my hat—if you call
hat—but the lid raises up and the rest of it goes down till it's below
chin, and then it ain't rightly a hat at all, but more like my head
shoved up through a jint o' stove-pipe. Look at it, says I—such a
for me to wear—one of the wealthiest men in this town, if I could git
rights.

" Oh, yes, this is a wonderful govment, wonderful. Why, looky here.
re was a free nigger there, from Ohio ; a mulatter, most as white as
vhite man. He had the whitest shirt on you ever see, too, and the
iiest hat ; and there ain't a man in that town that's got as fine clothes
what he had ; and he had a gold watch and chain, and a silver-headed
e—the awfulest old gray-headed nabob in the State. And what do you
ik ? they said he was a p'fessor in a college, and could talk all kinds

of languages, and knowed everything. And that ain't the wust. They s
he could *vote*, when he was at home. Well, that let me out. Thinks
what is the country a-coming to ? It was 'lection day, and I was just ab
to go and vote, myself, if I warn't too drunk to get there ; but wl
they told me there was a State in this country where they'd let t
nigger vote, I drawed out. I says I'll never vote agin. Them's the v
words I said ; they all heard me ; and the country may rot for all m
I'll never vote agin as long as I live. And to see the cool way of t
nigger—why, he wouldn't a give me the road if I hadn't shoved him
o' the way. I says to the people, why ain't this nigger put up at auct
and sold ?—that's what I want to know. And what do you reckon tl
said ? Why, they said he couldn't be sold till he'd been in the State
months, and he hadn't been there that long yet. There, now—that's
specimen. They call that a govment that can't sell a free nigger till l
been in the State six months. Here's a govment that calls itself a govme
and lets on to be a govment, and thinks it is a govment, and yet's
to set stock-still for six whole months before it can take ahold of a prowli
thieving, infernal, white-shirted free nigger, and——"

Pap was agoing on so, he never noticed where his old limber legs \
taking him to, so he went head over heels over the tub of salt pork, a
barked both shins, and the rest of his speech was all the hottest kind
language—mostly hove at the nigger and the govment, though he give
tub some, too, all along, here and there. He hopped around the ca.
considerable, first on one leg and then on the other, holding first one s.
and then the other one, and at last he let out with his left foot all o1
sudden and fetched the tub a rattling kick. But it warn't good judgme
because that was the boot that had a couple of his toes leaking out of
front end of it ; so now he raised a howl that fairly made a body's h
raise, and down he went in the dirt, and rolled there, and held his to
and the cussing he done then laid over anything he had ever done previc
He said so his own self, afterwards. He had heard old Sowberry Ha,
in his best days, and he said it laid over him, too ; but I reckon that
sort of piling it on, maybe.

After supper pap took the jug, and said he had enough whisky there for

drunks and one delirium
mens. That was always
word. I judged he would
blind drunk in about an
r, and then I would steal
key, or saw myself out,
or 'tother. He drank, and
nk, and tumbled down on
blankets, by-and-by; but
k didn't run my way. He
n't go sound asleep, but
uneasy. He groaned, and
aned, and thrashed around
way and that, for a long
e. At last I got so sleepy
ouldn't keep my eyes open,
I could do, and so before
knowed what I was about
vas sound asleep, and the
dle burning.

RAISING A HOWL.

I don't know how long I was asleep, but all of a sudden there was an
ful scream and I was up. There was pap, looking wild and skipping
und every which way and yelling about snakes. He said they was crawl-
up his legs; and then he would give a jump and scream, and say one
l bit him on the cheek—but I couldn't see no snakes. He started and
round and round the cabin, hollering "take him off! take him off!
s biting me on the neck!" I never see a man look so wild in the eyes.
tty soon he was all fagged out, and fell down panting; then he rolled
r and over, wonderful fast, kicking things every which way, and striking
l grabbing at the air with his hands, and screaming, and saying there was
vils ahold of him. He wore out, by-and-by, and laid still a while,
aning. Then he laid stiller, and didn't make a sound. I could hear

the owls and the wolves, away off in the woods, and it seemed terri
still. He was laying over by the corner. By-and-by he raised up, p
way, and listened, with his head to one side. He says very low:

"Tramp—tramp—tramp; that's the dead; tramp—tramp—tramp; the
coming after me; but I won't go— Oh, they're here! don't touch me—do
hands off—they're cold; let go— Oh, let a poor devil alone!"

Then he went down on all fours and crawled off begging them to
him alone, and he rolled himself up in his blanket and wallowed in under
old pine table, still a-begging; and then he went to crying. I could h
him through the blanket.

By-and-by he rolled out and jumped up on his feet looking wild, a
he see me and went for me. He chased me round and round the pla
with a clasp-knife, calling me the Angel of Death and saying he wo
kill me and then I couldn't come for him no more. I begged, and t
him I was only Huck, but he laughed *such* a screechy laugh, and roa
and cussed, and kept on chasing me up. Once when I turned short a
dodged under his arm he made a grab and got me by the jacket betw
my shoulders, and I thought I was gone; but I slid out of the jac
quick as lightning, and saved myself. Pretty soon he was all tired o
and dropped down with his back against the door, and said he would r
a minute and then kill me. He put his knife under him, and said
would sleep and get strong, and then he would see who was who.

So he dozed off, pretty soon. By-and-by I got the old split-bott
chair and clumb up, as easy as I could, not to make any noise, and
down the gun. I slipped the ramrod down it to make sure it was load
and then I laid it across the turnip barrel, pointing towards pap, and
down behind it to wait for him to stir. And how slow and still the ti
did drag along.

Chapter VII.

"GIT UP."

"Git up! what you 'bout!"

I opened my eyes and looked around, trying to make out where I was. It was after sun-up, and I had been sound asleep. Pap was standing over me, looking sour—and sick, too. He says—

"What you doin' with this gun?"

I judged he didn't know nothing about what he had been doing, so I says:

"Somebody tried to get in, so I was laying for him."

"Why didn't you roust me out?"

"Well I tried to, but I couldn't; I couldn't budge you."

"Well, all right. Don't stand there palavering all day, but out with and see if there's a fish on the lines for breakfast. I'll be along in a minute."

He unlocked the door and I cleared out, up the river bank. I noticed some pieces of limbs and such things floating down, and a sprinkling of bark; so I knowed the river had begun to rise. I reckoned I would have great times, now, if I was over at the town. The June rise used to be always luck for me; because as soon as that rise begins, here comes cord-wood floating down, and pieces of log rafts—sometimes a dozen

THE ART OF HUCKLEBERRY FINN **73**

logs together; so all you have to do is to catch them and sell them to wood yards and the sawmill.

I went along up the bank with one eye out for pap and 'tother one out what the rise might fetch along. Well, all at once, here comes a canoe; jus beauty, too, about thirteen or fourteen foot long, riding high like a duck. shot head first off of the bank, like a frog, clothes and all on, and struck for the canoe. I just expected there'd be somebody laying down in it, beca people often done that to fool folks, and when a chap had pulled a skiff out m

THE SHANTY.

to it they'd raise up and laugh at him. But it warn't so this time. It wa drift-canoe, sure enough, and I clumb in and paddled her ashore. Thinks the old man will be glad when he sees this—she's worth ten dollars. But wh I got to shore pap wasn't in sight yet, and as I was running her into a lit creek like a gully, all hung over with vines and willows, I struck another id I judged I'd hide her good, and then, stead of taking to the woods when I off, I'd go down the river about fifty mile and camp in one place for good, a not have such a rough time tramping on foot.

It was pretty close to the shanty, and I thought I heard the old man coming,
the time ; but I got her hid ; and then I out and looked around a bunch of
ows, and there was the old man down the path apiece just drawing a bead on
rd with his gun. So he hadn't seen anything.

When he got along, I was hard at it taking up a "trot" line. He abused me a
e for being so slow, but I told him I fell in the river and that was what made
so long. I knowed he would see I was wet, and then he would be asking
stions. We got five cat-fish off of the lines and went home.

While we laid off, after breakfast, to sleep up, both of us being about wore
, I got to thinking that if I could fix up some way to keep pap and the widow
n trying to follow me, it would be a certainer thing than trusting to luck to
far enough off before they missed me ; you see, all kinds of things might
pen. Well, I didn't see no way for a while, but by-and-by pap raised up a
ute, to drink another barrel of water, and he says :

" Another time a man comes a-prowling round here, you roust me out, you
r ? That man warn't here for no good. I'd a shot him. Next time, you
st me out, you hear ?"

Then he dropped down and went to sleep again—but what he had been saying
 me the very idea I wanted. I says to myself, I can fix it now so nobody
't think of following me.

About twelve o'clock we turned out and went along up the bank. The river
coming up pretty fast, and lots of drift-wood going by on the rise. By-and-
along comes part of a log raft—nine logs fast together. We went out with
skiff and towed it ashore. Then we had dinner. Anybody but pap would a
ted and seen the day through, so as to catch more stuff ; but that warn't pap's
e. Nine logs was enough for one time ; he must shove right over to town
 sell. So he locked me in and took the skiff and started off towing the raft
ut half-past three. I judged he wouldn't come back that night. I waited
I reckoned he had got a good start, then I out with my saw and went to
k on that log again. Before he was 'tother side of the river I was out of the
 ; him and his raft was just a speck on the water away off yonder.

I took the sack of corn meal and took it to where the canoe was hid, and
ved the vines and branches apart and put it in ; then I done the same with

THE ART OF HUCKLEBERRY FINN **75**

the side of bacon ; then the whisky jug ; I took all the coffee and sugar th
was, and all the ammunition ; I took the wadding ; I took the bucket and gou
I took a dipper and a tin cup, and my old saw and two blankets, and the ski
and the coffee-pot. I took fish-lines and matches and other things—everyth
that was worth a cent. I cleaned out the place. I wanted an axe, but th
wasn't any, only the one out at the wood pile, and I knowed why I was going
leave that. I fetched out the gun, and now I was done.

I had wore the ground a good deal, crawling out of the hole and dragging

SHOOTING THE PIG.

so many things. So I fixed that as good as I could from the outside by scatter
dust on the place, which covered up the smoothness and the sawdust. The
fixed the piece of log back into its place, and put two rocks under it and
against it to hold it there,—for it was bent up at that place, and didn't qu
touch ground. If you stood four or five foot away and didn't know it was saw
you wouldn't ever notice it ; and besides, this was the back of the cabin and
warn't likely anybody would go fooling around there.

It was all grass clear to the canoe ; so I hadn't left a track. I follow

nd to see. I stood on the bank and looked out over the river. All safe.
I took the gun and went up a piece into the woods and was hunting around
some birds, when I see a wild pig ; hogs soon went wild in them bottoms
r they had got away from the prairie farms. I shot this fellow and took
into camp.

took the axe and smashed in the door—I beat it and hacked it considerable,
ing it. I fetched the pig in and took him back nearly to the table and
ked into his throat with the ax, and laid him down on the ground to bleed—
y ground, because it *was* ground—hard packed, and no boards. Well, next I
an old sack and put a lot of big rocks in it,—all I could drag—and I started
om the pig and dragged it to the door and through the woods down to the
c and dumped it in, and down it sunk, out of sight. You could easy see that
ething had been dragged over the ground. I did wish Tom Sawyer was
e, I knowed he would take an interest in this kind of business, and throw in
fancy touches. Nobody could spread himself like Tom Sawyer in such a
g as that.

Well, last I pulled out some of my hair, and bloodied the ax good, and stuck it
he back side, and slung the ax in the corner. Then I took up the pig and held
to my breast with my jacket (so he couldn't drip) till I got a good piece be-
the house and then dumped him into the river. Now I thought of something

So I went and got the bag of meal and my old saw out of the canoe and
hed them to the house. I took the bag to where it used to stand, and ripped
le in the bottom of it with the was, for there warn't no knives and forks on
place—pap done everything with his clasp-knife, about the cooking. Then
rried the sack about a hundred yards across the grass and through the willows
of the house, to a shallow lake that was five mile wide and full of rushes—
ducks too, you might say, in the season. There was a slough or a creek
ing out of it on the other side, that went miles away, I don't know where,
it didn't go to the river. The meal sifted out and made a little track all the
to the lake. I dropped pap's whetstone there too, so as to look like it had
n done by accident. Then I tied up the rip in the meal sack with a string,
t wouldn't leak no more, and took it and my saw to the canoe again.

It was about dark, now ; so I dropped the canoe down the river under some

willows that hung over the bank, and waited for the moon to rise. I made
to a willow ; then I took a bite to eat, and by-and-by laid down in the cano
smoke a pipe and lay out a plan. I says to myself, they'll follow the track
that sackful of rocks to the shore and then drag the river for me. And th
follow that meal track to the lake and go browsing down the creek that l
out of it to find the robbers that killed me and took the things. They w
ever hunt the river for anything but my dead carcass. They'll soon get tire
that, and won't bother no more about me. All right ; I can stop anywhe
want to. Jackson's Island is good enough for me ; I know that island pr
well, and nobody ever comes there. And then I can paddle over to town, nig
and slink around and pick up things I want. Jackson's Island's the place.

I was pretty tired, and the first thing I knowed, I was asleep. Whe
woke up I didn't know where I was, for a minute. I set up and loo
around, a little scared. Then I remembered. The river looked miles and m
across. The moon was so bright I could a counted the drift logs that wer
slipping along, black and still, hundred of yards out from shore. Everything
dead quiet, and it looked late, and *smelt* late. You know what I mean—I d
know the words to put it in.

I took a good gap and a stretch, and was just going to unhitch and start, w
I heard a sound away over the water. I listened. Pretty soon I made it out.
was that dull kind of a regular sound that comes from oars working in rowlo
when it's a still night. I peeped out through the willow branches, and th
it was—a skiff, away across the water. I couldn't tell how many was in it.
kept a-coming, and when it was abreast of me I see there warn't but one ma
it. Thinks I, maybe it's pap, though I warn't expecting him. He drop
below me, with the current, and by-and-by he come a-swinging up shore in
easy water, and he went by so close I could a reached out the gun and touc
him. Well, it *was* pap, sure enough—and sober, too, by the way he laid to
oars.

I didn't lose no time. The next minute I was a-spinning down stream soft
quick in the shade of the bank. I made two mile and a half, and then str
out a quarter of a mile or more towards the middle of the river, because pr
soon I would be passing the ferry landing and people might see me and I

I got out amongst the drift-wood and then laid down in the bottom of the
oe and let her float. I laid there and had a good rest and a smoke out of my
e, looking away into the sky, not a cloud in it. The sky looks ever so deep
n you lay down on your back in the moonshine; I never knowed it before.
l how far a body can hear on the water such nights! I heard people talking at
ferry landing. I heard what they said, too, every word of it. One man said
as getting towards the long days and the short nights, now. 'Tother one said

TAKING A REST.

warn't one of the short ones, he reckoned—and then they laughed, and he said it
again and they laughed again; then they waked up another fellow and told
, and laughed, but he didn't laugh; he ripped out something brisk and said le
alone. The first fellow said he 'lowed to tell it to his old woman—she would
k it was pretty good; but he said that warn't nothing to some things he had
in his time. I heard one man say it was nearly three o'clock, and he hoped
light wouldn't wait more than about a week longer. After that, the talk got
her and further away, and I couldn't make out the words any more, but I could
the mumble; and now and then a laugh, too, but it seemed a long ways off.

I was away below the ferry now. I rose up and there was Jacks
Island, about two mile and a half down stream, heavy-timbered and stand
up out of the middle of the river, big and dark and solid, like a steaml
without any lights. There warn't any signs of the bar at the head—it
all under water, now.

It didn't take me long to get there. I shot past the head at a ripp
rate, the current was so swift, and then I got into the dead water and lan
on the side towards the Illinois shore. I run the canoe into a deep dent
the bank that I knowed about; I had to part the willow branches to get
and when I made fast nobody could a seen the canoe from the outside.

I went up and set down on a log at the head of the island and loo
out on the big river and the black driftwood, and away over to the to
three mile away, where there was three or four lights twinkling. A monstr
big lumber raft was about a mile up stream, coming along down, witl
lantern in the middle of it. I watched it come creeping down, and wher
was most abreast of where I stood I heard a man say, " Stern oars, the
heave her head to stabboard !" I heard that just as plain as if the man
by my side.

There was a little gray in the sky, now; so I stepped into the woods a
laid down for a nap before breakfast.

Chapter VIII.

The SUN was up so high when I waked, that I judged it was after eight o'clock. I laid there in the grass and the cool shade, thinking about things and feeling rested and ruther comfortable and satisfied. I could see the sun out at one or two holes, but mostly it was big trees all about, and gloomy in there amongst them. There was freckled places on the ground where the light sifted down through the leaves, and the freckled places swapped about a little, showing there was a little breeze up there. A couple of squirrels set on a limb and jabbered at me very friendly.

I was powerful lazy and comfortable—

IN THE WOODS.

n't want to get up and cook breakfast. Well, I was dozing off again,
n I thinks I hears a deep sound of "boom!" away up the river. I
es up and rests on my elbow and listens; pretty soon I hears it again.
opped up and went and looked out at a hole in the leaves, and I see
unch of smoke laying on the water a long ways up—about abreast the
y. And there was the ferry-boat full of people, floating along down. I
wed what was the matter, now. "Boom!" I see the white smoke

squirt out of the ferry-boat's side. You see, they was firing cannon over
water, trying to make my carcass come to the top.

I was pretty hungry, but it warn't going to do for me to start a ʄ
because they might see the smoke. So I set there and watched the cann
smoke and listened to the boom. The river was a mile wide, there,
it always looks pretty on a summer morning—so I was having a good enoʋ
time seeing them hunt for my remainders, if I only had a bite to ɛ
Well, then I happened to think how they always put quicksilver in loɛ
of bread and float them off because they always go right to the drown
carcass and stop there. So says I, I'll keep a lookout, and if any of the
floating around after me, I'll give them a show. I changed to the Illiɪ
edge of the island to see what luck I could have, and I warn't disappoinʈ
A big double loaf come along, and I most got it, with a long stick,
my foot slipped and she floated out further. Of course I was where
current set in the closest to the shore—I knowed enough for that. But by-and
along comes another one, and this time I won. I took out the plug ɛ
shook out the little dab of quicksilver, and set my teeth in. It was "bak
bread"—what the quality eat—none of your low-down corn-pone.

I got a good place amongst the leaves, and set there on a log, munch
the bread and watching the ferry-boat, and very well satisfied. And t
something struck me. I says, now I reckon the widow or the parson
somebody prayed that this bread would find me, and here it has gone ɛ
done it. So there ain't no doubt but there is something in that thi
That is, there's something in it when a body like the widow or the paɪ
prays, but it don't work for me, and I reckon it don't work for only ;
the right kind.

I lit a pipe and had a good long smoke and went on watching. ʼ
ferry-boat was floating with the current, and I allowed I'd have a cha
to see who was aboard when she come along, because she would come
close, where the bread did. When she'd got pretty well along down towɛ
me, I put out my pipe and went to where I fished out the bread,
laid down behind a log on the bank in a little open place. Where
log forked I could peep through.

By-and-by she come along, and she drifted in so close that they could
run out a plank and walked ashore. Most everybody was on the boat.
, and Judge Thatcher, and Bessie Thatcher, and Jo Harper, and Tom
yer, and his old Aunt Polly, and Sid and Mary, and plenty more. Every-
was talking about the murder, but the captain broke in and says :
'Look sharp, now ; the current sets in the closest here, and maybe he's
ed ashore and got tangled amongst the brush at the water's edge. I hope so,
way."

didn't hope so. They all crowded up and leaned over the rails, nearly in
face, and kept still, watching with all their might. I could see them first-

, but they couldn't see
Then the captain sung
:
'Stand away !" and the
on let off such a blast
t before me that it made
deef with the noise and
ty near blind with the
ke, and I judged I was
. If they'd a had some
ets in, I reckon they'd a
the corpse they was after.
l, I see I warn't hurt,
aks to goodness. The boat
ed on and went out of sight
nd the shoulder of the isl-
, I could hear the boom-
now and then, further and
her off, and by-and-by after
hour, I didn't hear it no
. The island was three
long. I judged they had

WATCHING THE BOAT.

to the foot, and was giving it up. But they didn't yet a while. They turned

around the foot of the island and started up the channel on the Missouri s
under steam, and booming once in a while as they went. I crossed ove
that side and watched them. When they got abreast the head of the island t
quit shooting and dropped over to the Missouri shore and went home to
town.

I knowed I was all right now. Nobody else would come a-hunting after
I got my traps out of the canoe and made me a nice camp in the thick wo
I made a kind of a tent out of my blankets to put my things under so the
couldn't get at them. I catched a cat-fish and haggled him open with my s

DISCOVERING THE CAMP FIRE.

and towards sundown I sta
my camp fire and had sup
Then I set out a line to ca
some fish for breakfast.

When it was dark I set by
camp fire smoking, and fee
pretty satisfied; but by-and-l
got sort of lonesome, and s
went and set on the bank
listened to the currents wash
along, and counted the stars
drift-logs and rafts that c
down, and then went to b
there ain't no better way to
in time when you are loneso
you can't stay so, you soon
over it.

And so for three days
nights. No difference—just
same thing. But the next
I went exploring around d
through the island. I was boss of it; it all belonged to me, so to say, an
wanted to know all about it; but mainly I wanted to put in the time.
found plenty strawberries, ripe and prime; and green summer-grapes,

n razberries ; and the green blackberries was just beginning to show.
y would all come handy by-and-by, I judged.

Well, I went fooling along in the deep woods till I judged I warn't far from
foot of the island.   I had my gun along, but I hadn't shot nothing ; it was
protection ; thought I would kill some game nigh home.   About this time
ighty near stepped on a good sized snake, and it went sliding off through
grass and flowers, and I after it, trying to get a shot at it.   I clipped along,
all of a sudden I bounded right on to the ashes of a camp fire that was
smoking.

My heart jumped up amongst my lungs.   I never waited for to look further,
uncocked my gun and went sneaking back on my tip-toes as fast as ever I
d.   Every now and then I stopped a second, amongst the thick leaves, and
ned ; but my breath come so hard I couldn't hear nothing else.   I slunk
g another piece further, then listened again ; and so on, and so on ; if I
a stump, I took it for a man ; if I trod on a stick and broke it, it made me
like a person had cut one of my breaths in two and I only got half, and the
t half, too.

When I got to camp I warn't feeling very brash, there warn't much sand in
craw ; but I says, this ain't no time to be fooling around.   So I got all my
s into my canoe again so as to have them out of sight, and I put out the fire
scattered the ashes around to look like an old last year's camp, and then
nb a tree.

I reckon I was up in the tree two hours ; but I didn't see nothing, I didn't
nothing—I only *thought* I heard and seen as much as a thousand things.
l, I couldn't stay up there forever ; so at last I got down, but I kept in the
k woods and on the lookout all the time.   All I could get to eat was berries
what was left over from breakfast.

By the time it was night I was pretty hungry.   So when it was good and
k, I slid out from shore before moonrise and paddled over to the Illinois
k—about a quarter of a mile.   I went out in the woods and cooked a supper,
I had about made up my mind I would stay there all night, when I hear a
nkety-plunk, plunkety-plunk, and says to myself, horses coming ; and next I
people's voices.   I got everything into the canoe as quick as I could, and

then went creeping through the woods to see what I could find out. I ha
got far when I hear a man say :

" We better camp here, if we can find a good place ; the horses is about
out. Let's look around."

I didn't wait, but shoved out and paddled away easy. I tied up in the
place, and reckoned I would sleep in the canoe.

I didn't sleep much. I couldn't, somehow, for thinking. And every tim
waked up I thought somebody had me by the neck. So the sleep didn't do
no good. By-and-by I says to myself, I can't live this way ; I'm agoing to
out who it is that's here on the island with me ; I'll find it out or bust. We
felt better, right off.

So I took my paddle and slid out from shore just a step or two, and then
the canoe drop along down amongst the shadows. The moon was shining,
outside of the shadows it made it most as light as day. I poked along well
an hour, everything still as rocks and sound asleep. Well by this time I
most down to the foot of the island. A little ripply, cool breeze begun to b
and that was as good as saying the night was about done. I give her a turn v
the paddle and brung her nose to shore ; then I got my gun and slipped out
into the edge of the woods. I set down there on a log and looked out thro
the leaves. I see the moon go off watch and the darkness begin to blanket
river. But in a little while I see a pale streak over the tree-tops, and knowed
day was coming. So I took my gun and slipped off towards where I had
across that camp fire, stopping every minute or two to listen. But I hadn't
luck, somehow ; I couldn't seem to find the place. But by-and-by, sure enou
I catched a glimpse of fire, away through the trees. I went for it, cautious
slow. By-and-by I was close enough to have a look, and there laid a man on
ground. It most give me the fan-tods. He had a blanket around his head,
his head was nearly in the fire. I set there behind a clump of bushes
about six foot of him, and kept my eyes on him steady. It was getting
daylight, now. Pretty soon he gapped, and stretched himself, and hove
the blanket, and it was Miss Watson's Jim ! I bet I was glad to see him
says :

" Hello, Jim ! " and skipped out.

He bounced up and stared at me wild.   Then he drops down on his knees,
puts his hands together and says :

"Doan' hurt me—don't !   I hain't ever done no harm to a ghos'.   I awluz

JIM AND THE GHOST.

d dead people, en done all I could for 'em.   You go en git in de river agin,
h you b'longs, en doan' do nuffn to Ole Jim, 'at 'uz awluz yo' fren'."

Well, I warn't long making him understand I warn't dead.   I was ever so glad
e Jim.   I warn't lonesome, now.   I told him I warn't afraid of *him* telling
people where I was.   I talked along, but he only set there and looked at me ;
r said nothing.   Then I says :

" It's good daylight.   Le's get breakfast.   Make up your camp fire good."

" What's de use er makin' up de camp fire to cook strawbries en sich truck ?
you got a gun, hain't you ?   Den we kin git sumfn better den strawbries."

" Strawberries and such truck," I says.   " Is that what you live on ?"

" I couldn' git nuffn else," he says.

" Why, how long you been on the island, Jim ?"

" I come heah de night arter you's killed. "

" What, all that time?"

" Yes-indeedy."

" And ain't you had nothing but that kind of rubbage to eat ? "

" No, sah—nuffn else."

" Well, you must be most starved, ain't you ? '

" I reck'n I could eat a hoss. I think I could. How long you ben o᠎ islan' ? "

" Since the night I got killed."

" No ! W'y, what has you lived on ? But you got a gun. Oh, yes, you g᠎ gun. Dat's good. Now you kill sumfn en I'll make up de fire."

So we went over to where the canoe was, and while he built a fire in a gr᠎ open place amongst the trees, I fetched meal and bacon and coffee, and coffee᠎ and frying-pan, and sugar and tin cups, and the nigger was set back consi᠎ able, because he reckoned it was all done with witchcraft. I catched a good᠎ cat-fish, too, and Jim cleaned him with his knife, and fried him.

When breakfast was ready, we lolled on the grass and eat it smoking ᠎ Jim laid it in with all his might, for he was most about starved. Then wher᠎ had got pretty well stuffed, we laid off and lazied.

By-and-by Jim says :

" But looky here, Huck, who wuz it dat 'uz killed in dat shanty, ef it wa᠎ you ? "

Then I told him the whole thing, and he said it was smart. He said ᠎ Sawyer couldn't get up no better plan than what I had. Then I says :

" How do you come to be here, Jim, and how'd you get here ? "

He looked pretty uneasy, and didn't say nothing for a minute. Then᠎ says :

" Maybe I better not tell."

" Why, Jim ? "

" Well, dey's reasons. But you wouldn' tell on me ef I 'uz to tell you, wo᠎ you, Huck ? "

" Blamed if I would, Jim."

" Well, I b'lieve you, Huck. I—I *run off.*"

" Jim ! "

'But mind, you said you wouldn't tell—you know you said you wouldn't tell,
k."

' Well, I did. I said I wouldn't, and I'll stick to it. Honest *injun* I will.
ple would call me a low down Ablitionist and despise me for keeping mum—
that don't make no difference. I ain't agoing to tell, and I ain't agoing back
e anyways. So now, le's know all about it."

' Well, you see, it 'uz dis way. Ole Missus—dat's Miss Watson—she pecks
ne all de time, en treats me pooty rough, but she awluz said she wouldn'
me down to Orleans. But I noticed dey wuz a nigger trader roun' de place
idable, lately, en I begin to git oneasy. Well, one night I creeps to de
pooty late, en de do' warn't quite shet, en I hear ole missus tell de
ler she gwyne to sell me down to Orleans, but she didn' want to, but she
d git eight hund'd dollars for me, en it 'uz sich a big stack o' money she
dn' resis'. De widder she try to git her to say she wouldn' do it, but I
er waited to hear de res'. I lit out mighty quick, I tell you.

' I tuck out en shin down de hill en 'spec to steal a skift 'long de sho'
'ers 'bove de town, but dey wuz people a-stirrin' yit, so I hid in de ole
ble-down cooper shop on de bank to wait for everybody to go 'way. Well,
uz dah all night. Dey wuz somebody roun' all de time. 'Long 'bout six
le mawnin', skifts begin to go by, en 'bout eight er nine every skift dat
t 'long wuz talkin' 'bout how yo' pap come over to de town en say you's
d. Dese las' skifts wuz full o' ladies en genlmen agoin' over for to see
place. Sometimes dey'd pull up at de sho' en take a res' b'fo' dey started
st, so by de talk I got to know all 'bout de killin'. I 'uz powerful sorry
s killed, Huck, but I ain't no mo', now.

' I laid dah under de shavins all day. I 'uz hungry, but I warn't afeared ;
ase I knowed ole missus en de widder wuz goin' to start to de camp-meetn'
t arter breakfas' en be gone all day, en dey knows I goes off wid de cattle
t daylight, so dey wouldn' 'spec to see me roun' de place, en so dey
ldn' miss me tell arter dark in de evenin'. De yuther servants wouldn'
s me, kase dey'd shin out en take holiday, soon as de ole folks 'uz out'n
way.

' Well, when it come dark I tuck out up de river road, en went 'bout

two mile er more to whah dey warn't no houses. I'd made up my
'bout what I's agwyne to do. You see ef I kep' on tryin' to git away a
de dogs 'ud track me; ef I stole a skift to cross over, dey'd miss dat s
you see, en dey'd know 'bout whah I'd lan' on de yuther side en wha
pick up my track. So I says, a raff is what I's arter; it doan' *make*
track.

"I see a light a-comin' roun' de p'int, bymeby, so I wade' in en sho
log ahead o' me, en swum more'n half-way acrost de river, en got in 'mo
de drift-wood, en kep' my head down low, en kinder swum agin de cur
tell de raff come along. Den I swum to de stern uv it, en tuck aholt.
clouded up en 'uz pooty dark for a little while. So I clumb up en
down on de planks. De men 'uz all 'way yonder in de middle, wha
lantern wuz. De river wuz arisin' en dey wuz a good current; so I reck
'at by fo' in de mawnin' I'd be twenty-five mile down de river, en den I'd
in, jis' b'fo' daylight, en swim asho' en take to de woods on de Illinoi s

"But I didn' have no luck. When we 'uz mos' down to de head e
islan', a man begin to come aft wid de lantern. I see it warn't no use
to wait, so I slid overboad, en struck out fer de islan'. Well, I had a no
I could lan' mos' anywhers, but I couldn't—bank too bluff. I 'uz mos
de foot er de islan' b'fo' I foun' a good place. I went into de woods
jedged I wouldn' fool wid raffs no mo', long as dey move de lantern r
so. I had my pipe en a plug er dog-leg, en some matches in my cap, en
warn't wet, so I 'uz all right."

"And so you ain't had no meat nor bread to eat all this time?
didn't you get mud-turkles?"

"How you gwyne to git'm? You can't slip up on um en grab um;
how's a body gwyne to hit um wid a rock? How could a body do it i
night? en I warn't gwyne to show mysef on de bank in de daytime."

"Well, that's so. You've had to keep in the woods all the time,
course. Did you hear 'em shooting the cannon?"

"Oh, yes. I knowed dey was arter you. I see um go by heah; wat
um thoo de bushes."

Some young birds come along, flying a yard or two at a time and light

said it was a sign it was going to rain. He said it was a sign when young
kens flew that way, and so he reckoned it was the same way when young
s done it. I was going to catch some of them, but Jim wouldn't let me.
said it was death. He said his father laid mighty sick once, and some of
n catched a bird, and his old granny said his father would die, and he

And Jim said you musn't count the things you are going to cook for dinner,
use that would bring bad luck. The same if you shook the table-cloth
r sundown. And he said if a man owned a bee-hive, and that man died,
bees must be told about it before sun-up next morning, or else the bees
ld all weaken down and quit work and die. Jim said bees wouldn't sting
ts ; but I didn't believe that, because I had tried them lots of times
elf, and they wouldn't sting me.

I had heard about some of these things before, but not all of them.
knowed all kinds of signs. He said he knowed most everything.
id it looked to me like all the signs was about bad luck, and so I asked
if there warn't any good-luck signs. He says :

" Mighty few—an' *dey* ain' no use to a body. What you want to
w when good luck's a-comin' for ? want to keep it off ? " And he said :
f you's got hairy arms en a hairy breas', it's a sign dat you's agwyne
e rich. Well, dey's some use in a sign like dat, ' kase it's so fur
d. You see, maybe you's got to be po' a long time fust, en so you
ht git discourage' en kill yo'sef 'f you didn' know by de sign dat you
ne to be rich bymeby."

" Have you got hairy arms and a hairy breast, Jim ? "

" What's de use to ax dat question ? don' you see I has ? "

" Well, are you rich ? "

" No, but I ben rich wunst, and gwyne to be rich agin   Wunst I had
en dollars, but I tuck to specalat'n', en got busted out."

" What did you speculate in, Jim ? "

" Well, fust I tackled stock."

" What kind of stock ? "

" Why, live stock. Cattle, you know. I put ten dollars in a cow.

But I ain' gwyne to resk no mo' money in stock.   De cow up 'n' ⟨
on my han's."

"So you lost the ten dollars."

"No, I didn' lose it all.   I on'y los' 'bout nine of it.   I sole de hide ⟨
taller for a dollar en ten cents."

"You had five dollars and ten cents left.   Did you speculate
more ?"

"Yes.   You know dat one-laigged nigger dat b'longs to old M⟨

MISTO BRADISH'S NIGGER.

Bradish ? well, he sot up ⟨
bank, en say anybody dat ⟨
in a dollar would git ⟨
dollars mo' at de en' er ⟨
year. Well, all de niggers w⟨
in, but dey didn' have mu⟨
I wuz de on'y one dat ⟨
much.   So I stuck out for ⟨
dan fo' dollars, en I said ⟨
didn' git it I'd start a b⟨
mysef.   Well o' course ⟨
nigger want' to keep me out⟨
de business, bekase he ⟨
dey warn't business 'nough ⟨
two banks, so he say I co⟨
put in my five dollars en ⟨
pay me thirty-five at de ⟨
er de year.

"So I done it.   De⟨
reck'n'd I'd inves' de thi⟨
five dollars right off en k⟨
things a-movin'.   Dey wu⟨

nigger name' Bob, dat had ketched a wood-flat, en his marster di⟨
know it; en I bought it off'n him en told him to take de thirty-⟨
dollars when de en' er de year come ; but somebody stole de wood-flat ⟨

t, en nex' day de one-laigged nigger say de bank 's busted. So dey
' none uv us git no money."

' What did you do with the ten cents, Jim ?"

'Well, I 'uz gwyne to spen' it, but I had a dream, en de dream tole
to give it to a nigger name' Balum—Balum's Ass dey call him for short,
one er dem chuckle-heads, you know. But he's lucky, dey say, en I
I warn't lucky. De dream say let Balum inves' de ten cents en he'd
e a raise for me. Well, Balum he tuck de money, en when he wuz
hurch he hear de preacher say dat whoever give to de po' len' to de
d, en boun' to git his money back a hund'd times. So Balum he tuck
give de ten cents to de po,' en laid low to see what wuz gwyne to
e of it."

"Well, what did come of it, Jim ?"

'Nuffn' never come of it. I couldn' manage to k'leck dat money no
; en Balum he couldn'. I ain' gwyne to len' no mo' money 'dout I
de security. Boun' to git yo' money back a hund'd times, de preacher
! Ef I could git de ten *cents* back, I'd call it squah, en be glad er
chanst."

"Well, it's all right, anyway, Jim, long as you're going to be rich
n some time or other."

"Yes—en I's rich now, come to look at it. I owns mysef, en I's
h eight hund'd dollars. I wisht I had de money, I wouldn' want no
."

Chapter IX

I WANTED to go and look a[t] place right about the middle [of] the island, that I'd found wh[en I] was exploring; so we started, [and] soon got to it, because the isl[and] was only three miles long an[d a] quarter of a mile wide.

This place was a tolerable l[ong,] steep hill or ridge, about f[orty] foot high. We had a rough t[ime] getting to the top, the sides [were] so steep and the bushes so th[ick.] We tramped and clumb aro[und] all over it, and by-and-by fo[und] a good big cavern in the ro[ck,] most up to the top on the s[ide] towards Illinois. The cavern [was] as big as two or three ro[oms] bunched together, and Jim co[uld] stand up straight in it. It [was] cool in there. Jim was for putt[ing] our traps in there, right aw[ay,] but I said we didn't want to [be]

EXPLORING THE CAVE.

climbing up and down there all the time.

Jim said if we had the canoe hid in a good place, and had all [the] traps in the cavern, we could rush there if anybody was to come to [the] island, and they would never find us without dogs. And besides, he s[aid] them little birds had said it was going to rain, and did I want the thi[ngs] to get wet?

So we went back and got the canoe and paddled up abreast the cavern, and
ged all the traps up there.   Then we hunted up a place close by to hide the
oe in, amongst the thick willows.   We took some fish off of the lines and
them again, and begun to get ready for dinner.

The door of the cavern was big enough to roll a hogshead in, and on one
 of the door the floor stuck out a little bit and was flat and a good place to
d a fire on.   So we built it there and cooked dinner.

We spread the blankets inside for a carpet, and eat our dinner in there.

IN THE CAVE.

put all the other things handy at the back of the cavern.   Pretty soon it
kened up and begun to thunder and lighten ; so the birds was right about it.
ctly it begun to rain, and it rained like all fury, too, and I never see the
l blow so.   It was one of these regular summer storms.   It would get so
k that it looked all blue-black outside, and lovely ; and the rain would thrash
g by so thick that the trees off a little ways looked dim and spider-webby ;
here would come a blast of wind that would bend the trees down and turn
he pale underside of the leaves ; and then a perfect ripper of a gust would
w along and set the branches to tossing their arms as if they was just wild ;

and next, when it was just about the bluest and blackest—*fst !* it was as bri
as glory and you'd have a little glimpse of tree-tops a-plunging about, away
yonder in the storm, hundreds of yards further than you could see before ; d
as sin again in a second, and now you'd hear the thunder let go with an av
crash and then go rumbling, grumbling, tumbling down the sky towards
under side of the world, like rolling empty barrels down stairs, where it's l
stairs and they bounce a good deal, you know.

"Jim, this is nice," I says. "I wouldn't want to be nowhere else but h
Pass me along another hunk of fish and some hot corn-bread."

"Well, you wouldn't a ben here, 'f it hadn't a ben for Jim. You'd a
down dah in de woods widout any dinner, en gittn' mos' drownded, too, dat
would, honey. Chickens knows when its gwyne to rain, en so do de birds, chi

The river went on raising and raising for ten or twelve days, till at last it
over the banks. The water was three or four foot deep on the island in the
places and on the Illinois bottom. On that side it was a good many miles wi
but on the Missouri side it was the same old distance across—a half a mi
because the Missouri shore was just a wall of high bluffs.

Daytimes we paddled all over the island in the canoe. It was mighty
and shady in the deep woods even if the sun was blazing outside. We w
winding in and out amongst the trees ; and sometimes the vines hung so th
we had to back away and go some other way. Well, on every old broken-d
tree, you could see rabbits, and snakes, and such things ; and when the isl
had been overflowed a day or two, they got so tame, on account of being hun,
that you could paddle right up and put your hand on them if you wanted
but not the snakes and turtles—they would slide off in the water. The ri
our cavern was in, was full of them. We could a had pets enough if we'd wa
them.

One night we catched a little section of a lumber raft—nice pine pla
It was twelve foot wide and about fifteen or sixteen foot long, and the top st
above water six or seven inches, a solid level floor. We could see saw-log
by in the daylight, sometimes, but we let them go ; we didn't show ourselve
daylight.

Another night, when we was up at the head of the island, just before dayli

e comes a frame house down, on the west side. She was a two-story, and
d over, considerable. We paddled out and got aboard—clumb in at an
stairs window. But it was too dark to see yet, so we made the canoe fast
set in her to wait for daylight.

The light begun to come before we got to the foot of the island. Then we
ked in at the window. We could make out a bed, and a table, and two old
rs, and lots of things around about on the floor; and there was clothes

JIM SEES A DEAD MAN.

ging against the wall. There was something laying on the floor in the far
er that looked like a man. So Jim says:

"Hello, you!"

But it didn't budge. So I hollered again, and then Jim says:

"De man ain't asleep—he's dead. You hold still—I'll go en see."

He went and bent down and looked, and says:

"It's a dead man. Yes, indeedy; naked, too. He's ben shot in de back.
ck'n he's ben dead two er three days. Come in, Huck, but doan' look at his
—it's too gashly."

I didn't look at him at all. Jim throwed some old rags over him, but
needn't done it; I didn't want to see him.   There was heaps of old gre
cards scattered around over the floor, and old whisky bottles, and a couple
masks made out of black cloth ; and all over the walls was the ignorantest k
of words and pictures, made with charcoal. There was two old dirty cal
dresses, and a sun-bonnet, and some women's under-clothes, hanging agai
the wall, and some men's clothing, too. We put the lot into the canoe ; it mi
come good. There was a boy's old speckled straw hat on the floor ; I took t
too. And there was a bottle that had had milk in it ; and it had a rag stop
for a baby to suck. We would a took the bottle, but it was broke. There
a seedy old chest, and an old hair trunk with the hinges broke. They stood op
but there warn't nothing left in them that was any account. The way things
scattered about, we reckoned the people left in a hurry and warn't fixed so a
carry off most of their stuff.

We got an old tin lantern, and a butcher knife without any handle, and a br
new Barlow knife worth two bits in any store, and a lot of tallow candles, an
tin candlestick, and a gourd, and a tin cup, and a ratty old bed-quilt off the b
and a reticule with needles and pins and beeswax and buttons and thread and
such truck in it, and a hatchet and some nails, and a fish-line as thick as
little finger, with some monstrous hooks on it, and a roll of buckskin, and a leat
dog-collar, and a horse-shoe, and some vials of medicine that didn't have no la
on them ; and just as we was leaving I found a tolerable good curry-comb, and
he found a ratty old fiddle-bow, and a wooden leg. The straps was broke off o
but barring that, it was a good enough leg, though it was too long for me and
long enough for Jim, and we couldn't find the other one, though we hunted
around.

And so, take it all around, we made a good haul. When we was ready to sh
off, we was a quarter of a mile below the island, and it was pretty broad day ;
made Jim lay down in the canoe and cover up with the quilt, because if he set
people could tell he was a nigger a good ways off. I paddled over to the Illi
shore, and drifted down most a half a mile doing it. I crept up the dead w
under the bank, and hadn't no accidents and didn't see nobody. We got h
all safe.

Chapter X.

THEY FOUND EIGHT DOLLARS.

AFTER breakfast I wanted to talk about the dead man and guess out how he come to be killed, but Jim didn't want to. He said it would fetch bad luck; and besides, he said, he might come and ha'nt us; he said a man that warn't buried was more likely to go a-ha'nting around than one that was planted and comfortable. That sounded pretty reasonable, so I didn't say no more; but I couldn't keep from studying over it and wishing I knowed who shot the man, and what they done it for.

We rummaged the clothes we'd got, and found eight dollars in silver sewed up in the lining of an old blanket over-coat. Jim said he reckoned the people in that house stole the coat, because ΄hey'd a knowed the money was there they wouldn't a left it. I said I reckoned y killed him, too; but Jim didn't want to talk about that. I says:

" Now you think it's bad luck; but what did you say when I fetched in the ke-skin that I found on the top of the ridge day before yesterday? You said ̇vas the worst bad luck in the world to touch a snake-skin with my hands. ll, here's your bad luck! We've raked in all this truck and eight dollars be-̇s. I wish we could have some bad luck like this every day, Jim."

"Never you mind, honey, never you mind. Don't you git too peart.
a-comin'. Mind I tell you, it's a-comin'."

It did come, too. It was a Tuesday that we had that talk. Well, after din
Friday, we was laying around in the grass at the upper end of the ridge, and
out of tobacco. I went to the cavern to get some, and found a rattlesnake
there. I killed him, and curled him up on the foot of Jim's blanket, ever
natural, thinking there'd be some fun when Jim found him there. Well,
night I forgot all about the snake, and when Jim flung himself down on

JIM AND THE SNAKE.

blanket while I struck a lig
the snake's mate was th
and bit him.

He jumped up yelling,
the first thing the light sho
was the varmint curled up
ready for another spring. I
him out in a second with
stick, and Jim grabbed pa
whisky jug and begun to p
it down.

He was barefooted, and
snake bit him right on the h
That all comes of my be
such a fool as to not remem
that wherever you leave a d
snake its mate always co
there and curls around it.
told me to chop off the sna
head and throw it away, a
then skin the body and roas
piece of it. I done it, and
eat it and said it would h

cure him. He made me take off the rattles and tie them around his wrist, t
He said that that would help. Then I slid out quiet and throwed the sna

r away amongst the bushes; for I warn't going to let Jim find out it was
ny fault, not if I could help it.

Jim sucked and sucked at the jug, and now and then he got out of his
d and pitched around and yelled; but every time he come to himself he went to
king at the jug again. His foot swelled up pretty big, and so did his leg;
by-and-by the drunk begun to come, and so I judged he was all right; but
druther been bit with a snake than pap's whisky.

Jim was laid up for four days and nights. Then the swelling was all gone and
was around again. I made up my mind I wouldn't ever take aholt of a
ke-skin again with my hands,
r that I see what had come of
Jim said he reckoned I would
eve him next time. And he
l that handling a snake-skin was
h awful bad luck that maybe
hadn't got to the end of it yet.
said he druther see the new
on over his left shoulder as much
a thousand times than take up a
ke-skin in his hand. Well, I
s getting to feel that way myself,
ugh I've always reckoned that
king at the new moon over your
shoulder is one of the carelessest
l foolishest things a body can do.
l Hank Bunker done it once, and
gged about it; and in less than
years he got drunk and fell off
he shot tower and spread himself

OLD HANK BUNKER.

so that he was just a kind of a layer, as you may say; and they slid him
eways between two barn doors for a coffin, and buried him so, so they say, but
dn't see it. Pap told me. But anyway, it all come of looking at the moon
t way, like a fool.

Well, the days went along, and the river went down between its banks aga[?] and about the first thing we done was to bait one of the big hooks with a skin[?] rabbit and set it and catch a cat-fish that was as big as a man, being six foot t[?] inches long, and weighed over two hundred pounds. We couldn't handle hi[?] of course ; he would a flung us into Illinois. We just set there and watched h[?] rip and tear around till he drownded. We found a brass button in his stoma[?] and a round ball, and lots of rubbage. We split the ball open with the hatch[?] and there was a spool in it. Jim said he'd had it there a long time, to coa[?]

"A FAIR FIT."

over so and make a ball of it. It was as big a fish as was ever catched in Mississippi, I reckon. Jim said he hadn't ever seen a bigger one. He woul[?] been worth a good deal over at the village. They peddle out such a fish as t[?] by the pound in the market house there ; everybody buys some of him ; meat's as white as snow and makes a good fry.

Next morning I said it was getting slow and dull, and I wanted to ge[?] stirring up, some way. I said I reckoned I would slip over the river and find[?] what was going on. Jim liked that notion ; but he said I must go in the d[?]

d look sharp. Then he studied it over and said, couldn't I put on some of
em old things and dress up like a girl ? That was a good notion, too. So we
ortened up one of the calico gowns and I turned up my trowser-legs to my
ees and got into it. Jim hitched it behind with the hooks, and it was a fair
 I put on the sun-bonnet and tied it under my chin, and then for a body to
k in and see my face was like looking down a joint of stove-pipe. Jim said
body would know me, even in the daytime, hardly. I practiced around all day
get the hang of the things, and by-and-by I could do pretty well in them, only
m said I didn't walk like a girl ; and he said I must quit pulling up my gown
get at my britches pocket. I took notice, and done better.

I started up the Illinois shore in the canoe just after dark.

I started across to the town from a little below the ferry landing, and the
ift of the current fetched me in at the bottom of the town. I tied up and
rted along the bank. There was a light burning in a little shanty that hadn't
en lived in for a long time, and I wondered who had took up quarters there. I
pped up and peeped in at the window. There was a woman about forty year
l in there, knitting by a candle that was on a pine table. I didn't know her
e ; she was a stranger, for you couldn't start a face in that town that I didn't
ow. Now this was lucky, because I was weakening ; I was getting afraid I
d come ; people might know my voice and find me out. But if this woman
d been in such a little town two days she could tell me all I wanted to know ;
I knocked at the door, and made up my mind I wouldn't forget I was a girl.

Chapter XI.

"COME IN."

"COME in," says the woman, and I di
She says:

"Take a cheer."

I done it. She looked me all ov
with her little shiny eyes, and says:

"What might your name be?"

"Sarah Williams."

"Where 'bouts do you live? In t
neighborhood?"

"No'm. In Hookerville, seven m
below. I've walked all the way and I
all tired out."

"Hungry, too, I reckon. I'll fi
you something."

"No'm, I ain't hungry. I was
hungry I had to stop two mile bel
here at a farm; so I ain't hungry
more. It's what makes me so late. My mother's down sick, and out of mon
and everything, and I come to tell my uncle Abner Moore. He lives at t
upper end of the town, she says. I hain't ever been here before. Do y
know him?"

"No; but I don't know everybody yet. I haven't lived here quite two week
It's a considerable ways to the upper end of the town. You better stay here
night. Take off your bonnet."

" No," I says, " I'll rest a while, I reckon, and go on. I ain't afeard of the
k."

She said she wouldn't let me go by myself, but her husband would be in by-
-by, maybe in a hour and a half, and she'd send him along with me. Then she
to talking about her husband, and about her relations up the river, and her
tions down the river, and about how much better off they used to was, and how
y didn't know but they'd made a mistake coming to our town, instead of let-
g well alone—and so on and so on, till I was afeard *I* had made a mistake com-
to her to find out what was going on in the town ; but by-and-by she
pped onto pap and the murder, and then I was pretty willing to let her clatter
t along. She told about me and Tom Sawyer finding the six thousand
lars (only she got it ten) and all about pap and what a hard lot he was,
what a hard lot I was, and at last she got down to where I was murdered.
ys :

" Who done it ? We've heard considerable about these goings on, down in
okerville, but we don't know who 'twas that killed Huck Finn."

" Well, I reckon there's a right smart chance of people *here* that 'd like to
w who killed him. Some thinks old Finn done it himself."

" No—is that so ? "

" Most everybody thought it at first. He'll never know how nigh he come to
ting lynched. But before night they changed around and judged it was done
a runaway nigger named Jim."

" Why *he*——"

I stopped. I reckoned I better keep still. She run on, and never noticed I
put in at all.

" The nigger run off the very night Huck Finn was killed. So there's a re-
rd out for him—three hundred dollars. And there's a reward out for old Finn
—two hundred dollars. You see, he come to town the morning after the
rder, and told about it, and was out with 'em on the ferry-boat hunt, and
ht away after he up and left. Before night they wanted to lynch him, but he
s gone, you see. Well, next day they found out the nigger was gone ; they
nd out he hadn't ben seen sence ten o'clock the night the murder was done.
then they put it on him, you see, and while they was full of it, next day back

comes old Finn and went boo-hooing to Judge Thatcher to get money to hu for the nigger all over Illinois with. The judge give him some, and that eveni he got drunk and was around till after midnight with a couple of mighty hard loo ing strangers, and then went off with them. Well, he hain't come back sen and they ain't looking for him back till this thing blows over a little, for peo thinks now that he killed his boy and fixed things so folks would think robbers do it, and then he'd get Huck's money without having to bother a long time with lawsuit. People do say he warn't any too good to do it. Oh, he's sly, I reck If he don't come back for a year, he'll be all right. You can't prove anything him, you know; everything will be quieted down then, and he'll walk into Huc money as easy as nothing."

"Yes, I reckon so, 'm. I don't see nothing in the way of it. Has everybo quit thinking the nigger done it ?"

"Oh, no, not everybody. A good many thinks he done it. But they'll the nigger pretty soon, now, and maybe they can scare it out of him."

"Why, are they after him yet ?"

"Well, you're innocent, ain't you ! Does three hundred dollars lay rou every day for people to pick up ? Some folks thinks the nigger ain't far fr here. I'm one of them—but I hain't talked it around. A few days ago I w talking with an old couple that lives next door in the log shanty, and they happen to say hardly anybody ever goes to that island over yonder that they call Jackso Island. Don't anybody live there ? says I. No, nobody, says they. I didn't any more, but I done some thinking. I was pretty near certain I'd seen smo over there, about the head of the island, a day or two before that, so I says to m self, like as not that nigger's hiding over there ; anyway, says I, it's worth t trouble to give the place a hunt. I hain't seen any smoke sence, so I reck maybe he's gone, if it was him ; but husband's going over to see—him and anotl man. He was gone up the river ; but he got back to-day and I told him as so as he got here two hours ago."

I had got so uneasy I couldn't set still. I had to do something with hands ; so I took up a needle off of the table and went to threading it. hands shook, and I was making a bad job of it. When the woman stopp talking, I looked up, and she was looking at me pretty curious, and smiling

le. I put down the needle and thread and let on to be interested—and I was,
—and says :

"Three hundred dollars is a power of money. I wish my mother could get

Is your husband going
r there to-night ?"

"Oh, yes. He went up
n with the man I was
ling you of, to get a boat
l see if they could borrow
ther gun. They'll go over
er midnight."

"Couldn't they see better
they was to wait till day-
e ?"

"Yes. And couldn't the
ger see better, too ? After
lnight he'll likely be asleep,
l they can slip around
ough the woods and hunt
his camp fire all the better
the dark, if he's got one."

"I didn't think of that."

The woman kept looking

" HIM AND ANOTHER MAN."

me pretty curious, and I didn't feel a bit comfortable. Pretty soon she says :

"What did you say your name was, honey ?"

"M—Mary Williams."

Somehow it didn't seem to me that I said it was Mary before, so I didn't
k up; seemed to me I said it was Sarah ; so I felt sort of cornered, and
s afeared maybe I was looking it, too. I wished the woman would say some-
ng more ; the longer she set still, the uneasier I was. But now she says :

"Honey, I thought you said it was Sarah when you first come in ?"

"Oh, yes'm, I did. Sarah Mary Williams. Sarah's my first name. Some
ls me Sarah, some calls me Mary."

" Oh, that's the way of it ? "

" Yes'm."

I was feeling better, then, but I wished I was out of there, anyway. couldn't look up yet.

Well, the woman fell to talking about how hard times was, and how p₀ they had to live, and how the rats was as free as if they owned the pla and so forth, and so on, and then I got easy again. She was right abo the rats. You'd see one stick his nose out of a hole in the corner ev₀ little while. She said she had to have things handy to throw at them wh she was alone, or they wouldn't give her no peace. She showed me a ▶ of lead, twisted up into a knot, and said she was a good shot with generly, but she'd wrenched her arm a day or two ago, and didn't kn₀ whether she could throw true, now. But she watched for a chance, a directly she banged away at a rat, but she missed him wide, and said " Ouch it hurt her arm so. Then she told me to try for the next one. I want to be getting away before the old man got back, but of course I didn't let ₀ I got the thing, and the first rat that showed his nose I let drive, and if h₀ a stayed where he was he'd a been a tolerable sick rat. She said that that was fir rate, and she reckoned I would hive the next one. She went and got the lum of lead and fetched it back and brought along a hank of yarn, which she wan₀ me to help her with. I held up my two hands and she put the hank over th₀ and went on talking about her and her husband's matters. But she broke to say :

" Keep your eye on the rats. You better have the lead in your lap, handy₀

So she dropped the lump into my lap, just at that moment, and I clapped ₀ legs together on it and she went on talking. But only about a minute. Th₀ she took off the hank and looked me straight in the face, but very pleasant, a₀ says :

" Come, now—what's your real name ? "

" Wh-what, mum ? "

" What's your real name ? Is it Bill, or Tom, or Bob ?—or what is it ? "

I reckon I shook like a leaf, and I didn't know hardly what to do. But says :

" Please to don't poke fun at a poor girl like me, mum. If I'm in the way,
e, I'll——"

" No, you won't. Set down and stay where you are. I ain't going to hurt
, and I ain't going to tell on you, nuther. You just tell me your secret, and
st me. I'll keep it ; and what's more, I'll help you. So'll my old man, if you
at him to. You see, you're a runaway 'prentice—that's all. It ain't any-
ng. There ain't any harm in it. You've been treated bad, and you made up
ar mind to cut. Bless you, child, I wouldn't tell on you. Tell me all about
now—that's a good boy."

So I said it wouldn't be no use to try to play it any longer, and I would just
ke a clean breast and tell her everything, but she mustn't go back on her
mise. Then I told her my father and mother was dead, and the law had
and me out to a mean old farmer in the country thirty mile back from the
er, and he treated me so bad I couldn't stand it no longer ; he went away to
gone a couple of days, and so I took my chance and stole some of his daugh-
's old clothes, and cleared out, and I had been three nights coming the thirty
les ; I traveled nights, and hid day-times and slept, and the bag of bread and
at I carried from home lasted me all the way and I had a plenty. I said I
ieved my uncle Abner Moore would take care of me, and so that was why I
uck out for this town of Goshen."

" Goshen, child ? This ain't Goshen. This is St. Petersburg. Goshen's ten
le further up the river. Who told you this was Goshen ?"

" Why, a man I met at day-break this morning, just as I was going to turn
o the woods for my regular sleep. He told me when the roads forked I must
ke the right hand, and five mile would fetch me to Goshen."

" He was drunk I reckon. He told you just exactly wrong."

" Well, he did act like he was drunk, but it ain't no matter now. I got to be
ving along. I'll fetch Goshen before day-light."

" Hold on a minute. I'll put you up a snack to eat. You might want it."
So she put me up a snack, and says :

" Say—when a cow's laying down, which end of her gets up first ? Answer
prompt, now—don't stop to study over it. Which end gets up first ?"

" The hind end, mum."

" Well, then, a horse ? "

" The for'rard end, mum."

Which side of a tree does the most moss grow on ? "

SHE PUTS UP A SNACK.

" North side."

" If fifteen cows is browsing a hillside, how many of them e with their heads pointed the sa direction ? "

" The whole fifteen, mum.'

" Well, I reckon you *have* liv in the country. I thought may you was trying to hocus again. What's your real nam now ? "

" George Peters, mum."

" Well, try to remember George. Don't forget and tell it's Elexander before you go, a then get out by saying it's Geor Elexander when I catch y And don't go about women that old calico. You do a g tolerable poor, but you mig fool men, maybe. Bless y child, when you set out to thre a needle, don't hold the thread still and fetch the needle up to it ; h the needle still and poke the thread at it—that's the way a woman most alw does ; but a man always does 'tother way. And when you throw at a rat anything, hitch yourself up a tip-toe, and fetch your hand up over your head awkard as you can, and miss your rat about six or seven foot. Throw stiff-arm from the shoulder, like there was a pivot there for it to turn on—like a girl ; from the wrist and elbow, with your arm out to one side, like a boy. And mi you, when a girl tries to catch anything in her lap, she throws her knees apa

don't clap them together, the way you did when you catched the lump of
l.   Why, I spotted you for a boy when you was threading the needle ; and I
trived the other things just to make certain.   Now trot along to your uncle,
ah Mary Williams George Elexander Peters, and if you get into trouble you
d word to Mrs. Judith Loftus, which is me, and I'll do what I can to get you
of it.   Keep the river road, all the way, and next time you tramp, take shoes

"HUMP YOURSELF."

socks with you. The river road's a rocky one, and your feet 'll be in a
dition when you get to Goshen, I reckon."

I went up the bank about fifty yards, and then I doubled on my tracks and
ped back to where my canoe was, a good piece below the house. I jumped in
was off in a hurry. I went up stream far enough to make the head of the
nd, and then started across. I took off the sun-bonnet, for I didn't want no
ders on, then. When I was about the middle, I hear the clock begin to
ke ; so I stops and listens ; the sound come faint over the water, but clear—
en. When I struck the head of the island I never waited to blow, though I

was most winded, but I shoved right into the timber where my old camp us
to be, and started a good fire there on a high-and-dry spot.

Then I jumped in the canoe and dug out for our place a mile and a h
below, as hard as I could go. I landed, and slopped through the timber a
up the ridge and into the cavern. There Jim laid, sound asleep on the groun
I roused him out and says :

"Git up and hump yourself, Jim ! There ain't a minute to lose. They
after us !"

Jim never asked no questions, he never said a word ; but the way he work
for the next half an hour showed about how he was scared. By that ti
everything we had in the world was on our raft and she was ready to be show
out from the willow cove where she was hid. We put out the camp fire
the cavern the first thing, and didn't show a candle outside after that.

I took the canoe out from shore a little piece and took a look, but if the
was a boat around I couldn't see it, for stars and shadows ain't good to see I
Then we got out the raft and slipped along down in the shade, past the f
of the island dead still, never saying a word.

Chapter XII.

ON THE RAFT.

IT MUST a been close onto one o'clock when we got below the island at last, and the raft did seem to go mighty slow. If a boat was to come along, we was going to take to the canoe and break for the Illinois shore; and it was well a boat didn't come, for we hadn't ever thought to put the gun into the canoe, or a fishing-line or anything to eat. We was in ruther too much of a sweat to think of so many things. It warn't good judgment to put *everything* on the raft.

If the men went to the island, I just expect they found the camp fire I built, and watched it all night for Jim to come. Anyways, they stayed away from us, and if my building the fire never fooled them it warn't no fault of mine. I played it as low-down on them as I could.

When the first streak of day begun to show, we tied up to a tow-head in a bend on the Illinois side, and hacked off cotton-wood branches with the hatchet and covered up the raft with them so she looked like there had been a cave-in in the bank there. A tow-head is a sand-bar that has cotton-woods on it as thick as harrow-teeth.

We had mountains on the Missouri shore and heavy timber on the Illinois side,

and the channel was down the Missouri shore at that place, so we warn't afr
of anybody running across us.   We laid there all day and watched the rafts a
steamboats spin down the Missouri shore, and up-bound steamboats fight
big river in the middle.   I told Jim all about the time I had jabbering w
that woman ; and Jim said she was a smart one, and if she was to start after
herself *she* wouldn't set down and watch a camp fire—no, sir, she'd fetcl
dog.   Well, then, I said, why couldn't she tell her husband to fetch a dog ? J
said he bet she did think of it by the time the men was ready to start, and
believed they must a gone up town to get a dog and so they lost all that time,
else we wouldn't be here on a tow-head sixteen or seventeen mile below the vill
—no, indeedy, we would be in that same old town again.   So I said I didn't c
what was the reason they didn't get us, as long as they didn't.

When it was beginning to come on dark, we poked our heads out of the c
tonwood thicket and looked up, and down, and across ; nothing in sight ; so J
took up some of the top planks of the raft and built a snug wigwam to get un
in blazing weather and rainy, and to keep the things dry.   Jim made a floor
the wigwam, and raised it a foot or more above the level of the raft, so now
blankets and all the traps was out of the reach of steamboat waves.   Right in
middle of the wigwam we made a layer of dirt about five or six inches deep w
a frame around it for to hold it to its place ; this was to build a fire on in slo
weather or chilly ; the wigwam would keep it from being seen.   We made an
tra steering oar, too, because one of the others might get broke, on a snag
something.   We fixed up a short forked stick to hang the old lantern on ;
cause we must always light the lantern whenever we see a steamboat coming do
stream, to keep from getting run over ; but we wouldn't have to light it for
stream boats unless we see we was in what they call a "crossing ;" for the ri
was pretty high yet, very low banks being still a little under water ; so up-bou
boats didn't always run the channel, but hunted easy water.

This second night we run between seven and eight hours, with a current t
was making over four mile an hour.   We catched fish, and talked, and we too
swim now and then to keep off sleepiness.   It was kind of solemn, drifting do
the big still river, laying on our backs looking up at the stars, and we did
ever feel like talking loud, and it warn't often that we laughed, only a li

d of a low chuckle. We had mighty good weather, as a general thing, and noth-
ever happened to us at all, that night, nor the next, nor the next.

Every night we passed towns, some of them away up on black hillsides, noth-
but just a shiny bed of lights, not a house could you see. The fifth night
passed St. Louis, and it was like the whole world lit up. In St. Petersburg
y used to say there was twenty or thirty thousand people in St. Louis, but I
er believed it till I see that wonderful spread of lights at two o'clock that still
ht. There warn't a sound there ; everybody was asleep.

Every night, now, I used to slip ashore, towards ten o'clock, at some little
age, and buy ten or fifteen cents' worth of meal or bacon or other stuff to eat ;
I sometimes I lifted a chicken that warn't roosting comfortable, and took him

ng. Pap always said, take a
cken when you get a chance,
ause if you don't want him
rself you can easy find some-
y that does, and a good deed
't ever forgot. I never see
when he didn't want the
cken himself, but that is what
used to say, anyway.

Mornings, before daylight, I
ped into corn fields and bored a watermelon, or a mush-
on, or a punkin, or some
corn, or things of that kind.
always said it warn't no
m to borrow things, if you
meaning to pay them back,
etime ; but the widow said
varn't anything but a soft
ne for stealing, and no decent

HE SOMETIMES LIFTED A CHICKEN.

y would do it. Jim said he reckoned the widow was partly right and pap
partly right ; so the best way would be for us to pick out two or three

things from the list and say we wouldn't borrow them any more—then he reck_c
it wouldn't be no harm to borrow the others. So we talked it over all one ni,
drifting along down the river, trying to make up our minds whether to drop
watermelons, or the cantelopes, or the mushmelons, or what. But towards
light we got it all settled satisfactory, and concluded to drop crabapples
p'simmons. We warn't feeling just right, before that, but it was all comfort
now. I was glad the way it come out, too, because crabapples ain't ever g_c
and the p'simmons wouldn't be ripe for two or three months yet.

We shot a water-fowl, now and then, that got up too early in the mornin
didn't go to bed early enough in the evening. Take it all around, we lived pr'
high.

The fifth night below St. Louis we had a big storm after midnight, wi
power of thunder and lightning, and the rain poured down in a solid sheet.
stayed in the wigwam and let the raft take care of itself. When the light
glared out we could see a big straight river ahead, and high rocky bluffs on
sides. By-and-by says I, "Hel-*lo*, Jim, looky yonder!" It was a steamboat
had killed herself on a rock. We was drifting straight down for her. The light
showed her very distinct. She was leaning over, with part of her upper _c
above water, and you could see every little chimbly-guy clean and clear, an
chair by the big bell, with an old slouch hat hanging on the back of it when
flashes come.

Well, it being away in the night, and stormy, and all so mysterious-lik
felt just the way any other boy would a felt when I see that wreck lay
there so mournful and lonesome in the middle of the river. I wanted
get aboard of her and slink around a little, and see what there was there.
I says :

"Le's land on her, Jim."

But Jim was dead against it, at first. He says :

"I doan' want to go fool'n 'long er no wrack. We's doin' blame' well, en
better let blame' well alone, as de good book says. Like as not dey's a watch
on dat wrack.'

"Watchman your grandmother," I says ; "there ain't nothing to watch
the texas and the pilot-house ; and do you reckon anybody's going to resk

for a texas and a pilot-house such a night as this, when it's likely to break up
wash off down the river any minute ? " Jim couldn't say nothing to that,
he didn't try. " And besides," I says, " we might borrow something worth
ing, out of the captain's stateroom. Seegars, *I* bet you—and cost five cents
ce, solid cash. Steamboat captains is always rich, and get sixty dollars a
th, and *they* don't care a cent what a thing costs, you know, long as they
t it. Stick a candle in your pocket ; I can't rest, Jim, till we give her a
maging. Do you reckon Tom Sawyer would ever go by this thing ? Not
pie, he wouldn't. He'd call it an adventure—that's what he'd call it ;
he'd land on that wreck if it was his last act. And wouldn't he throw
e into it ?—wouldn't he spread himself, nor nothing ? Why, you'd think it
Christopher C'lumbus discovering Kingdom-Come. I wish Tom Sawyer
here."

Jim he grumbled a little, but give in. He said we mustn't talk any more
n we could help, and then talk mighty low. The lightning showed us the
ck again, just in time, and we fetched the starboard derrick, and made
there.

The deck was high out, here. We went sneaking down the slope of it to
oard, in the dark, towards the texas, feeling our way slow with our feet, and
ading our hands out to fend off the guys, for it was so dark we couldn't see
sign of them. Pretty soon we struck the forward end of the skylight, and
mb onto it ; and the next step fetched us in front of the captain's door, which
open, and by Jimminy, away down through the texas-hall we see a light !
all in the same second we seem to hear low voices in yonder !

Jim whispered and said he was feeling powerful sick, and told me to come
g. I says, all right ; and was going to start for the raft ; but just then I
rd a voice wail out and say :

" Oh, please don't, boys ; I swear I won't ever tell ! "

Another voice said, pretty loud :

It's a lie, Jim Turner. You've acted this way before. You always want
e'n your share of the truck, and you've always got it, too, because you've
re 't if you didn't you'd tell. But this time you've said it jest one time too
y. You're the meanest, treacherousest hound in this country."

By this time Jim was gone for the raft. I was just a-biling with curiosi
and I says to myself, Tom Sawyer wouldn't back out now, and so I won't eith
I'm agoing to see what's going on here. So I dropped on my hands and kn
in the little passage, and crept aft in the dark, till there warn't. but about
stateroom betwixt me and the cross-hall of the texas. Then, in there I see a m
stretched on the floor and tied hand and foot, and two men standing over h

"PLEASE DON'T, BILL "

and one of them had a dim lantern in his hand, and the other one had a pis
This one kept pointing the pistol at the man's head on the floor and saying—

"I'd *like* to ! And I orter, too, a mean skunk !"

The man on the floor would shrivel up, and say : "Oh, please don't, Bill
hain't ever goin' to tell."

And every time he said that, the man with the lantern would laugh, and s

"'Deed you *ain't !* You never said no truer thing 'n that, you bet yo
And once he said : "Hear him beg ! and yit if we hadn't got the best of I
and tied him, he'd a killed us both. And what *for ?* Jist for noth'n. Jist

se we stood on our *rights*—that's what for. But I lay you ain't a-goin' to
eaten nobody any more, Jim Turner. Put *up* that pistol, Bill."

Bill says :

" I don't want to, Jake Packard. I'm for killin' him—and didn't he kill old
tfield jist the same way—and don't he deserve it ? "

" But I don't *want* him killed, and I've got my reasons for it."

" Bless yo' heart for them words, Jake Packard ! I'll never forgit you, long's
ve ! " says the man on the floor, sort of blubbering.

Packard didn't take no notice of that, but hung up his lantern on a nail, and
ted towards where I was, there in the dark, and motioned Bill to come. I
wfished as fast as I could, about two yards, but the boat slanted so that I
ldn't make very good time ; so to keep from getting run over and catched I
wled into a stateroom on the upper side. The man come a-pawing along in
dark, and when Packard got to my stateroom, he says :

" Here—come in here."

And in he come, and Bill after him. But before they got in, I was up in the
er berth, cornered, and sorry I come. Then they stood there, with their
ds on the ledge of the berth, and talked. I couldn't see them, but I could
where they was, by the whisky they'd been having. I was glad I didn't
nk whisky ; but it wouldn't made much difference, anyway, because most of
time they couldn't a treed me because I didn't breathe. I was too scared. And
ides, a body *couldn't* breathe, and hear such talk. They talked low and earnest.
wanted to kill Turner. He says :

" He's said he'll tell, and he will. If we was to give both our shares to him
, it wouldn't make no difference after the row, and the way we've served him.
re's you're born, he'll turn State's evidence ; now you hear *me*. I'm for put-
g him out of his troubles."

" So'm I," says Packard, very quiet.

" Blame it, I'd sorter begun to think you wasn't. Well, then, that's all right.
' go and do it."

" Hold on a minute ; I hain't had my say yit. You listen to me. Shooting's
d, but there's quieter ways if the thing's *got* to be done. But what *I* say, is
s ; it ain't good sense to go court'n around after a halter, if you can git at

what you're up to in some way that's jist as good and at the same time don't br
you into no resks.   Ain't that so ? "

"You bet it is.   But how you goin' to manage it this time ? "

" Well, my idea is this : we'll rustle around and gether up whatever pickins we
overlooked in the staterooms, and shove for shore and hide the truck.   T
we'll wait.   Now I say it ain't agoin' to be more 'n two hours befo' this wr
breaks up and washes off down the river.   See ?   He'll be drownded, and wo
have nobody to blame for it but his own self.   I reckon that's a considerble si
better'n killin' of him.   I'm unfavorable to killin' a man as long as you can
around it ; it ain't good sense, it ain't good morals.   Ain't I right ? "

"IT AIN'T GOOD MORALS."

"Yes—I reck'n you a
But s'pose she *don't* br
up and wash off ? "

"Well, we can wait
two hours, anyway, and
can't we ? "

"All right, then ; co
along."

So they started, and I
out, all in a cold sweat, a
scrambled forward.   It
dark as pitch there ; bu
said in a kind of a coa
whisper, "Jim !" and
answered up, right at
elbow, with a sort of a mo
and I says :

"Quick, Jim, it ain't
time for fooling around a
moaning ; there's a gang
murderers in yonder, a

if we don't hunt up their boat and set her drifting down the river so th
fellows can't get away from the wreck, there's one of 'em going to be in a bad

if we find their boat we can put *all* of 'em in a bad fix—for the Sheriff 'll get
Quick—hurry! I'll hunt the labboard side, you hunt the stabboard. You
rt at the raft, and——"

"Oh, my lordy, lordy! *Raf'?* Dey ain' no raf' no mo', she done broke loose
gone!—'en here we is!"

"OH! LORDY LORDY!"

Chapter XIII

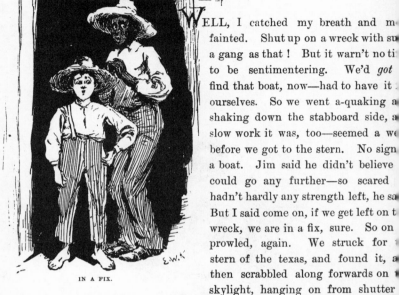

IN A FIX.

WELL, I catched my breath and m[ost]
fainted. Shut up on a wreck with su[ch]
a gang as that! But it warn't no ti[me]
to be sentimentering. We'd *got* [to]
find that boat, now—had to have it [for]
ourselves. So we went a-quaking a[nd]
shaking down the stabboard side, a[nd]
slow work it was, too—seemed a we[ek]
before we got to the stern. No sign [of]
a boat. Jim said he didn't believe [he]
could go any further—so scared [he]
hadn't hardly any strength left, he sa[ys].
But I said come on, if we get left on t[he]
wreck, we are in a fix, sure. So on [we]
prowled, again. We struck for [the]
stern of the texas, and found it, a[nd]
then scrabbled along forwards on [the]
skylight, hanging on from shutter [to]
shutter, for the edge of the skylight was in the water. When we got pretty cl[ose]
to the cross-hall door, there was the skiff, sure enough! I could just barely [see]
her. I felt ever so thankful. In another second I would a been aboard of h[er],
but just then the door opened. One of the men stuck his head out, only abou[t a]
couple of foot from me, and I thought I was gone; but he jerked it in aga[in],
and says:

"Heave that blame lantern out o' sight, Bill!"

He flung a bag of something into the boat, and then got in himself, and

wn. It was Packard. Then Bill *he* come out and got in. Packard says, in a
ɣ voice :

"All ready—shove off !"

I couldn't hardly hang onto the shutters, I was so weak. But Bill says :

"Hold on—'d you go through him ?"

"No. Didn't you ?"

"No. So he's got his share o' the cash, yet."

"Well, then, come along—no use to take truck and leave money."

"Say—won't he suspicion what we're up to ?"

"Maybe he won't. But we got to have it anyway. Come along."

So they got out and went in.

The door slammed to, because it was on the careened side ; and in a half
ɔnd I was in the boat, and Jim come a tumbling after me. I out with my
ife and cut the rope, and away we went !

We didn't touch an oar, and we didn' speak nor whisper, nor hardly even
eathe. We went gliding swift along, dead silent, past the tip of the paddle-
x, and past the stern ; then in a second or two more we was a hundred yards
low the wreck, and the darkness soaked her up, every last sign of her, and
ɜ was safe, and knowed it.

When we was three or four hundred yards down stream, we see the lantern
ow like a little spark at the texas door, for a second, and we knowed by that
at the rascals had missed their boat, and was beginning to understand that they
ıs in just as much trouble, now, as Jim Turner was.

Then Jim manned the oars, and we took out after our raft. Now was the first
ne that I begun to worry about the men—I reckon I hadn't had time to before.
ɔegun to think how dreadful it was, even for murderers, to be in such a fix. I
ɣs to myself, there ain't no telling but I might come to be a murderer myself,
t, and then how would *I* like it ? So says I to Jim:

"The first light we see, we'll land a hundred yards below it or above it, in a
ıce where it's a good hiding-place for you and the skiff, and then I'll go and
up some kind of a yarn, and get somebody to go for that gang and get them
t of their scrape, so they can be hung when their time comes."

But that idea was a failure ; for pretty soon it begun to storm again, and this

time worse than ever. The rain poured down, and never a light showed; eve
body in bed, I reckon. We boomed along down the river, watching for lights a
watching for our raft. After a long time the rain let up, but the clouds sta
and the lightning kept whimpering, and by-and-by a flash showed us a bla
thing ahead, floating, and we made for it.

It was the raft, and mighty glad was we to get aboard of it again. We see

"HELLO, WHAT'S UP?"

light, now, away down to the right, on shore. So I said I would go for it. The s
was half full of plunder which that gang had stole, there on the wreck. We hust
it onto the raft in a pile, and I told Jim to float along down, and show a lig
when he judged he had gone about two mile, and keep it burning till I com
then I manned my oars and shoved for the light. As I got down towards it, th
or four more showed—up on a hillside. It was a village. I closed in above t
shore-light, and laid on my oars and floated. As I went by, I see it was a lante
hanging on the jackstaff of a double-hull ferry-boat. I skimmed around for t
watchman, a-wondering whereabouts he slept; and by-and-by I found him ro

; on the bitts, forward, with his head down between his knees. I give his
)ulder two or three little shoves, and begun to cry.

He stirred up, in a kind of a startlish way ; but when he see it was only me, he
·k a good gap and stretch, and then he says :

"Hello, what's up ? Don't cry, bub. What's the trouble ? "

I says :

" Pap, and mam, and sis, and—— "

Then I broke down. He says :

" Oh, dang it, now, *don't* take on so, we all has to have our troubles and this'n
:ome out all right. What's the matter with 'em ? "

" They're—they're—are you the watchman of the boat ? "

" Yes," he says, kind of pretty-well-satisfied like. " I'm the captain and the
ner, and the mate, and the pilot, and watchman, and head deck-hand ; and
netimes I'm the freight and passengers. I ain't as rich as old Jim Hornback,
l I can't be so blame' generous and good to Tom, Dick and Harry as what he
and slam around money the way he does ; but I've told him a many a time 't I
uldn't trade places with him ; for, says I, a sailor's life's the life for me, and
a derned if *I'd* live two mile out o' town, where there ain't nothing ever goin'
not for all his spondulicks and as much more on top of it. Says I—— "

I broke in and says :

" They're in an awful peck of trouble, and—— "

" *Who* is ? "

" Why, pap, and mam, and sis, and Miss Hooker ; and if you'd take your
ry-boat and go up there—— "

" Up where ? Where are they ? "

" On the wreck."

" What wreck ? "

" Why, there ain't but one."

" What, you don't mean the *Walter Scott?* "

" Yes."

" Good land ! what are they doin' *there*, for gracious sakes ? "

" Well, they didn't go there a-purpose."

" I bet they didn't ! Why, great goodness, there ain't no chance for 'em if

they don't git off mighty quick ! Why, how in the nation did they ever git i
such a scrape ?"

"Easy enough. Miss Hooker was a-visiting, up there to the town——"

"Yes, Booth's Landing—go on."

"She was a-visiting, there at Booth's Landing, and just in the edge of
evening she started over with her nigger woman in the horse-ferry, to stay
night at her friend's house, Miss What-you-may-call-her, I disremember
name, and they lost their steering-oar, and swung around and went a-floati
down, stern-first, about two mile, and saddle-baggsed on the wreck, and the fe
man and the nigger woman and the horses was all lost, but Miss Hooker s
made a grab and got aboard the wreck. Well, about an hour after dark,
come along down in our trading-scow, and it was so dark we didn't notice t
wreck till we was right on it ; and so *we* saddle-baggsed ; but all of us was sav
but Bill Whipple—and oh, he *was* the best cretur !—I most wish't it had be
me, I do."

"My George ! It's the beatenest thing I ever struck. And *then* what
you all do ?"

"Well, we hollered and took on, but it's so wide there, we couldn't ma
nobody hear. So pap said somebody got to get ashore and get help someh
I was the only one that could swim, so I made a dash for it, and Miss Hoo
she said if I didn't strike help sooner, come here and hunt up her uncle, and h
fix the thing. I made the land about a mile below, and been fooling along e
since, trying to get people to do something, but they said, ' What, in such a ni
and such a current ? there ain't no sense in it ; go for the steam-ferry.' Now
you'll go, and——"

"By Jackson, I'd *like* to, and blame it I don't know but I will ; but who
the dingnation's agoin' to *pay* for it ? Do you reckon your pap——"

"Why *that's* all right. Miss Hooker she told me, *particular*, that her un
Hornback——"

"Great guns ! is *he* her uncle ? Looky here, you break for that lig
over yonder-way, and turn out west when you git there, and about a quar
of a mile out you'll come to the tavern ; tell 'em to dart you out to Jim Ho
back's and he'll foot the bill. And don't you fool around any, because h

ıt to know the news. Tell him I'll have his niece all safe before he can
to town. Hump yourself, now; I'm agoing up around the corner here, to
st out my engineer."

I struck for the light, but as soon as he turned the corner I went back
l got into my skiff and bailed her out and then pulled up shore in
easy water about six hundred yards, and tucked myself in among some
odboats; for I couldn't rest easy till I could see the ferry-boat start. But
e it all around, I was feeling ruther comfortable on accounts of taking all
s trouble for that gang, for not many would a done it. I wished the

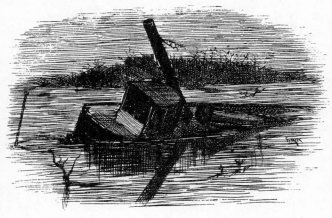

THE WRECK.

low knowed about it. I judged she would be proud of me for helping
ese rapscallions, because rapscallions and dead beats is the kind the widow
l good people takes the most interest in.

Well, before long, here comes the wreck, dim and dusky, sliding along
wn! A kind of cold shiver went through me, and then I struck out for
r. She was very deep, and I see in a minute there warn't much chance
anybody being alive in her. I pulled all around her and hollered a little,
t there wasn't any answer; all dead still. I felt a little bit heavy-hearted
ut the gang, but not much, for I reckoned if they could stand it, I could.

Then here comes the ferry-boat; so I shoved for the middle of the ri
on a long down-stream slant; and when I judged I was out of eye-reach
laid on my oars, and looked back and see her go and smell around the wre
for Miss Hooker's remainders, because the captain would know her un
Hornback would want them; and then pretty soon the ferry-boat give it
and went for shore, and I laid into my work and went a-booming down the riv

WE TURNED IN AND SLEPT.

It did seem a powerful long time before Jim's light showed up; and when
did show, it looked like it was a thousand mile off. By the time I got there t
sky was beginning to get a little gray in the east; so we struck for an islan
and hid the raft, and sunk the skiff, and turned in and slept like dead peop

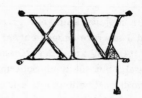

Chapter XIV.

TURNING OVER THE TRUCK.

By-and-by, when we got up, we turned over the truck the gang had stole off of the wreck, and found boots, and blankets, and clothes, and all sorts of other things, and a lot of books, and a spyglass, and three boxes of seegars. We hadn't ever been this rich before, in neither of our lives. The seegars was prime. We laid off all the afternoon in the woods talking, and me reading the books, and having a general good time. I told Jim all about what happened inside the wreck, and at the ferry-boat; and I said these kinds of things was adventures; but he said he didn't want no more adventures. He said that when I went in the texas and he crawled back to get on the raft and found her gone, he nearly died; because he judged it was all up with *him*, anyway it could be fixed; for if he didn't get saved he would get drownded; and if he did get saved, whoever saved him would send him back to me so as to get the reward, and then Miss Watson would sell him South, sure. Well, he was right; he was most always right; he had an uncommon level head, for a nigger.

I read considerable to Jim about kings, and dukes, and earls, and such, and how gaudy they dressed, and how much style they put on, and called each other

your majesty, and your grace, and your lordship, and so on, 'stead of miste
and Jim's eyes bugged out, and he was interested.   He says :

"I didn' know dey was so many un um.   I hain't hearn 'bout none un u
skasely, but ole King Sollermun, onless you counts dem kings dat's in a pack
k'yards.   How much do a king git?"

"Get?" I says ; "why, they get a thousand dollars a month if they want
they can have just as much as they want ; everything belongs to them."

"*Ain'* dat gay?   En what dey got to do, Huck?"

SOLOMON AND HIS MILLION WIVES.

"*They* don't do nothing!   Why how you talk.   They just set around."

"No—is dat so?"

"Of course it is.   They just set around.   Except maybe when there 's a wa
then they go to the war.   But other times they just lazy around ; or go hawki
—just hawking and sp— Sh!—d' you hear a noise?"

We skipped out and looked ; but it warn't nothing but the flutter of
steamboat's wheel, away down coming around the point ; so we come back.

"Yes," says I, "and other times, when things is dull, they fuss with t

·lyment; and if everybody don't go just so he whacks their heads off.   But
·stly they hang round the harem."

"Roun' de which?"

"Harem."

"What's de harem?"

"The place where he keep his wives.   Don't you know about the harem?
.omon had one ; he had about a million wives."

"Why, yes, dat's so; I—I'd done forgot it.   A harem's a bo'd'n-house, I
k'n.   Mos' likely dey has rackety times in de nussery.   En I reck'n de wives
urrels considable ; en dat 'crease de racket.   Yit dey say Sollermun de wises'
n dat ever live'.   I doan' take no stock in dat.   Bekase why : would a wise
n want to live in de mids' er sich a blimblammin' all de time?   No—'deed he
uldn'.   A wise man 'ud take en buil' a biler-factry; en den he could shet
·vn de biler-factry when he want to res'."

"Well, but he *was* the wisest man, anyway ; because the widow she told me
her own self."

"I doan k'yer what de widder say, he *warn't* no wise man, nuther.   He had
ne er de dad-fetchedes' ways I ever see.   Does you know 'bout dat chile dat he
gwyne to chop in two?"

"Yes, the widow told me all about it."

"*Well*, den!   Warn' dat de beatenes' notion in de worl'?   You jes' take en
k at it a minute.   Dah's de stump, dah—dat's one er de women : heah's you—
;'s de yuther one ; I's Sollermun ; en dish-yer dollar bill's de chile.   Bofe un
1 claims it.   What does I do?   Does I shin aroun' mongs' de neighbors en fine
t which un you de bill *do* b'long to, en han' it over to de right one, all safe en
ın', de way dat anybody dat had any gumption would?   No—I take en whack
bill in *two*, en give half un it to you, en de yuther half to de yuther woman.
t's de way Sollermun was gwyne to do wid de chile.   Now I want to ast you:
at's de use er dat half a bill ?—can't buy noth'n wid it.   En what use is a half
·hile?   I would'n give a dern for a million un um."

"But hang it, Jim, you've clean missed the point—blame it, you've missed it
housand mile."

"Who ? Me ? Go 'long.   Doan' talk to *me* 'bout yo' pints.   I reck'n I knows

sense when I sees it ; en dey ain' no sense in sich doin's as dat.   De 'spute war
'bout a half a chile, de 'spute was 'bout a whole chile ; en de man dat think
kin settle a 'spute 'bout a whole chile wid a half a chile, doan' know enough
come in out'n de rain.   Doan' talk to me 'bout Sollermun, Huck, I knows h
by de back."

" But I tell you you don't get the point."

" Blame de pint ! I reck'n I knows what I knows.   En mine you, de *real* p
is down furder—it's down deeper.   It lays in de way Sollermun was raised.   Y

THE STORY OF " SOLLERMUN."

take a man dat's got on'y one er two chillen ; is dat man gwyne to be wasefu
chillen ? No, he ain't ; he can't 'ford it.   *He* know how to value 'em.   But y
take a man dat's got 'bout five million chillen runnin' roun' de house, en i
diffunt.   *He* as soon chop a chile in two as a cat.   Dey's plenty mo'.   A chile
two, mo' er less, warn't no consekens to Sollermun, dad fetch him ! "

I never see such a nigger.   If he got a notion in his head once, there war
no getting it out again.   He was the most down on Solomon of any nigger I ev
see.   So I went to talking about other kings, and let Solomon slide.   I told abc
Louis Sixteenth that got his head cut off in France long time age ; and about

le boy the dolphin, that would a been a king, but they took and shut him up jail, and some say he died there.

" Po' little chap."

" But some says he got out and got away, and come to America."

" Dat's good ! But he'll be pooty lonesome—dey ain' no kings here, is dey, ck ?"

" No."

"Den he cain't git no situation.   What he gwyne to do ?"

" Well, I don't know.   Some of them gets on the police, and some of them rns people how to talk French."

" Why, Huck, doan' de French people talk de same way we does ?"

" *No*, Jim; you couldn't understand a word they said—not a single word."

" Well, now, I be ding-busted !   How do dat come ?"

" *I* don't know ; but it's so.   I got some of their jabber out of a book. Spose nan was to come to you and say *Polly-voo-franzy*—what would you think ?"

" I wouldn' think nuff 'n ; I'd take en bust him over de head.   Dat is, if he rn't white.   I wouldn't 'low no nigger to call me dat."

" Shucks, it ain't calling you anything.   It's only saying do you know how to k French."

" Well, den, why couldn't he *say* it ?"

" Why, he *is* a-saying it.   That's a Frenchman's *way* of saying it."

" Well, it's a blame' ridicklous way, en I doan' want to hear no mo' 'bout it. y ain' no sense in it."

" Looky here, Jim ; does a cat talk like we do ?"

" No, a cat don't."

" Well, does a cow ?"

" No, a cow don't, nuther."

" Does a cat talk like a cow, or a cow talk like a cat ?"

" No, dey don't."

"It's natural and right for 'em to talk different from each other, ain't it ?"

" 'Course."

" And ain't it natural and right for a cat and a cow to talk different from *us* ?"

" Why, mos' sholy it is."

" Well, then, why ain't it natural and right for a *Frenchman* to talk differe
from us ?   You answer me that."

"Is a cat a man, Huck ? "

" No."

" Well, den, dey ain't no sense in a cat talkin' like a man.   Is a cow a ma
—er is a cow a cat ?"

" No, she ain't either of them."

" Well, den, she ain' got no business to talk like either one er the yuther
'em.   Is a Frenchman a man ?"

" Yes."

" *Well,* den !   Dad blame it, why doan' he *talk* like a man ?   You answer
dat ! "

I see it warn't no use wasting words—you can't learn a nigger to argue.
I quit.

Chapter XV.

"WE WOULD SELL THE RAFT."

W E judged that three nights more would fetch us to Cairo, at the bottom of Illinois, where the Ohio River comes in, and that was what we was after. We would sell the raft and get on a steamboat and go way up the Ohio amongst the free States, and then be out of trouble.

Well, the second night a fog begun to come on, and we made for a tow-head to tie to, for it wouldn't do to try to run in fog; but when I paddled ahead in the canoe, with the line, to make fast, there warn't anything but little saplings to tie to. I passed the line around one of them right on the edge of the cut bank, but there was a stiff current, and the

t come booming down so lively she tore it out by the roots and away she at. I see the fog closing down, and it made me so sick and scared I ldn't budge for most a half a minute it seemed to me—and then there rn't no raft in sight; you couldn't see twenty yards. I jumped into the oe and run back to the stern and grabbed the paddle and set her back a oke. But she didn't come. I was in such a hurry I hadn't untied her. ot up and tried to untie her, but I was so excited my hands shook so I ldn't hardly do anything with them.

As soon as I got started I took out after the raft, hot and heavy, right

down the tow-head. That was all right as far as it went, but the tow-he
warn't sixty yards long, and the minute I flew by the foot of it I shot c
into the solid white fog, and hadn't no more idea which way I was goi
than a dead man.

Thinks I, it won't do to paddle ; first I know I'll run into the bank or
tow-head or something ; I got to set still and float, and yet it's mighty fidg
business to have to hold your hands still at such a time. I whooped a
listened. Away down there, somewheres, I hears a small whoop, and
comes my spirits. I went tearing after it, listening sharp to hear it aga
The next time it come, I see I warn't heading for it but heading away to the rig
of it. And the next time, I was heading away to the left of it—and not gaini
on it much, either, for I was flying around, this way and that and 'tother, but
was going straight ahead all the time.

I did wish the fool would think to beat a tin pan, and beat it all the tir
but he never did, and it was the still places between the whoops that was maki
the trouble for me. Well, I fought along, and directly I hears the who
behind me. I was tangled good, now. That was somebody else's whoop,
else I was turned around.

I throwed the paddle down. I heard the whoop again ; it was behind
yet, but in a different place; it kept coming, and kept changing its place, an
kept answering, till by-and-by it was in front of me again and I knowed the c
rent had swung the canoe's head down stream and I was all right, if that was J
and not some other raftsman hollering. I couldn't tell nothing about voices i
fog, for nothing don't look natural nor sound natural in a fog.

The whooping went on, and in about a minute I come a booming down or
cut bank with smoky ghosts of big trees on it, and the current throwed me
to the left and shot by, amongst a lot of snags that fairly roared, the current w
tearing by them so swift.

In another second or two it was solid white and still again. I set perfec
still, then, listening to my heart thump, and I reckon I didn't draw a brea
while it thumped a hundred.

I just give up, then. I knowed what the matter was. That cut bank v
an island, and Jim had gone down 'tother side of it. It warn't no tow-head, t

could float by in ten minutes. It had the big timber of a regular island ;
might be five or six mile long and more than a half a mile wide.

I kept quiet, with my ears cocked, about fifteen minutes, I reckon. I was
ting along, of course, four or five mile an hour ; but you don't ever think of
t. No, you *feel* like you are laying dead still on the water ; and if a little
mpse of a snag slips by, you don't think to yourself how fast *you're* going, but
catch your breath and think, my ! how that snag's tearing along. If you

AMONG THE SNAGS.

nk it ain't dismal and lonesome out in a fog that way, by yourself, in the
ht, you try it once—you'll see.

Next, for about a half an hour, I whoops now and then ; at last I hears the
swer a long ways off, and tries to follow it, but I couldn't do it, and directly I
lged I'd got into a nest of tow-heads, for I had little dim glimpses of them on
th sides of me, sometimes just a narrow channel between ; and some that I
ıldn't see, I knowed was there, because I'd hear the wash of the current against
old dead brush and trash that hung over the banks. Well, I warn't long
ng the whoops, down amongst the tow-heads ; and I only tried to chase them

a little while, anyway, because it was worse than chasing a Jack-o-lantern. Y
never knowed a sound dodge around so, and swap places so quick and so much

I had to claw away from the bank pretty lively, four or five times, to ke
from knocking the islands out of the river ; and so I judged the raft must be h
ting into the bank every now and then, or else it would get further ahead a
clear out of hearing—it was floating a little faster than what I was.

Well, I seemed to be in the open river again, by-and-by, but I couldn't h
no sign of a whoop nowheres. I reckoned Jim had fetched up on a snag, may

ASLEEP ON THE RAFT.

and it was all up with him. I was good and tired, so I laid down in the ca
and said I wouldn't bother no more. I didn't want to go to sleep, of course ; l
I was so sleepy I couldn't help it ; so I thought I would take just one lit
cat-nap.

But I reckon it was more than a cat-nap, for when I waked up the stars v
shining bright, the fog was all gone, and I was spinning down a big bend st
first. First I didn't know where I was ; I thought I was dreaming ; and wh
things begun to come back to me, they seemed to come up dim out of l
week.

It was a monstrous big river here, with the tallest and the thickest kind of
ber on both banks ; just a solid wall, as well as I could see, by the stars.   I
ced away down stream, and seen a black speck on the water.   I took out after
but when I got to. it it warn't nothing but a couple of saw-logs made fast
ether.   Then I see another speck, and chased that ; then another, and this
e I was right.   It was the raft.

When I got to it Jim was setting there with his head down between his knees,
ep, with his right arm hanging over the steering oar.   The other oar was
shed off, and the raft was littered up with leaves and branches and dirt.   So
'd had a rough time.

I made fast and laid down under Jim's nose on the raft, and begun to gap,
stretch my fists out against Jim, and says :

"Hello, Jim, have I been asleep ?   Why didn't you stir me up ?"

"Goodness gracious, is dat you, Huck ?   En you ain' dead—you ain' drownded
ou's back agin ?   It's too good for true, honey, it's too good for true.   Lemme
c at you, chile, lemme feel o' you.   No, you ain' dead ! you's back agin,' live
ioun', jis de same ole Huck—de same ole Huck, thanks to goodness !"

" What's the matter with you, Jim ?   You been a drinking ?"

"Drinkin' ?   Has I ben a drinkin' ?   Has I had a chance to be a drinkin' ?"

" Well, then, what makes you talk so wild ?"

" How does I talk wild ?"

" *How?* why, hain't you been talking about my coming back, and all that
f, as if I'd been gone away ?"

"Huck—Huck Finn, you look me in de eye ; look me in de eye.   *Hain't* you
gone away ?"

" Gone away ?   Why, what in the nation do you mean ?   *I* hain't been gone
wheres.   Where would I go to ?"

" Well, looky here, boss, dey's sumf'n wrong, dey is.   Is I *me,* or who *is* I ?
heah, or whah *is* I ?   Now dat's what I wants to know ?"

" Well, I think you're here, plain enough, but I think you're a tangle-headed
fool, Jim."

"I is, is I ?   Well you answer me dis.   Didn't you tote out de line in de
oe, fer to make fas' to de tow-head ?"

" No, I didn't. What tow-head ? I hain't seen no tow-head."

" You hain't seen no tow-head ? Looky here—didn't de line pull loose en raf' go a hummin' down de river, en leave you en de canoe behine in de fog

" What fog ? "

" Why *de* fog. De fog dat's ben aroun' all night. En didn't you whoop, didn't I whoop, tell we got mix' up in de islands en one un us got los' en 'totl one was jis' as good as los', 'kase he didn' know whah he wuz ? En didn't I b up agin a lot er dem islands en have a turrible time en mos' git drownded ? N ain' dat so, boss—ain't it so ? You answer me dat."

" Well, this is too many for me, Jim. I hain't seen no fog, nor no islan nor no troubles, nor nothing. I been setting here talking with you all night you went to sleep about ten minutes ago, and I reckon I done the same. Y couldn't a got drunk in that time, so of course you've been dreaming."

" Dad fetch it, how is I gwyne to dream all dat in ten minutes ? "

" Well, hang it all, you did dream it, because there didn't any of it happe

" But Huck, it's all jis' as plain to me as——"

" It don't make no difference how plain it is, there ain't nothing in it. know, because I've been here all the time."

Jim didn't say nothing for about five minutes, but set there studying over Then he says :

" Well, den, I reck'n I did dream it, Huck ; but dog my cats ef it ain't powerfullest dream I ever see. En I hain't ever had no dream b'fo' dat's ti me like dis one."

" Oh, well, that's all right, because a dream does tire a body like everythi sometimes. But this one was a staving dream—tell me all about it, Jim."

So Jim went to work and told me the whole thing right through, just a happened, only he painted it up considerable. Then he said he must start and " 'terpret" it, because it was sent for a warning. He said the first tow-h stood for a man that would try to do us some good, but the current was anotl man that would get us away from him. The whoops was warnings that wo come to us every now and then, and if we didn't try hard to make out to und stand them they'd just take us into bad luck, 'stead of keeping us out of The lot of tow-heads was troubles we was going to get into with quarrelsc

ple and all kinds of mean folks, but if we minded our business and didn't
back and aggravate them, we would pull through and get out of the fog and
the big clear river, which was the free States, and wouldn't have no more
ble.

It had clouded up pretty dark just after I got onto the raft, but it was
ring up again, now.

" Oh, well, that's all interpreted well enough, as far as it goes, Jim," I says ;
ut what does *these* things stand for ? "

It was the leaves and rubbish on the raft, and the smashed oar. You could
them first rate, now.

Jim looked at the trash, and then looked at me, and back at the trash again.
had got the dream fixed so strong in his head that he couldn't seem to shake
ose and get the facts back into its place again, right away. But when he
get the thing straightened around, he looked at me steady, without ever
ling, and says :

" What do dey stan' for ? I's gwyne to tell you. When I got all wore out
work, en wid de callin' for you, en went to sleep, my heart wuz mos' broke
ase you wuz los', en I didn' k'yer no mo' what become er me en de raf'. En
n I wake up en fine you back agin', all safe en soun', de tears come en I
ld a got down on my knees en kiss' yo' foot I's so thankful. En all you wuz
akin 'bout wuz how you could make a fool uv ole Jim wid a lie. Dat truck
is *trash ;* en trash is what people is dat puts dirt on de head er dey fren's
makes 'em ashamed."

Then he got up slow, and walked to the wigwam, and went in there, without
ing anything but that. But that was enough. It made me feel so mean I
ld almost kissed *his* foot to get him to take it back.

It was fifteen minutes before I could work myself up to go and humble
self to a nigger—but I done it, and I warn't ever sorry for it afterwards,
ther. I didn't do him no more mean tricks, and I wouldn't done that one if
a knowed it would make him feel that way.

Chapter XVI

"IT AMOUNTED TO SOMETHING BEING A RAFTSMAN."

WE slept most all day, and started out at night, a little ways behind a monstrous long raft that was as long going by as a procession. She had four long sweeps at each end, so we judged she carried as many as thirty men, likely. She had five big wigwams aboard, wide apart, and an open camp fire in the middle, and a tall flag-pole at each end. There was a power of style about her. It amounted to something being a raftsman on such a craft as that.

We went drifting down into a big bend, and the night clouded up and got hot. The river was very wide, and was walled with solid timber on both sides; you couldn't see a break in it hardly ever, or a light. We talked about Cairo, and wondered whether we would know it when we got to it. I said likely we wouldn't, because I had heard there warn't but about a dozen houses there, and if they didn't happen to have them lit up, how was we going to know we was passing a town? Jim said if two big rivers joined together there, that would show. But I said maybe might think we was passing the foot of an island and coming into the same river again. That disturbed Jim—and me too. So the question was, what do? I said, paddle ashore the first time a light showed, and tell them pap behind, coming along with a trading-scow, and was a green hand at the business

wanted to know how far it was to Cairo. Jim thought it was a good idea,
ve took a smoke on it and waited.

There warn't nothing to do, now, but to look out sharp for the town, and not
s it without seeing it. He said he'd be mighty sure to see it, because he'd be
ee man the minute he seen it, but if he missed it he'd be in the slave country
in and no more show for freedom. Every little while he jumps up and says :
" Dah she is !"

But it warn't. It was Jack-o-lanterns, or lightning-bugs ; so he set down
n, and went to watching, same as before. Jim said it made him all over
ibly and feverish to be so close to freedom. Well, I can tell you it made me
over trembly and feverish, too, to hear him, because I begun to get it through
head that he *was* most free—and who was to blame for it ? Why, *me.* I
ldn't get that out of my conscience, no how nor no way. It got to troubling
so I couldn't rest ; I couldn't stay still in one place. It hadn't ever come
ie to me before, what this thing was that I was doing. But now it did ; and
taid with me, and scorched me more and more. I tried to make out to
telf that *I* warn't to blame, because *I* didn't run Jim off from his rightful
ler ; but it warn't no use, conscience up and says, every time, "But you
wed he was running for his freedom, and you could a paddled ashore and told
ebody." That was so—I couldn't get around that, noway. That was where
inched. Conscience says to me, "What had poor Miss Watson done to you,
; you could see her nigger go off right under your eyes and never say one
;le word ? What did that poor old woman do to you, that you could treat
so mean ? Why, she tried to learn you your book, she tried to learn you
r manners, she tried to be good to you every way she knowed how. *That's*
at she done."

I got to feeling so mean and so miserable I most wished I was dead. I
eted up and down the raft, abusing myself to myself, and Jim was fidgeting
and down past me. We neither of us could keep still. Every time he danced
ind and says, " Dah's Cairo !" it went through me like a shot, and I thought
; *was* Cairo I reckoned I would die of miserableness.

Jim talked out loud all the time while I was talking to myself. He was saying
r the first thing he would do when he got to a free State he would go to

saving up money and never spend a single cent, and when he got enough
would buy his wife, which was owned on a farm close to where Miss Wats
lived ; and then they would both work to buy the two children, and if th
master wouldn't sell them, they'd get an Ab'litionist to go and steal them.

It most froze me to hear such talk. He wouldn't ever dared to talk such t
in his life before. Just see what a difference it made in him the minute he judg
he was about free. It was according to the old saying, " give a nigger an inch a
he'll take an ell." Thinks I, this is what comes of my not thinking. Here was t
nigger which I had as good as helped to run away, coming right out flat-foo
and saying he would steal his children—children that belonged to a man I did
even know ; a man that hadn't ever done me no harm.

I was sorry to hear Jim say that, it was such a lowering of him.
conscience got to stirring me up hotter than ever, until at last I says to it, "]
up on me—it ain't too late, yet—I'll paddle ashore at the first light, and tell."
felt easy, and happy, and light as a feather, right off. All my troubles was go
I went to looking out sharp for a light, and sort of singing to myself. By-a
by one showed. Jim sings out :

" We's safe, Huck, we's safe ! Jump up and crack yo' heels, dat's de g
ole Cairo at las', I jis knows it ! "

I says :

" I'll take the canoe and go see, Jim. It mightn't be, you know."

He jumped and got the canoe ready, and put his old coat in the bottom
me to set on, and give me the paddle ; and as I shoved off, he says :

" Pooty soon I'll be a-shout'n for joy, en I'll say, it's all on accounts o' Hu
I's a free man, en I couldn't ever ben free ef it hadn' ben for Huck ; Huck d
it. Jim won't ever forgit you, Huck ; you's de bes' fren' Jim's ever had ;
you's de *only* fren' ole Jim's got now."

I was paddling off, all in a sweat to tell on him ; but when he says this
seemed to kind of take the tuck all out of me. I went along slow then, an
warn't right down certain whether I was glad I started or whether I warn't. Wl
I was fifty yards off, Jim says :

" Dah you goes, de ole true Huck ; de on'y white genlman dat ever kep'
promise to ole Jim."

Well, I just felt sick. But I says, I *got* to do it—I can't get *out* of it. Right

1, along comes a skiff with two men in it, with guns, and they stopped and I

ped. One of them says :

"What's that, yonder ?"

"A piece of a raft," I says.

"Do you belong on it ?"

"Yes, sir."

"Any men on it ?"

"Only one, sir."

"Well, there's five niggers run off to-night, up yonder above the head of

bend. Is your man white or black ?"

I didn't answer up prompt. I tried to, but the words wouldn't come.

ied, for a second or two, to brace up and out with it, but I warn't man

ugh—hadn't the spunk of a rabbit. I see I was weakening ; so I just give up

ng, and up and says—

"He's white."

"I reckon we'll go and see for ourselves."

"I wish you would, " says I, " because it's pap that's there, and maybe you'd

me tow the raft ashore where the light is. He's sick—and so is mam and

y Ann."

"Oh, the devil ! we're in a hurry, boy. But I s'pose we've got to. Come—

kle to your paddle, and let's get along."

I buckled to my paddle and they laid to their oars. When we had made a

ke or two, I says :

"Pap'll be mighty much obleeged to you, I can tell you. Everybody goes away

n I want them to help me tow the raft ashore, and I can't do it by myself."

"Well, that's infernal mean. Odd, too. Say, boy, what's the matter with

r father ?"

"It's the—a—the—well, it ain't anything, much."

They stopped pulling. It warn't but a mighty little ways to the raft, now.

says :

"Boy, that's a lie. What *is* the matter with your pap ? Answer up square,

, and it'll be the better for you."

"I will, sir, I will, honest—but don't leave us, please. It's the—the—gen
men, if you'll only pull ahead, and let me heave you the head-line, you w
have to come a-near the raft—please do."

"Set her back, John, set her back!" says one.   They backed wa
"Keep away, boy—keep to looard. Confound it, I just expect the wind
blowed it to us. Your pap's got the small-pox, and you know it precious w
Why didn't you come out and say so? Do you want to spread it all over?"

"BOY, THAT'S A LIE."

"Well," says I, a-blubbering, "I've told everybody before, and then t
just went away and left us."

"Poor devil, there's something in that. We are right down sorry for y
but we—well, hang it, we don't want the small-pox, you see. Look here,
tell you what to do. Don't you try to land by yourself, or you'll smash ev
thing to pieces. You float along down about twenty miles and you'll come t
town on the left-hand side of the river. It will be long after sun-up, then,
when you ask for help, you tell them your folks are all down with chills
fever. Don't be a fool again, and let people guess what is the matter. Now w
trying to do you a kindness; so you just put twenty miles between us, that

boy. It wouldn't do any good to land yonder where the light is—it's only od-yard. Say—I reckon your father's poor, and I'm bound to say he's in ty hard luck. Here—I'll put a twenty dollar gold piece on this board, and get it when it floats by. I feel mighty mean to leave you, but my dom ! it won't do to fool with small-pox, don't you see ? "

' Hold on, Parker," says the other man, " here's a twenty to put on the board me. Good-bye, boy, you do as Mr. Parker told you, and you'll be all right."

' HERE I IS, HUCK."

' That's so, my boy—good-bye, good-bye. If you see any runaway niggers, get help and nab them, and you can make some money by it."

' Good-bye, sir," says I, " I won't let no runaway niggers get by me if I can it."

They went off, and I got aboard the raft, feeling bad and low, because I wed very well I had done wrong, and I see it warn't no use for me to try arn to do right ; a body that don't get *started* right when he's little, ain't

got no show—when the pinch comes there ain't nothing to back him up and k
him to his work, and so he gets beat.   Then I thought a minute, and say
myself, hold on,—s pose you'd a done right and give Jim up ; would you
better than what you do now ?   No, says I, I'd feel bad—I'd feel just the sa
way I do now.   Well, then, says I, what's the use you learning to do right, w
it's troublesome to do right and ain't no trouble to do wrong, and the wage
just the same ?   I was stuck.   I couldn't answer that.   So I reckoned I would
bother no more about it, but after this always do whichever come handiest
the time.

I went into the wigwam ; Jim warn't there.   I looked all around ;
warn't anywhere.   I says :

" Jim! "

" Here I is, Huck.   Is dey out o' sight yit ?   Don't talk loud."

He was in the river, under the stern oar, with just his nose out.   I told
they was out of sight, so he come aboard.   He says :

" I was a-listenin' to all de talk, en I slips into de river en was gwyne
shove for sho' if dey come aboard.   Den I was gwyne to swim to de raf' a
when dey was gone.   But lawsy, how you did fool 'em, Huck !   Dat *wuz*
smartes' dodge !   I tell you, chile, I 'speck it save' ole Jim—ole Jim ain't gw
to forgit you for dat, honey."

Then we talked about the money.   It was a pretty good raise, twenty dol
apiece.   Jim said we could take deck passage on a steamboat now, and
money would last us as far as we wanted to go in the free States.   He said twe
mile more warn't far for the raft to go, but he wished we was already there.

Towards daybreak we tied up, and Jim was mighty particular about hid
the raft good.   Then he worked all day fixing things in bundles, and getting
ready to quit rafting.

That night about ten we hove in sight of the lights of a town away d
in a left-hand bend.

I went off in the canoe, to ask about it.   Pretty soon I found a man out
the river with a skiff, setting a trot-line.   I ranged up and says :

" Mister, is that town Cairo ? "

" Cairo ? no.   You must be a blame' fool."

" What town is it, mister ? "

" If you want to know, go and find out. If you stay here botherin' around for about a half a minute longer, you'll get something you won't want."

I paddled to the raft. Jim was awful disappointed, but I said never mind, ro would be the next place, I reckoned.

We passed another town before daylight, and I was going out again ; but it s high ground, so I didn't go. No high ground about Cairo, Jim said. I had got it. We laid up for the day, on a tow-head tolerable close to the left-hand k. I begun to suspicion something. So did Jim. I says :

" Maybe we went by Cairo in the fog that night."

He says :

" Doan' less' talk about it, Huck. Po' niggers can't have no luck. I awluz ected dat rattle-snake skin warn't done wid it's work."

" I wish I'd never seen that snake-skin, Jim—I do wish I'd never laid eyes it."

" It ain't yo' fault, Huck ; you didn' know. Don't you blame yo'self ut it."

When it was daylight, here was the clear Ohio water in shore, sure ugh, and outside was the old regular Muddy ! So it was all up with Cairo. We talked it all over. It wouldn't do to take to the shore ; we couldn't take raft up the stream, of course. There warn't no way but to wait for dark, start back in the canoe and take the chances. So we slept all day amongst cotton-wood thicket, so as to be fresh for the work, and when we went back he raft about dark the canoe was gone !

We didn't say a word for a good while. There warn't anything to say. We h knowed well enough it was some more work of the rattle-snake skin ; so at was the use to talk about it ? It would only look like we was finding fault, that would be bound to fetch more bad luck—and keep on fetching it, too, we knowed enough to keep still.

By-and-by we talked about what we better do, and found there warn't no way just to go along down with the raft till we got a chance to buy a canoe to go k in. We warn't going to borrow it when there warn't anybody around, the pap would do, for that might set people after us.

So we shoved out, after dark, on the raft.

Anybody that don't believe yet, that it's foolishness to handle a snake-sk
after all that that snake-skin done for us, will believe it now, if they read on a
see what more it done for us.

The place to buy canoes is off of rafts laying up at shore. But we didn't
no rafts laying up ; so we went along during three hours and more. Well,
night got gray, and ruther thick, which is the next meanest thing to fog. Y
can't tell the shape of the river, and you can't see no distance. It got to be v
late and still, and then along comes a steamboat up the river. We lit the
tern, and judged she would see it. Up-stream boats didn't generly come clos
us ; they go out and follow the bars and hunt for easy water under the reefs ;
nights like this they bull right up the channel against the whole river.

We could hear her pounding along, but we didn't see her good till she
close. She aimed right for us. Often they do that and try to see how close t
can come without touching ; sometimes the wheel bites off a sweep, and then
pilot sticks his head out and laughs, and thinks he's mighty smart. Well, h
she comes, and we said she was going to try to shave us ; but she didn't seen
be sheering off a bit. She was a big one, and she was coming in a hurry,
looking like a black cloud with rows of glow-worms around it ; but all c
sudden she bulged out, big and scary, with a long row of wide-open furnace d
shining like red-hot teeth, and her monstrous bows and guards hanging ri
over us. There was a yell at us, and a jingling of bells to stop the engine
pow-wow of cussing, and whistling of steam—and as Jim went overboard on
side and I on the other, she come smashing straight through the raft.

I dived—and I aimed to find the bottom, too, for a thirty-foot wheel had
to go over me, and I wanted it to have plenty of room. I could always s
under water a minute ; this time I reckon I staid under water a minute an
half. Then I bounced for the top in a hurry, for I was nearly busting. I pop
out to my arm-pits and blowed the water out of my nose, and puffed a bit.
course there was a booming current ; and of course that boat started her engi
again ten seconds after she stopped them, for they never cared much for ra
men ; so now she was churning along up the river, out of sight in the th
weather, though I could hear her.

I sung out for Jim about a dozen times, but I didn't get any answer; so I bbed a plank that touched me while I was "treading water," and struck out shore, shoving it ahead of me. But I made out to see that the drift of the rent was towards the left-hand shore, which meant that I was in a crossing; changed off and went that way.

It was one of these long, slanting, two-mile crossings; so I was a good long e in getting over. I made a safe landing, and clum up the bank. I couldn't but a little ways, but I went poking along over rough ground for a quarter of ile or more, and then I run across a big old-fashioned double log house before oticed it. I was going to rush by and get away, but a lot of dogs jumped out went to howling and barking at me, and I knowed better than to move ther peg.

CLIMBING UP THE BANK.

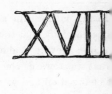

Chapter XVII

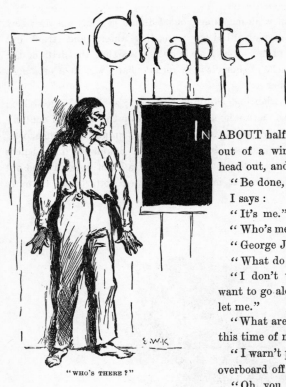

"WHO'S THERE?"

ABOUT half a minute somebody spoke out of a window, without putting his head out, and says :

"Be done, boys ! Who's there ?"

I says :

"It's me."

"Who's me ?"

"George Jackson, sir."

"What do you want ?"

"I don't want nothing, sir. I only want to go along by, but the dogs won't let me."

"What are you prowling around here this time of night, for—hey ?"

"I warn't prowling around, sir ; I fell overboard off of the steamboat."

"Oh, you did, did you ? Strike a light there, somebody. What did you say your name was ?"

"George Jackson, sir. I'm only a boy."

"Look here ; if you're telling the truth, you needn't be afraid—nobody'll hurt you. But don't try to budge ; stand right where you are. Rouse out Bob and Tom, some of you, and fetch the guns. George Jackson, is there anybody with you ?"

"No, sir, nobody."

I heard the people stirring around in the house, now, and see a light. The man sung out :

'Snatch that light away, Betsy, you old fool—ain't you got any sense ? Put
1 the floor behind the front door. Bob, if you and Tom are ready, take your
es."

"All ready."

"Now, George Jackson, do you know the Shepherdsons ?"

"No, sir—I never heard of them."

"Well, that may be so, and it mayn't. Now, all ready. Step forward,
rge Jackson. And mind, don't you hurry—come mighty slow. If there's
body with you, let him keep back—if he shows himself he'll be shot. Come
ig, now. Come slow ; push the door open, yourself—just enough to squeeze
d' you hear ?"

I didn't hurry, I couldn't if I'd a wanted to. I took one slow step at a time,
there warn't a sound, only I thought I could hear my heart. The dogs were
till as the humans, but they followed a little behind me. When I got to the
e log door-steps, I heard them unlocking and unbarring and unbolting. I
my hand on the door and pushed it a little and a little more, till somebody
, "There, that's enough—put your head in." I done it, but I judged they
ld take it off.

The candle was on the floor, and there they all was, looking at me, and me at
n, for about a quarter of a minute. Three big men with guns pointed at me,
ch made me wince, I tell you ; the oldest, gray and about sixty, the other two
ty or more—all of them fine and handsome—and the sweetest old gray-headed
y, and back of her two young women which I couldn't see right well. The
gentleman says :

"There—I reckon it's all right. Come in."

As soon as I was in, the old gentleman he locked the door and barred it and
ed it, and told the young men to come in with their guns, and they all went
a big parlor that had a new rag carpet on the floor, and got together in a
er that was out of range of the front windows—there warn't none on the
. They held the candle, and took a good look at me, and all said, "Why *he*
t a Shepherdson—no, there ain't any Shepherdson about him." Then the
man said he hoped I wouldn't mind being searched for arms, because he
n't mean no harm by it—it was only to make sure. So he didn't pry

into my pockets, but only felt outside with his hands, and said it was all rig
He told me to make myself easy and at home, and tell all about myself ; but
old lady says :

"Why bless you, Saul, the poor thing's as wet as he can be ; and d
you reckon it may be he's hungry ?"

"True for you, Rachel—I forgot."

So the old lady says :

"Betsy" (this was a nigger woman), "you fly around and get him somet
to eat, as quick as you can, poor thing; and one of you girls go and wake
Buck and tell him— Oh, here he is himself. Buck, take this little stranger
get the wet clothes off from him and dress him up in some of yours that's dry.

"BUCK."

Buck looked about as old as m
thirteen or fourteen or along th
though he was a little bigger than
He hadn't on anything but a sh
and he was very frowsy-headed.
come in gaping and digging one
into his eyes, and he was draggin
gun along with the other one.
says :

"Ain't they no Shepherds
around ?"

They said, no, 'twas a false ala
"Well," he says, "if they'd a
some, I reckon I'd a got one."

They all laughed, and Bob says
"Why, Buck, they might h
scalped us all, you've been so slow
coming."

"Well, nobody come after me,
it ain't right. I'm always kep' dov
I don't get no show."

"Never mind, Buck, my boy," says the old man, "you'll have show enou

in good time, don't you fret about that.   Go 'long with you now, and do
your mother told you."

When we got up stairs to his room, he got me a coarse shirt and a round-
ut and pants of his, and I put them on.   While I was at it he asked me what
name was, but before I could tell him, he started to telling me about a blue
and a young rabbit he had catched in the woods day before yesterday, and he
ed me where Moses was when the candle went out.   I said I didn't know ; I
ln't heard about it before, no way.

" Well, guess," he says.

" How'm I going to guess," says I, " when I never heard tell about it
ore ? "

" But you can guess, can't you ?   It's just as easy."

" *Which* candle ? "   I says.

" Why, any candle," he says.

" I don't know where he was," says I; " where was he ? "

" Why he was in the *dark !*   That's where he was ! "

" Well, if you knowed where he was, what did you ask me for ? "

" Why, blame it, it's a riddle, don't you see ?   Say, how long are you going to
y here ?   You got to stay always.   We can just have booming times—they
i't have no school now.   Do you own a dog ?   I've got a dog—and he'll go in
 river and bring out chips that you throw in.   Do you like to comb up,
idays, and all that kind of foolishness ?   You bet I don't, but ma she makes
 Confound these ole britches, I reckon I'd better put 'em on, but I'd ruther
, it's so warm.   Are you all ready ?   All right—come along, old hoss."

Cold corn-pone, cold corn-beef, butter and butter-milk—that is what they
l for me down there, and there ain't nothing better that ever I've come across
.   Buck and his ma and all of them smoked cob pipes, except the nigger
man, which was gone, and the two young women.   They all smoked and
ked, and I eat and talked.   The young women had quilts around them,
 their hair down their backs.   They all asked me questions, and I told
m how pap and me and all the family was living on a little farm down at
 bottom of Arkansaw, and my sister Mary Ann run off and got married and
er was heard of no more, and Bill went to hunt them and he warn't heard of

no more, and Tom and Mort died, and then there warn't nobody but just me ɛ
pap left, and he was just trimmed down to nothing, on account of his troubl
so when he died I took what there was left, because the farm didn't belong to
and started up the river, deck passage, and fell overboard ; and that was ho
come to be here. So they said I could have a home there as long as I wanted
Then it was most daylight, and everybody went to bed, and I went to bed w
Buck, and when I waked up in the morning, drat it all, I had forgot what
name was. So I laid there about an hour trying to think, and when Bɪ
waked up, I says :

"Can you spell, Buck ? "

"Yes," he says.

"I bet you can't spell my name," says I.

"I bet you what you dare I can," says he.

"All right," says I, "go ahead."

"G-o-r-g-e J-a-x-o-n—there now," he says.

"Well," says I, "you done it, but I didn't think you could. It ain't
slouch of a name to spell—right off without studying."

I set it down, private, because somebody might want *me* to spell it, next, ɛ
so I wanted to be handy with it and rattle it off like I was used to it.

It was a mighty nice family, and a mighty nice house, too. I hadn't seen
house out in the country before that was so nice and had so much style. It did
have an iron latch on the front door, nor a wooden one with a buckskin stri
but a brass knob to turn, the same as houses in a town. There warn't no ʰ
in the parlor, not a sign of a bed ; but heaps of parlors in towns has beds
them. There was a big fireplace that was bricked on the bottom, and the bri
was kept clean and red by pouring water on them and scrubbing them w
another brick ; sometimes they washed them over with red water-paint that tʰ
call Spanish-brown, same as they do in town. They had big brass dog-irons t
could hold up a saw-log. There was a clock on the middle of the mantel-pie
with a picture of a town painted on the bottom half of the glass front, an
round place in the middle of it for the sun, and you could see the pendul
swing behind it. It was beautiful to hear that clock tick ; and sometimes wʰ
one of these peddlers had been along and scoured her up and got her in gᵉ

pe, she would start in and strike a hundred and fifty before she got tuck-
l out. They wouldn't took any money for her.

Well, there was a big outlandish parrot on each side of the clock, made out of
ething like chalk, and painted up gaudy. By one of the parrots was a cat
le of crockery, and a crockery dog by the other ; and when you pressed down
them they squeaked, but didn't open their mouths nor look different nor
rested. They squeaked through underneath. There was a couple of big
l-turkey-wing fans spread out behind those things. On a table in the middle
he room was a kind of a lovely crockery basket that had apples and oranges
peaches and grapes piled up in it which was much redder and yellower and
ttier than real ones is, but they warn't real because you could see where pieces
got chipped off and showed the white chalk or whatever it was, underneath.
This table had a cover made out of beautiful oil-cloth, with a red and blue
ead-eagle painted on it, and a painted border all around. It come all the way
n Philadelphia, they said. There was some books too, piled up perfectly
ct, on each corner of the table. One was a big family Bible, full of pictures.
e was " Pilgrim's Progress," about a man that left his family it didn't say why.
ead considerable in it now and then. The statements was interesting, but
gh. Another was " Friendship's Offering," full of beautiful stuff and poetry ;
I didn't read the poetry. Another was Henry Clay's Speeches, and another
Dr. Gunn's Family Medicine, which told you all about what to do if a body
sick or dead. There was a Hymn Book, and a lot of other books. And
re was nice split-bottom chairs, and perfectly sound, too—not bagged down in
middle and busted, like an old basket.

They had pictures hung on the walls—mainly Washingtons and Lafayettes,
battles, and Highland Marys, and one called " Signing the Declaration." There
s some that they called crayons, which one of the daughters which was dead
de her own self when she was only fifteen years old. They was different from
pictures I ever see before ; blacker, mostly, than is common. One was a
man in a slim black dress, belted small under the arm-pits, with bulges like a
bage in the middle of the sleeves, and a large black scoop-shovel bonnet with
lack veil, and white slim ankles crossed about with black tape, and very wee
ck slippers, like a chisel, and she was leaning pensive on a tombstone on her

right elbow, under a weeping willow, and her other hand hanging down her s
holding a white handkerchief and a reticule, and underneath the picture it s
"Shall I Never See Thee More Alas." Another one was a young lady with I
hair all combed up straight to the top of her head, and knotted there in front
a comb like a chair-back, and she was crying into a handkerchief and had a de
bird laying on its back in her other hand with its heels up, and underneath t
picture it said "I Shall Never Hear Thy Sweet Chirrup More Alas." There v
one where a young lady was at a window looking up at the moon, and te
running down her cheeks; and she had an open letter in one hand with bla

sealing-wax showing on one edge
it, and she was mashing a locl
with a chain to it against her mou
and underneath the picture it s
"And Art Thou Gone Yes Th
Art Gone Alas." These was
nice pictures, I reckon, but I did
somehow seem to take to them,
cause if ever I was down a litt
they always give me the fan-to
Everybody was sorry she died,
cause she had laid out a lot more
these pictures to do, and a be
could see by what she had done wl
they had lost. But I reckon
that with her disposition, she v
having a better time in the gra
yard. She was at work on wl
they said was her greatest pict
when she took sick, and every e
and every night it was her prayer

"IT MADE HER LOOK SPIDERY."

be allowed to live till she got it done, but she never got the chance. It wa
picture of a young woman in a long white gown, standing on the rail of a brie
all ready to jump off, with her hair all down her back, and looking up to t

on, with the tears running down her face, and she had two arms folded
oss her breast, and two arms stretched out in front, and two more reaching
towards the moon—and the idea was, to see which pair would look best and
n scratch out all the other arms ; but, as I was saying, she died before she
; her mind made up, and now they kept this picture over the head of the
l in her room, and every time her birthday come they hung flowers on it.
her times it was hid with a little curtain. The young woman in the picture
l a kind of a nice sweet face, but there was so many arms it made her look
• spidery, seemed to me.

This young girl kept a scrap-book when she was alive, and used to paste
tuaries and accidents and cases of patient suffering in it out of the *Pres-
terian Observer,* and write poetry after them out of her own head. It was
·y good poetry. This is what she wrote about a boy by the name of Stephen
•wling Bots that fell down a well and was drownded :

ODE TO STEPHEN DOWLING BOTS, DEC'D.

> And did young Stephen sicken,
>   And did young Stephen die ?
> And did the sad hearts thicken,
>   And did the mourners cry ?

> No ; such was not the fate of
>   Young Stephen Dowling Bots ;
> Though sad hearts round him thickened,
>   'Twas not from sickness' shots.

> No whooping-cough did rack his frame,
>   Nor measles drear, with spots ;
> Not these impaired the sacred name
>   Of Stephen Dowling Bots.

Despised love struck not with woe
  That head of curly knots,
Nor stomach troubles laid him low,
  Young Stephen Dowling Bots.

O no.   Then list with tearful eye,
  Whilst I his fate do tell.
His soul did from this cold world fly,
  By falling down a well.

They got him out and emptied him ;
  Alas it was too late ;
His spirit was gone for to sport aloft
  In the realms of the good and great.

"THEY GOT HIM OUT AND EMPTIED HIM."

160 THE ART OF HUCKLEBERRY FINN

If Emmeline Grangerford could make poetry like that before she was fourteen, re ain't no telling what she could a done by-and-by. Buck said she ld rattle off poetry like nothing. She didn't ever have to stop to think. said she would slap down a line, and if she couldn't find anything to me with it she would just scratch it out and slap down another one, l go ahead. She warn't particular, she could write about anything you ose to give her to write about, just so it was sadful. Every time a man l, or a woman died, or a child died, she would be on hand with her ribute " before he was cold. She called them tributes. The neighbors l it was the doctor first, then Emmeline, then the undertaker—the under- er never got in ahead of Emmeline but once, and then she hung fire on a me for the dead person's name, which was Whistler. She warn't ever same, after that ; she never complained, but she kind of pined away l did not live long. Poor thing, many's the time I made myself go up the little room that used to be hers and get out her poor old scrap- k and read in it when her pictures had been aggravating me and I l soured on her a little. I liked all that family, dead ones and all, and n't going to let anything come between us. Poor Emmeline made poetry ut all the dead people when she was alive, and it didn't seem right that re warn't nobody to make some about her, now she was gone ; so I tried sweat out a verse or two myself, but I couldn't seem to make it go, lehow. They kept Emmeline's room trim and nice and all the things fixed it just the way she liked to have them when she was alive, and nobody r slept there. The old lady took care of the room herself, though there s plenty of niggers, and she sewed there a good deal and read her Bible re, mostly.

Well, as I was saying about the parlor, there was beautiful curtains on windows : white, with pictures painted on them, of castles with vines all vn the walls, and cattle coming down to drink. There was a little old no, too, that had tin pans in it, I reckon, and nothing was ever so lovely as near the young ladies sing, " The Last Link is Broken " and play " The Battle Prague " on it. The walls of all the rooms was plastered, and most had pets on the floors, and the whole house was whitewashed on the outside.

It was a double house, and the big open place betwixt them was roof
and floored, and sometimes the table was set there in the middle of t
day, and it was a cool, comfortable place. Nothing couldn't be better. A
warn't the cooking good, and just bushels of it too !

THE HOUSE.

Chapter XVIII

COL. GRANGERFORD.

Col. GRANGERFORD was a gentleman, you see. He was a gentleman all over; and so was his family. He was well born, as the saying is, and that's worth as much in a man as it is in a horse, so the Widow Douglass said, and nobody ever denied that she was of the first aristocracy in our town; and pap he always said it, too, though he warn't no more quality than a mudcat, himself. Col. Grangerford was very tall and very slim, and had a darkish-paly complexion, not a sign of red in it anywheres; he was clean-shaved every morning, all over his thin face, and he had the thinnest kind of lips, and the thinnest kind of nostrils, and a high nose, and heavy eyebrows, and the blackest kind of eyes, sunk so deep back that they seemed like they was looking out of caverns at you, as you may say. His forehead was high, and his hair was black and straight, and hung to his shoulders. His hands was long and thin, and every day of his life he put on a clean shirt and a full suit from head to foot made out of linen so white it hurt your eyes to look at it; and on Sundays he wore a blue tail-coat with brass buttons on it. He carried a mahogany cane with a silver

head to it. There warn't no frivolishness about him, not a bit, and he war
ever loud. He was as kind as he could be—you could feel that, you know, a
so you had confidence. Sometimes he smiled, and it was good to see ; but wh
he straightened himself up like a liberty-pole, and the lightning begun to flic
out from under his eyebrows you wanted to climb a tree first, and find out wl
the matter was afterwards. He didn't ever have to tell anybody to mind th
manners—everybody was always good mannered where he was. Everybe
loved to have him around, too ; he was sunshine most always—I mean he ma
it seem like good weather. When he turned into a cloud-bank it was aw
dark for a half a minute and that was enough ; there wouldn't nothing go wro
again for a week.

When him and the old lady come down in the morning, all the family got
out of their chairs and give them good-day, and didn't set down again till tl
had set down. Then Tom and Bob went to the sideboard where the decant
was, and mixed a glass of bitters and handed it to him, and he held it in
hand and waited till Tom's and Bob's was mixed, and then they bowed and s
" Our duty to you, sir, and madam ; " and *they* bowed the least bit in the wo
and said thank you, and so they drank, all three, and Bob and Tom poured
spoonful of water on the sugar and the mite of whisky or apple brandy in
bottom of their tumblers, and give it to me and Buck, and we drank to the
people too.

Bob was the oldest, and Tom next. Tall, beautiful men with very bre
shoulders and brown faces, and long black hair and black eyes. They dres
in white linen from head to foot, like the old gentleman, and wore bro
Panama hats.

Then there was Miss Charlotte, she was twenty-five, and tall and proud a
grand, but as good as she could be, when she warn't stirred up ; but when
was, she had a look that would make you wilt in your tracks, like her fath
She was beautiful.

So was her sister, Miss Sophia, but it was a different kind. She was gen
and sweet, like a dove, and she was only twenty

Each person had their own nigger to wait on them—Buck, too. My nig

d a monstrous easy time, because I warn't used to having anybody do anything
me, but Buck's was on the jump most of the time.

This was all there was of the family, now ; but there used to be more—three
s ; they got killed ; and Emmeline that died.

The old gentleman owned a lot of farms, and over a hundred niggers.
metimes a stack of people would come there, horseback, from ten or fifteen
le around, and stay five or six days, and have such junketings round about and
the river, and dances and picnics in the woods, day-times, and balls at the
use, nights. These people was
stly kin-folks of the family.
e men brought their guns
h them. It was a handsome
of quality, I tell you.

There was another clan of
stocracy around there—five
six families—mostly of the
ne of Shepherdson. They
s as high-toned, and well
n, and rich and grand, as the
be of Grangerfords. The
epherdsons and the Granger-
ds used the same steamboat
ding, which was about two
le above our house ; so some-
1es when I went up there
h a lot of our folks I used to
a lot of the Shepherdsons
re, on their fine horses.

One day Buck and me was
ay out in the woods, hunt-
, and heard a horse coming. We was crossing the road. Buck says :
"Quick ! Jump for the woods !"

YOUNG HARNEY SHEPHERDSON.

We done it, and then peeped down the woods through the leave Pretty soon a splendid young man come galloping down the road, setting h horse easy and looking like a soldier. He had his gun across his pommel. had seen him before. It was young Harney Shepherdson. I heard Buck's g go off at my ear, and Harney's hat tumbled off from his head. He grabb his gun and rode straight to the place where we was hid. But we did wait. We started through the woods on a run. The woods warn't thick, I looked over my shoulder, to dodge the bullet, and twice I seen Harney cov Buck with his gun ; and then he rode away the way he come—to get his hat reckon, but I couldn't see. We never stopped running till we got home. T old gentleman's eyes blazed a minute—'twas pleasure, mainly, I judged—th

MISS CHARLOTTE.

his face sort of smoothed down, and says, kind of gentle :

" I don't like that shooting from b hind a bush. Why didn't you step in the road, my boy ? "

" The Shepherdsons don't, fathe They always take advantage."

Miss Charlotte she held her head like a queen while Buck was tellin his tale, and her nostrils spread and h eyes snapped. The two young me looked dark, but never said nothin Miss Sophia she turned pale, but t color come back when she found t man warn't hurt.

Soon as I could get Buck down the corn-cribs under the trees by ou selves, I says :

" Did you want to kill him, Buck

"Well, I bet I did."

" What did he do to you ? "

" Him ? He never done nothing to me."

" Well, then, what did you want to kill him for ? "

" Why nothing—only it's on account of the feud."

" What's a feud ? "

" Why, where was you raised ? Don't you know what a feud is ? "

" Never heard of it before—tell me about it."

" Well," says Buck, " a feud is this way. A man has a quarrel with another
n, and kills him ; then that other man's brother kills *him ;* then the other
thers, on both sides, goes for one another ; then the *cousins* chip in—and by-
d-by everybody's killed off, and there ain't no more feud. But it's kind of
w, and takes a long time."

" Has this one been going on long, Buck ? "

" Well I should *reckon !* it started thirty year ago, or som'ers along there.
ere was trouble 'bout something and then a lawsuit to settle it ; and the suit
nt agin one of the men, and so he up and shot the man that won the suit—
ich he would naturally do, of course. Anybody would."

" What was the trouble about, Buck ?—land ? "

" I reckon maybe—I don't know."

" Well, who done the shooting ?—was it a Grangerford or a Shepherd-
? "

" Laws, how do *I* know ? it was so long ago."

" Don't anybody know ? "

" Oh, yes, pa knows, I reckon, and some of the other old folks ; but they
n't know, now, what the row was about in the first place."

" Has there been many killed, Buck ? "

" Yes—right smart chance of funerals. But they don't always kill. Pa's
t a few buck-shot in him ; but he don't mind it 'cuz he don't weigh much
yway. Bob's been carved up some with a bowie, and Tom's been hurt once or
ice."

" Has anybody been killed this year, Buck ? "

" Yes, we got one and they got one. 'Bout three months ago, my cousin
d, fourteen year old, was riding through the woods, on t'other side of the river.

and didn't have no weapon with him, which was blame' foolishness, and in a lon
some place he hears a horse a-coming behind him, and sees old Baldy Shepher
son a-linkin' after him with his gun in his hand and his white hair a-flying in t
wind ; and 'stead of jumping off and taking to the brush, Bud 'lowed he cou
outrun him ; so they had it, nip and tuck, for five mile or more, the old m
a-gaining all the time ; so at last Bud seen it warn't any use, so he stopped a
faced around so as to have the bullet holes in front, you know, and the old m
he rode up and shot him down. But he didn't git much chance to enjoy h
luck, for inside of a week our folks laid *him* out."

"I reckon that old man was a coward, Buck."

"I reckon he *warn't* a coward. Not by a blame' sight. There ain't a cowa
amongst them Shepherdsons—not a one. And there ain't no cowards among
the Grangerfords, either. Why, that old man kep' up his end in a fight one da
for a half an hour, against three Grangerfords, and come out winner. They w
all a-horseback ; he lit off of his horse and got behind a little wood-pile, and ke
his horse before him to stop the bullets ; but the Grangerfords staid on the
horses and capered around the old man, and peppered away at him, and
peppered away at them. Him and his horse both went home pretty leaky a
crippled, but the Grangerfords had to be *fetched* home—and one of 'em w
dead, and another died the next day. No, sir, if a body's out hunting f
cowards, he don't want to fool away any time amongst them Shepherdsons, bec
they don't breed any of that *kind*."

Next Sunday we all went to church, about three mile, everybody a-horsebac
The men took their guns along, so did Buck, and kept them between their kne
or stood them handy against the wall. The Shepherdsons done the same.
was pretty ornery preaching—all about brotherly love, and such-like tiresomene
but everybody said it was a good sermon, and they all talked it over goir
home, and had such a powerful lot to say about faith, and good works, and fr
grace, and preforeordestination, and I don't know what all, that it did seem
me to be one of the roughest Sundays I had run across yet.

About an hour after dinner everybody was dozing around, some in their chai
and some in their rooms, and it got to be pretty dull. Buck and a dog w

etched out on the grass in the sun, sound asleep. I went up to our room, and
lged I would take a nap myself. I found that sweet Miss Sophia standing in
r door, which was next to ours, and she took me in her room and shut the
or very soft, and asked me if I liked her, and I said I did ; and she asked me
I would do something for her and not tell anybody, and I said I would. Then
e said she'd forgot her Testament, and left it in the seat at church, between
o other books and would I slip out quiet and go there and fetch it to her,
d not say nothing to nobody. I said I would. So I slid out and slipped off
the road, and there warn't anybody at the church, except maybe a hog or
o, for there warn't any lock on the door, and hogs likes a puncheon floor

summer-time because it's cool.
you notice, most folks don't go to
urch only when they've got to ;
t a hog is different.

Says I to myself something's up
it ain't natural for a girl to be
such a sweat about a Testament ;
I give it a shake, and out drops a
tle piece of paper with *"Half-past
o"* wrote on it with a pencil. I
nsacked it, but couldn't find any-
ing else. I couldn't make any-
ing out of that, so I put the paper
the book again, and when I got
me and up stairs, there was Miss
phia in her door waiting for me.
e pulled me in and shut the door ;
en she looked in the Testament
l she found the paper, and as soon
she read it she looked glad ;

"AND ASKED ME IF I LIKED HER."

d before a body could think, she grabbed me and give me a squeeze, and said I
s the best boy in the world, and not to tell anybody. She was mighty red in

the face, for a minute, and her eyes lighted up and it made her powerful prett
I was a good deal astonished, but when I got my breath I asked her what t
paper was about, and she asked me if I had read it, and I said no, and she ask
me if I could read writing, and I told her " no, only coarse-hand," and then s
said the paper warn't anything but a book-mark to keep her place, and I mig
go and play now.

I went off down to the river, studying over this thing, and pretty soon
noticed that my nigger was following along behind. When we was out of sig
of the house, he looked back and around a second, and then comes a-runnin
and says :

" Mars Jawge, if you'll come down into de swamp, I'll show you a whe
stack o' water-moccasins."

Thinks I, that's mighty curious ; he said that yesterday. He oughter kn
a body don't love water-moccasins enough to go around hunting for them. Wh
is he up to anyway ? So I says—

" All right, trot ahead."

I followed a half a mile, then he struck out over the swamp and wad
ankle deep as much as another half mile. We come to a little flat piece of la
which was dry and very thick with trees and bushes and vines, and he says—

" You shove right in dah, jist a few steps, Mars Jawge, dah's whah dey is.
seed 'm befo', I don't k'yer to see 'em no mo'."

Then he slopped right along and went away, and pretty soon the trees h
him. I poked into the place a-ways, and come to a little open patch as big as
bedroom, all hung around with vines, and found a man laying there asleep—a
by jings it was my old Jim !

I waked him up, and I reckoned it was going to be a grand surprise to him
see me again, but it warn't. He nearly cried, he was so glad, but he warn
surprised. Said he swum along behind me, that night, and heard me yell eve
time, but dasn't answer, because he didn't want nobody to pick *him* up, and ta
him into slavery again. Says he—

" I got hurt a little, en couldn't swim fas', so I wuz a considable ways behi
you, towards de las' ; when you landed I reck'ned I could ketch up wid you on

' 'dout havin' to shout at you, but when I see dat house I begin to go slow. I
off too fur to hear what dey say to you—I wuz 'fraid o' de dogs—but when it
all quiet agin, I knowed you's in de house, so I struck out for de woods to
it for day. Early in de mawnin' some er de niggers come along, gwyne to de
ds, en dey tuck me en showed me dis place, whah de dogs can't track me on
ounts o' de water, en dey brings me truck to eat every night, en tells me how
's a gitt'n along."

" Why didn't you tell my Jack to fetch me here sooner, Jim ? "

" Well, 'twarn't no use to 'sturb you, Huck, tell we could do sumfn—but we's
right, now. I ben a-buyin' pots en pans en vittles, as I got a chanst, en a
tchin' up de raf', nights, when——"

" *What* raft, Jim ? "

" Our ole raf'."

" You mean to say our old raft warn't smashed all to flinders ? "

" No, she warn't. She was tore up a good deal—one en' of her was—but dey
rn't no great harm done, on'y our traps was mos' all los'. Ef we hadn' dive'
deep en swum so fur under water, en de night hadn' ben so dark, en we warn't
sk'yerd, en ben sich punkin-heads, as de sayin' is, we'd a seed de raf'. But it's
' as well we didn't, 'kase now she's all fixed up agin mos' as good as new, en
's got a new lot o' stuff, too, in de place o' what 'uz los'."

" Why, how did you get hold of the raft again, Jim—did you catch her ? "

" How I gwyne to ketch her, en I out in de woods ? No, some er de niggers
in' her ketched on a snag, along heah in de ben', en dey hid her in a crick,
ongst de willows, en dey wuz so much jawin' 'bout which un 'um she b'long to de
s', dat I come to heah 'bout it pooty soon, so I ups en settles de trouble by tellin'
n she don't b'long to none uv um, but to you en me ; en I ast 'm if dey gwyne to
b a young white genlman's propaty, en git a hid'n for it ? Den I gin 'm ten
ts apiece, en dey 'uz mighty well satisfied, en wisht some mo' raf's 'ud come
ng en make 'm rich agin. Dey's mighty good to me, dese niggers is, en
atever I wants 'm to do fur me, I doan' have to ast 'm twice, honey. Dat
ck's a good nigger, en pooty smart."

" Yes, he is. He ain't ever told me you was here ; told me to come, and he'd

show me a lot of water-moccasins. If anything happens, *he* ain't mixed up in
He can say he never seen us together, and it'll be the truth."

I don't want to talk much about the next ·day. I reckon I'll cut it pret
short. I waked up about dawn, and was agoing to turn over and go to sle
again, when I noticed how still it was—didn't seem to be anybody stirrin
That warn't usual. Next I noticed that Buck was up and gone. Well, I ge
up, a-wondering, and goes down stairs—nobody around ; everything as still
a mouse. Just the same outside; thinks I, what does it mean ? Down by tl
wood-pile I comes across my Jack, and says :

" What's it all about ? "

Says he :

" Don't you know, Mars Jawge ? "

" No," says I, " I don't."

" Well, den, Miss Sophia's run off ! 'deed she has. She run off in de nigh
sometime—nobody don't know jis' when—run off to git married to dat you
Harney Shepherdson, you know—leastways, so dey 'spec. De fambly foun'
out, 'bout half an hour ago—maybe a little mo'—en' I *tell* you dey warn't no tir
los'. Sich another hurryin' up guns en hosses *you* never see ! De women fol
has gone for to stir up de relations, en ole Mars Saul en de boys tuck dey guns
rode up de river road for to try to ketch dat young man en kill him 'fo' he k
git acrost de river wid Miss Sophia. I reck'n dey's gwyne to be mighty roug
times."

" Buck went off 'thout waking me up."

" Well I reck'n he *did!* Dey warn't gwyne to mix you up in it. Ma
Buck he loaded up his gun en 'lowed he's gwyne to fetch home a Shepherdson
bust. Well, dey'll be plenty un 'm dah, I reck'n, en you bet you he'll fetch o
ef he gits a chanst."

I took up the river road as hard as I could put. By-and-by I begin to he
guns a good ways off. When I come in sight of the log store and the wood-pi
where the steamboats lands, I worked along under the trees and brush till I g
to a good place, and then I clumb up into the forks of a cotton-wood that was o
of reach, and watched. There was a wood-rank four foot high, a little ways

nt of the tree, and first I was going to hide behind that ; but maybe it was
kier I didn't.

There was four or five men cavorting around on their horses in the open
ce before the log store, cussing and yelling, and trying to get at a couple of
ing chaps that was behind the wood-rank alongside of the steamboat landing—
t they couldn't come it. Every time one of them showed himself on the river

" BEHIND THE WOOD-PILE."

le of the wood-pile he got shot at. The two boys was squatting back to back
hind the pile, so they could watch both ways.

By-and-by the men stopped cavorting around and yelling. They started
ling towards the store ; then up gets one of the boys, draws a steady bead over
e wood-rank, and drops one of them out of his saddle. All the men jumped
' of their horses and grabbed the hurt one and started to carry him to the store;
d that minute the two boys started on the run. They got half-way to the tree
vas in before the men noticed. Then the men see them, and jumped on their
rses and took out after them. They gained on the boys, but it didn't do no
od, the boys had too good a start ; they got to the wood-pile that was in front

of my tree, and slipped in behind it, and so they had the bulge on the men aga
One of the boys was Buck, and the other was a slim young chap about ninete
years old.

The men ripped around awhile, and then rode away. As soon as they w
out of sight, I sung out to Buck and told him.   He didn't know what to make
my voice coming out of the tree, at first.   He was awful surprised.   He told
to watch out sharp and let him know when the men come in sight again ; s
they was up to some devilment or other—wouldn't be gone long.   I wished I w
out of that tree, but I dasn't come down.   Buck begun to cry and rip, and 'low
that him and his cousin Joe (that was the other young chap) would make up
this day, yet.   He said his father and his two brothers was killed, and two
three of the enemy.   Said the Shepherdsons laid for them, in ambush.   Bu
said his father and brothers ought to waited for their relations—the Shepherds
was too strong for them.   I asked him what was become of young Harney a
Miss Sophia.   He said they'd got across the river and was safe.   I was glad
that ; but the way Buck did take on because he didn't manage to kill Harr
that day he shot at him—I hain't ever heard anything like it.

All of a sudden, bang ! bang ! bang ! goes three or four guns—the men h
slipped around through the woods and come in from behind without their hors
The boys jumped for the river—both of them hurt—and as they swum down t
current the men run along the bank shooting at them and singing out, " K
them, kill them !"   It made me so sick I most fell out of the tree.   I ain't agoi
to tell *all* that happened—it would make me sick again if I was to do that.
wished I hadn't ever come ashore that night, to see such things.   I ain't e
going to get shut of them—lots of times I dream about them.

I staid in the tree till it begun to get dark, afraid to come down.   Sometim
I heard guns away off in the woods ; and twice I seen little gangs of men gall
past the log store with guns ; so I reckoned the trouble was still agoing on.
was mighty down-hearted ; so I made up my mind I wouldn't ever go an
that house again, because I reckoned I was to blame, somehow.   I judged th
that piece of paper meant that Miss Sophia was to meet Harney somewheres
half-past two and run off; and I judged I ought to told her father about th

er and the curious way she acted, and then maybe he would a locked her up
this awful mess wouldn't ever happened.

When I got down out of the tree, I crept along down the river bank a
ce, and found the two bodies laying in the edge of the water, and tugged
hem till I got them ashore ; then I covered up their faces, and got away as
ck as I could. I cried a little when I was covering up Buck's face, for he
mighty good to me.

It was just dark, now. I never went near the house, but struck through the
ds and made for the swamp. Jim warn't on his island, so I tramped off in
urry for the crick, and crowded through the willows, red-hot to jump aboard
get out of that awful country—the raft was gone ! My souls, but I was
red ! I couldn't get my breath for most a minute. Then I raised a yell. A
ce not twenty-five foot from me, says—

"Good lan' ! is dat you, honey ? Doan' make no noise."

It was Jim's voice—nothing ever sounded so good before. I run along the
k a piece and got aboard, and Jim he grabbed me and hugged me, he was so
d to see me. He says—

"Laws bless you, chile, I 'uz right down sho' you's dead agin. Jack's been
h, he say he reck'n you's ben shot, kase you didn' come home no mo' ; so
jes' dis minute a startin' de raf' down towards de mouf er de crick, so's to be
ready for to shove out en leave soon as Jack comes agin en tells me for certain
is dead. Lawsy, I's mighty glad to git you back agin, honey."

I says—

"All right—that's mighty good ; they won't find me, and they'll think I've
n killed, and floated down the river—there's something up there that'll help
m to think so—so don't you lose no time, Jim, but just shove off for the big
ter as fast as ever you can."

I never felt easy till the raft was two mile below there and out in the middle
the Mississippi. Then we hung up our signal lantern, and judged that we was
e and safe once more. I hadn't had a bite to eat since yesterday ; so Jim he got
some corn-dodgers and buttermilk, and pork and cabbage, and greens—
re ain't nothing in the world so good, when it's cooked right—and whilst I eat

my supper we talked, and had a good time. I was powerful glad to get aw
from the feuds, and so was Jim to get away from the swamp. We said the
warn't no home like a raft, after all. Other places do seem so cramped up a
smothery, but a raft don't. You feel mighty free and easy and comfortable
a raft.

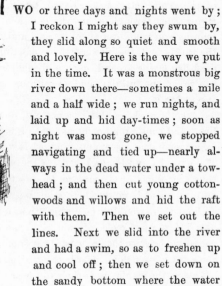

Chapter XIX

HIDING DAY-TIMES.

TWO or three days and nights went by; I reckon I might say they swum by, they slid along so quiet and smooth and lovely. Here is the way we put in the time. It was a monstrous big river down there—sometimes a mile and a half wide; we run nights, and laid up and hid day-times; soon as night was most gone, we stopped navigating and tied up—nearly always in the dead water under a tow-head; and then cut young cotton-woods and willows and hid the raft with them. Then we set out the lines. Next we slid into the river and had a swim, so as to freshen up and cool off; then we set down on the sandy bottom where the water

is about knee deep, and watched the daylight come. Not a sound, anywheres—perfectly still—just like the whole world was asleep, only sometimes the ll-frogs a-cluttering, maybe. The first thing to see, looking away over the ter, was a kind of dull line—that was the woods on t'other side—you couldn't ke nothing else out; then a pale place in the sky; then more paleness, eading around; then the river softened up, away off, and warn't black more, but gray; you could see little dark spots drifting along, ever so far

away—trading scows, and such things; and long black streaks—rafts; som
times you could hear a sweep screaking; or jumbled up voices, it was so sti
and sounds come so far; and by-and-by you could see a streak on the wa
which you know by the look of the streak that there's a snag there in a sw
current which breaks on it and makes that streak look that way; and you
the mist curl up off of the water, and the east reddens up, and the river, and y
make out a log cabin in the edge of the woods, away on the bank on t'other si
of the river, being a wood-yard, likely, and piled by them cheats so you c
throw a dog through it anywheres; then the nice breeze springs up, and com
fanning you from over there, so cool and fresh, and sweet to smell, on account
the woods and the flowers; but sometimes not that way, because they've l
dead fish laying around, gars, and such, and they do get pretty rank; and n
you've got the full day, and everything smiling in the sun, and the song-bi
just going it!

A little smoke couldn't be noticed, now, so we would take some fish off of t
lines, and cook up a hot breakfast. And afterwards we would watch the lo
someness of the river, and kind of lazy along, and by-and-by lazy off to sle
Wake up, by-and-by, and look to see what done it, and maybe see a steambo
coughing along up stream, so far off towards the other side you couldn't t
nothing about her only whether she was stern-wheel or side-wheel; then for ab
an hour there wouldn't be nothing to hear nor nothing to see—just solid lonesor
ness. Next you'd see a raft sliding by, away off yonder, and maybe a galoot o
chopping, because they're most always doing it on a raft; you'd see the ax flash, a
come down—you don't hear nothing; you see that ax go up again, and by the ti
it's above the man's head, then you hear the *k'chunk!*—it had took all that ti
to come over the water. So we would put in the day, lazying around, listeni
to the stillness. Once there was a thick fog, and the rafts and things that w
by was beating tin pans so the steamboats wouldn't run over them. A scow c
raft went by so close we could hear them talking and cussing and laughing
heard them plain; but we couldn't see no sign of them; it made you feel craw
it was like spirits carrying on that way in the air. Jim said he believed it w
spirits; but I says:

" No, spirits wouldn't say, ' dern the dern fog.' "

Soon as it was night, out we shoved; when we got her out to about the ldle, we let her alone, and let her float wherever the current wanted her then we lit the pipes, and dangled our legs in the water and talked about kinds of things—we was always naked, day and night, whenever the squitoes would let us—the new clothes Buck's folks made for me was good to be comfortable, and besides I didn't go much on clothes, no-y.

Sometimes we'd have that whole river all to ourselves for the longest e. Yonder was the banks and the islands, across the water ; and maybe a rk—which was a candle in a cabin window—and sometimes on the water could see a spark or two—on a raft or a scow, you know ; and maybe could hear a fiddle or a song coming over from one of them crafts. It's ly to live on a raft. We had the sky, up there, all speckled with stars, we used to lay on our backs and look up at them, and discuss about ther they was made, or only just happened—Jim he allowed they was made, I allowed they happened ; I judged it would have took too long to *make* many. Jim said the moon could a *laid* them ; well, that looked kind of sonable, so I didn't say nothing against it, because I've seen a frog lay st as many, so of course it could be done. We used to watch the stars that , too, and see them streak down. Jim allowed they'd got spoiled and was e out of the nest.

Once or twice of a night we would see a steamboat slipping along in the k, and now and then she would belch a whole world of sparks up out ter chimbleys, and they would rain down in the river and look awful pretty ; n she would turn a corner and her lights would wink out and her pow-wow t off and leave the river still again ; and by-and-by her waves would get to a long time after she was gone, and joggle the raft a bit, and after that you ldn't hear nothing for you couldn't tell how long, except maybe frogs something.

After midnight the people on shore went to bed, and then for two or ee hours the shores was black—no more sparks in the cabin windows. These

sparks was our clock—the first one that showed again meant morning was comin
so we hunted a place to hide and tie up, right away.

One morning about day-break, I found a canoe and crossed over a chute
the main shore—it was only two hundred yards—and paddled about a mile
a crick amongst the cypress woods, to see if I couldn't get some berries. Ju
as I was passing a place where a kind of a cow-path crossed the crick, here con
a couple of men tearing up the path as tight as they could foot it. I thoug

"AND DOGS A-COMING."

I was a goner, for whe
ever anybody was after an
body I judged it was *me*—
maybe Jim. I was abo
to dig out from there in
hurry, but they was pre
close to me then, and su
out and begged me to sa
their lives—said they had
been doing nothing, and w
being chased for it—said the
was men and dogs a-comin
They wanted to jump rig
in, but I says—

"Don't you do it.
don't hear the dogs a
horses yet; you've
time to crowd through t
brush and get up the cr
a little ways; then you ta
to the water and wade do
to me and get in—that'll throw the dogs off the scent."

They done it, and soon as they was aboard I lit out for our tow-head, a
in about five or ten minutes we heard the dogs and the men away off, shouti
We heard them come along towards the crick, but couldn't see them; th

ned to stop and fool around a while ; then, as we got further and further
y all the time, we couldn't hardly hear them at all ; by the time we had
a mile of woods behind us and struck the river, everything was quiet,
we paddled over to the tow-head and hid in the cotton-woods and was
.

One of these fellows was about seventy, or upwards, and had a bald head
very gray whiskers.   He had an old battered-up slouch hat on, and a greasy
e woolen shirt, and ragged old blue jeans britches stuffed into his boot tops,
. home-knit galluses—no, he only had one.   He had an old long-tailed blue
s coat with slick brass buttons, flung over his arm, and both of them had
fat ratty-looking carpet-bags.

The other fellow was about thirty and dressed about as ornery.   After break-
; we all laid off and talked, and the first thing that come out was that these
ps didn't know one another.

" What got you into trouble ? " says the baldhead to t'other chap.

" Well, I'd been selling an article to take the tartar off the teeth—and it does
e it off, too, and generly the enamel along with it—but I staid about one night
ger than I ought to, and was just in the act of sliding out when I ran across
on the trail this side of town, and you told me they were coming, and begged
to help you to get off.   So I told you I was expecting trouble myself and
ld scatter out *with* you.   That's the whole yarn—what's yourn ? "

" Well, I'd ben a-runnin' a little temperance revival thar, 'bout a week, and
the pet of the women-folks, big and little, for I was makin' it mighty warm
the rummies, I *tell* you, and takin' as much as five or six dollars a night—ten
ts a head, children and niggers free—and business a growin' all the time ;
en somehow or another a little report got around, last night, that I had a way
uttin' in my time with a private jug, on the sly.   A nigger rousted me out
mornin', and told me the people was getherin' on the quiet, with their dogs
horses, and they'd be along pretty soon and give me 'bout half an hour's
t, and then run me down, if they could ; and if they got me they'd tar and
ther me and ride me on a rail, sure.   I didn't wait for no breakfast—I warn't
gry."

"Old man," says the young one, "I reckon we might double-team together ; what do you think ? "

"I ain't undisposed. What's your line—mainly ? "

"Jour printer, by trade ; do a little in patent medicines ; theatre-acto tragedy, you know ; take a turn at mesmerism and phrenology when there' chance ; teach singing-geography school for a change ; sling a lecture, sometii —oh, I do lots of things—most anything that comes handy, so it ain't wo What's your lay ? "

"I've done considerble in the doctoring way in my time. Layin' on o' hand my best holt—for cancer, and paralysis, and sich things ; and I k'n tel fortune pretty good, when I've got somebody along to find out the facts me. Preachin's my line, too ; and workin' camp-meetin's ; and missionar around."

Nobody never said anything for a while ; then the young man hove a sigh a says—

"Alas ! "

"What 're you alassin' about ? " says the baldhead.

"To think I should have lived to be leading such a life, and be degrac down into such company." And he begun to wipe the corner of his eye wit rag.

"Dern your skin, ain't the company good enough for you?" says the ba head, pretty pert and uppish.

"Yes, it *is* good enough for me ; it's as good as I deserve ; for who fetc me so low, when I was so high ? *I* did myself. I don't blame *you*, gentlemei far from it ; I don't blame anybody. I deserve it all. Let the cold world do worst ; one thing I know—there's a grave somewhere for me. The world may on just as its always done, and take everything from me—loved ones, proper everything—but it can't take that. Some day I'll lie down in it and forget it and my poor broken heart will be at rest." He went on a-wiping.

"Drot your pore broken heart," says the baldhead ; "what are you he ing your pore broken heart at *us* f'r ? *We* hain't done nothing."

"No, I know you haven't. I ain't blaming you, gentlemen. I brou

elf down—yes, I did it myself. It's right I should suffer—perfectly right—I
't make any moan."

" Brought you down from whar ? Whar was you brought down from ? "

" Ah, you would not believe me ; the world never believes—let it pass—'tis
matter. The secret of my
h—— "

" The secret of your birth ?
you mean to say—— "

" Gentlemen," says the young
ı, very solemn, " I will reveal
o you, for I feel I may have
fidence in you. By rights I
a duke ! "

Jim's eyes bugged out when
heard that ; and I reckon
ıe did, too. Then the bald-
d says : " No ! you can't
ın it ? "

" Yes. My great-grandfather,
st son of the Duke of Bridge-
er, fled to this country about
end of the last century, to
ıthe the pure air of freedom ;
ried here, and died, leaving a

" BY RIGHTS I AM A DUKE ! "

his own father dying about the same time. The second son of the late duke
ed the title and estates—the infant real duke was ignored. I am the lineal
ıendant of that infant—I am the rightful Duke of Bridgewater ; and here am
ɔrlorn, torn from my high estate, hunted of men, despised by the cold world,
ged, worn, heart-broken, and degraded to the companionship of felons on
ft ! "

Jim pitied him ever so much, and so did I. We tried to comfort him, but he
it warn't much use, he couldn't be much comforted ; said if we was a mind to

acknowledge him, that would do him more good than most anything else ; so said we would, if he would tell us how.   He said we ought to bow, when spoke to him, and say "Your Grace," or "My Lord," or "Your Lordship" and he wouldn't mind it if we called him plain "Bridgewater," which he s was a title, anyway, and not a name ; and one of us ought to wait on him dinner, and do any little thing for him he wanted done.

Well, that was all easy, so we done it.   All through dinner Jim st around and waited on him, and says, "Will yo' Grace have some o' dis, some o' dat ? " and so on, and a body could see it was mighty pleasing him.

But the old man got pretty silent, by-and-by—didn't have much to s and didn't look pretty comfortable over all that petting that was going on arou that duke.   He seemed to have something on his mind.   So, along in the aft noon, he says :

"Looky here, Bilgewater," he says, "I'm nation sorry for you, but you ai the only person that's had troubles like that."

"No ?"

"No, you ain't.   You ain't the only person that's ben snaked do wrongfully out'n a high place."

"Alas ! "

"No, you ain't the only person that's had a secret of his birth."   And jings, *he* begins to cry.

"Hold !   What do you mean ? "

"Bilgewater, kin I trust you ? " says the old man, still sort of sobbing

"To the bitter death ! "   He took the old man by the hand and squeezed and says, "The secret of your being : speak ! "

"Bilgewater, I am the late Dauphin ! "

You bet you Jim and me stared, this time.   Then the duke says ·

"You are what ? "

"Yes, my friend, it is too true—your eyes is lookin' at this very mom on the pore disappeared Dauphin, Looy the Seventeen, son of Looy the Sixt and Marry Antonette."

"You! At your age! No! You mean you're the late Charlemagne; you

st be six or seven hundred
rs old, at the very least."

"Trouble has done it,
gewater, trouble has done
  trouble has brung these
y hairs and this premature
litude. Yes, gentlemen,
. see before you, in blue
as and misery, the wan-
in', exiled, trampled-on and
erin' r i g h t f u l King of
nce."

Well, he cried and took on
  that me and Jim didn't
w hardly what to do, we
s so sorry—and so glad and
ud we'd got him with us,
. So we set in, like we done
ore with the duke, and tried
comfort *him.* But he said

"I AM THE LATE DAUPHIN."

warn't no use, nothing but to be dead and done with it all could do him any
d; though he said it often made him feel easier and better for a while if
ple treated him according to his rights, and got down on one knee to speak to
, and always called him "Your Majesty," and-waited on him first at meals,
 didn't set down in his presence till he asked them. So Jim and me set to
jestying him, and doing this and that and t'other for him, and standing up till
told us we might set down. This done him heaps of good, and so he got
erful and comfortable. But the duke kind of soured on him, and didn't look a
satisfied with the way things was going; still, the king acted real friendly
ards him, and said the duke's great-grandfather and all the other Dukes of
gewater was a good deal thought of by *his* father and was allowed to come to

the palace considerable ; but the duke staid huffy a good while, till by-and
the king says :

" Like as not we got to be together a blamed long time, on this h-yer ra
Bilgewater, and so what's the use o' your bein' sour ? It'll only make thi
oncomfortable. It ain't my fault I warn't born a duke, it ain't your fault
warn't born a king—so what's the use to worry ? Make the best o' things
way you find 'em, says I—that's my motto. This ain't no bad thing that we
struck here—plenty grub and an easy life—come, give us your hand, Duke, a
less all be friends."

The duke done it, and Jim and me was pretty glad to see it. It took away
the uncomfortableness, and we felt mighty good over it, because it would a b
a miserable business to have any unfriendliness on the raft ; for what you wa
above all things, on a raft, is for everybody to be satisfied, and feel right a
kind towards the others.

It didn't take me long to make up my mind that these liars warn't no ki
nor dukes, at all, but just low-down humbugs and frauds. But I never s
nothing, never let on ; kept it to myself ; it's the best way ; then you don't h
no quarrels, and don't get into no trouble. If they wanted us to call them ki
and dukes, I hadn't no objections, 'long as it would keep peace in the famil
and it warn't no use to tell Jim, so I didn't tell him. If I never learnt noth
else out of pap, I learnt that the best way to get along with his kind of peo
is to let them have their own way.

Chapter XX

ON THE RAFT.

THEY ASKED us considerable many questions; wanted to know what we covered up the raft that way for, and laid by in the day-time instead of running—was Jim a runaway nigger? Says I—

"Goodness sakes, would a runaway nigger run *south*?"

No, they allowed he wouldn't. I had to account for things some way, so I says:

"My folks was living in Pike County, in Missouri, where I was born, and they all died off but me and pa and my brother Ike. Pa, he 'lowed he'd break up and go down and live with Uncle Ben, who's got a little one-horse place on the river, forty-four mile ow Orleans. Pa was pretty poor, and had some debts; so when he'd ared up there warn't nothing left but sixteen dollars and our nigger, Jim. at warn't enough to take us fourteen hundred mile, deck passage nor no other . Well, when the river rose, pa had a streak of luck one day; he ketched s piece of a raft; so we reckoned we'd go down to Orleans on it. Pa's luck n't hold out; a steamboat run over the forrard corner of the raft, one night, we all went overboard and dove under the wheel; Jim and me come up, all ht, but pa was drunk, and Ike was only four years old, so they never come up

no more. Well, for the next day or two we had considerable trouble, becau
people was always coming out in skiffs and trying to take Jim away from m
saying they believed he was a runaway nigger. We don't run day-times no mo
now ; nights they don't bother us."

The duke says—

"Leave me alone to cipher out a way so we can run in the day-time if we wa
to. I'll think the thing over—I'll invent a plan that'll fix it. We'll let it alo
for to-day, because of course we don't want to go by that town yonder in da
light—it mightn't be healthy."

Towards night it begun to darken up and look like rain ; the heat lightni
was squirting around, low down in the sky, and the leaves was beginning
shiver—it was going to be pretty ugly, it was easy to see that. So the duke a
the king went to overhauling our wigwam, to see what the beds was like. M
bed was a straw tick—better than Jim's, which was a corn-shuck tick ; ther
always cobs around about in a shuck tick, and they poke into you and hurt ; a
when you roll over, the dry shucks sound like you was rolling over in a pile
dead leaves ; it makes such a rustling that you wake up. Well, the duke allow
he would take my bed ; but the king allowed he wouldn't. He says—

"I should a reckoned the difference in rank would a sejested to you that
corn-shuck bed warn't just fitten for me to sleep on. Your Grace'll take t
shuck bed yourself."

Jim and me was in a sweat again, for a minute, being afraid there was goi
to be some more trouble amongst them ; so we was pretty glad when the du
says—

"'Tis my fate to be always ground into the mire under the iron heel
oppression. Misfortune has broken my once haughty spirit ; I yield, I subm
'tis my fate. I am alone in the world—let me suffer ; I can bear it."

We got away as soon as it was good and dark. The king told us to stand w
out towards the middle of the river, and not show a light till we got a long wa
below the town. We come in sight of the little bunch of lights by-and-by—t
was the town, you know—and slid by, about a half a mile out, all right. Wh
we was three-quarters of a mile below, we hoisted up our signal lantern ; a

ut ten o'clock it come on to rain and blow and thunder and lighten like every-
ng; so the king told us to both stay on watch till the weather got better;
n him and the duke crawled into the wigwam and turned in for the night. It
s my watch below, till twelve, but I wouldn't a turned in, anyway, if I'd had a
; because a body don't see such a storm as that every day in the week, not by
ong sight. My souls, how the wind did scream along! And every second or
there'd come a glare that lit up the white-caps for a half a mile around, and
'd see the islands looking dusty through the rain, and the trees thrashing
und in the wind; then comes a *h-wack!*—bum! bum! bumble-umble-um-
m-bum-bum-bum—and the thunder would go rumbling and grumbling away,
l quit—and then *rip* comes another flash and another sockdolager. The waves
st washed me off the raft, sometimes, but I hadn't any clothes on, and didn't
nd. We didn't have no trouble about snags; the lightning was glaring
l flittering around so constant that we could see them plenty soon enough to
ow her head this way or that and miss them.

I had the middle watch, you know, but I was pretty sleepy by that time, so Jim
said he would stand the first half of it for me; he was always mighty good,
t way, Jim was. I crawled into the wigwam, but the king and the duke had
eir legs sprawled around so there warn't no show for me; so I laid outside—I
ln't mind the rain, because it was warm, and the waves warn't running so
gh, now. About two they come up again, though, and Jim was going to call
, but he changed his mind because he reckoned they warn't high enough yet
do any harm; but he was mistaken about that, for pretty soon all of a sudden
ng comes a regular ripper, and washed me overboard. It most killed Jim
aughing. He was the easiest nigger to laugh that ever was, anyway.

I took the watch, and Jim he laid down and snored away; and by-and-by the
rm let up for good and all; and the first cabin-light that showed, I rousted
m out and we slid the raft into hiding-quarters for the day.

The king got out an old ratty deck of cards, after breakfast, and him and the
ke played seven-up a while, five cents a game. Then they got tired of it, and
owed they would "lay out a campaign," as they called it. The duke went
wn into his carpet-bag and fetched up a lot of little printed bills, and read

them out loud. One bill said "The celebrated Dr. Armand de Montalban
Paris," would "lecture on the Science of Phrenology" at such and such a pla
on the blank day of blank, at ten cents admission, and "furnish charts of char
ter at twenty-five cents apiece." The duke said that was *him.* In another bill
was the "world renowned Shaksperean tragedian, Garrick the Younger, of Dru
Lane, London." In other bills he had a lot of other names and done ot
wonderful things, like finding water and gold with a "divining rod," "dissip
ing witch-spells," and so on. By-and-by he says—

"But the histrionic muse is the darling. Have you ever trod the boar
Royalty ?"

"No," says the king.

THE KING AS JULIET.

"You shall, then, befo
you're three days older, Fall
Grandeur," says the duke. "T
first good town we come to, w
hire a hall and do the sword-fig
in Richard III. and the balco
scene in Romeo and Juliet. H
does that strike you ?"

"I'm in, up to the hub, .
anything that will pay, Bilg
water, but you see I don't kn
nothing about play-actn', a
hain't ever seen much of it.
was too small when pap used
have 'em at the palace. Do y
reckon you can learn me ?"

"Easy !"

"All right. I'm jist
freezn' for something fresh, anyway. Less commence, right away."

So the duke he told him all about who Romeo was, and who Juliet was, a
said he was used to being Romeo, so the king could be Juliet.

"But if Juliet's such a young gal, Duke, my peeled head and my white hiskers is goin' to look oncommon odd on her, maybe."

"No, don't you worry—these country jakes won't ever think of that. Besides, you know, you'll be in costume, and that makes all the difference in the world ; Juliet's in a balcony, enjoying the moonlight before she goes to bed, and she's got on her night-gown and her ruffled night-cap. Here are the costumes for the parts."

He got out two or three curtain-calico suits, which he said was meedyevil armor for Richard III. and t'other chap, and a long white cotton night-shirt and a ruffled night-cap to match. The king was satisfied ; so the duke got out his book and read the parts over in the most splendid spread-eagle way, prancing around and acting at the same time, to show how it had got to be done ; then give the book to the king and told him to get his part by heart.

There was a little one-horse town about three mile down the bend, and after dinner the duke said he had ciphered out his idea about how to run daylight without it being dangersome for Jim ; so he allowed he would go down to the town and fix that thing. The king allowed he would go, and see if he couldn't strike something. We was out of coffee, so Jim said I better go along with them in the canoe and get some.

When we got there, there warn't nobody stirring ; streets empty, and perfectly dead and still, like Sunday. We found a sick nigger sunning himself in a back yard, and he said everybody that warn't too young or too sick or too old, was gone to camp-meeting, about two mile back in the woods. The king got the directions, and allowed he'd go and work that camp-meeting for all it was worth, and I might go, too.

The duke said what he was after was a printing office. We found it ; a little bit of a concern, up over a carpenter shop—carpenters and printers all gone to the meeting, and no doors locked. It was a dirty, littered-up place, and had ink marks, and handbills with pictures of horses and runaway niggers on them, all over the walls. The duke shed his coat and said he was all right, now. So me and the king lit out for the camp-meeting.

We got there in about a half an hour, fairly dripping, for it was a most awful

hot day. There was as much as a thousand people there, from twenty mi
around. The woods was full of teams and wagons, hitched everywheres, feedi
out of the wagon troughs and stomping to keep off the flies. There was she
made out of poles and roofed over with branches, where they had lemonade an
gingerbread to sell, and piles of watermelons and green corn and such-like truc

The preaching was going on under the same kinds of sheds, only they w
bigger and held crowds of people. The benches was made out of outside slabs
logs, with holes bored in the round side to drive sticks into for legs. Th

"COURTING ON THE SLY."

didn't have no backs. T
preachers had high platfor
to stand on, at one end of t
sheds. The women had on su
bonnets : and some had linse
woolsey frocks, some gingha
ones, and a few of the you
ones had on calico. Some of t
young men was barefooted, a
some of the children didn't ha
on any clothes but just a to
linen shirt. Some of the o
women was knitting, and sor
of the young folks was courti
on the sly.

The first shed we come t
the preacher was lining out
hymn. He lined out two lin
everybody sung it, and it w
kind of grand to hear it, the
was so many of them and th

done it in such a rousing way ; then he lined out two more for them to sing
and so on. The people woke up more and more, and sung louder and loude
and towards the end, some begun to groan, and some begun to shout. Then t

eacher begun to preach ; and begun in earnest, too ; and went weaving first to
e side of the platform and then the other, and then a leaning down over the
nt of it, with his arms and his body going all the time, and shouting his words
t with all his might ; and every now and then he would hold up his Bible and
read it open, and kind of pass it around this way and that, shouting, " It's the
izen serpent in the wilderness ! Look upon it and live ! " And people would
out out, " Glory!—A-a-*men !* " And so he went on, and the people groaning
d crying and saying amen :

" Oh, come to the mourners' bench ! come, black with sin ! (*amen !*) come,
k and sore ! (*amen !*) come, lame and halt, and blind ! (*amen !*) come, pore
d needy, sunk in shame ! (*a-a-men !*) come all that's worn, and soiled, and
fering !—come with a broken spirit ! come with a contrite heart ! come in
ir rags and sin and dirt ! the waters that cleanse is free, the door of heaven
nds open—oh, enter in and be at rest ! " (*a-a-men ! glory, glory hallelujah !*)
And so on. You couldn't make out what the preacher said, any more, on
ount of the shouting and crying. Folks got up, everywheres in the crowd,
d worked their way, just by main strength, to the mourners' bench, with the
rs running down their faces ; and when all the mourners had got up there to
e front benches in a crowd, they sung, and shouted, and flung themselves
wn on the straw, just crazy and wild.

Well, the first I knowed, the king got agoing ; and you could hear him over
erybody ; and next he went a-charging up on to the platform and the preacher
begged him to speak to the people, and he done it. He told them he was a
ate—been a pirate for thirty years, out in the Indian Ocean, and his crew
s thinned out considerable, last spring, in a fight, and he was home now, to
ke out some fresh men, and thanks to goodness he'd been robbed last night,
d put ashore off of a steamboat without a cent, and he was glad of it, it was
e blessedest thing that ever happened to him, because he was a changed man
w, and happy for the first time in his life ; and poor as he was, he was
ing to start right off and work his way back to the Indian Ocean and put
the rest of his life trying to turn the pirates into the true path ; for he
uld do it better than anybody else, being acquainted with all the pirate crews

in that ocean; and though it would take him a long time to get there, witho[ut]
money, he would get there anyway, and every time he convinced a pirate
would say to him, "Don't you thank me, don't you give me no credit, it

"A PIRATE FOR THIRTY YEARS."

belongs to them dear people [at]
Pokeville camp-meeting, natur[al]
brothers and benefactors of the ra[ce]
—and that dear preacher there, t[he]
truest friend a pirate ever had!"

And then he busted into tea[rs,]
and so did everybody. Then som[e-]
body sings out, "Take up a colle[c-]
tion for him, take up a collection[!"]
Well, a half a dozen made a jum[p]
to do it, but somebody sings o[ut,]
"Let *him* pass the hat around[!"]
Then everybody said it, the preac[her]
too.

So the king went all throu[gh]
the crowd with his hat, swabbi[ng]
his eyes, and blessing the peop[le]
and praising them and thanki[ng]
them for being so good to t[he]

poor pirates away off there; and every little while the prettiest kind of gir[ls,]
with the tears running down their cheeks, would up and ask him would he [let]
them kiss him, for to remember him by; and he always done it; and some [of]
them he hugged and kissed as many as five or six times—and he was invited [to]
stay a week; and everybody wanted him to live in their houses, and said the[y'd]
think it was an honor; but he said as this was the last day of the camp-meeti[ng]
he couldn't do no good, and besides he was in a sweat to get to the Indian Oce[an]
right off and go to work on the pirates.

When we got back to the raft and he come to count up, he found he had c[ol-]
lected eighty-seven dollars and seventy-five cents. And then he had fetch[ed]

ay a three-gallon jug of whisky, too, that he found under a wagon when we
s starting home through the woods. The king said, take it all around, it laid
r any day he'd ever put in in the missionarying line. He said it warn't no use
king, heathens don't amount to shucks, alongside of pirates, to work a camp-
eting with.

The duke was thinking *he'd* been doing pretty well, till the king come to
w up, but after that he didn't think so so much. He had set up and printed
two little jobs for farmers, in that printing office—horse bills—and took the
ney, four dollars. And he had got in ten dollars worth of advertisements for
e paper, which he said he would put in for four dollars if they would pay in

vance—so they done it. The
ice of the paper was two dol-
s a year, but he took in three
bscriptions for half a dollar
iece on condition of them
ying him in advance; they
re going to pay in cord-wood
d onions, as usual, but he
d he had just bought the con-
rn and knocked down the
ice as low as he could afford it,
d was going to run it for
sh. He set up a little piece
poetry, which he made, him-
lf, out of his own head—three
rses—kind of sweet and sad-
sh — the name of it was,
Yes, crush, cold world, this
eaking heart "—and he left
at all set up and ready to

ANOTHER LITTLE JOB.

int in the paper and didn't charge nothing for it. Well, he took in nine
llars and a half, and said he'd done a pretty square day's work for it.

Then he showed us another little job he'd printed and hadn't charged fo
because it was for us. It had a picture of a runaway nigger, with a bundle
a stick, over his shoulder, and "$200 reward" under it. The reading was
about Jim, and just described him to a dot. It said he run away from S
Jacques' plantation, forty mile below New Orleans, last winter, and likely we
north, and whoever would catch him and send him back, he could have t
reward and expenses.

"Now," says the duke, "after to-night we can run in the daytime if
want to. Whenever we see anybody coming, we can tie Jim hand and fo
with a rope, and lay him in the wigwam and show this handbill and say we captur
him up the river, and were too poor to travel on a steamboat, so we got th
little raft on credit from our friends and are going down to get the rewar
Handcuffs and chains would look still better on Jim, but it wouldn't go w
with the story of us being so poor. Too much like jewelry. Ropes are the co
rect thing—we must preserve the unities, as we say on the boards."

We all said the duke was pretty smart, and there couldn't be no trouble abo
running daytimes. We judged we could make miles enough that night to g
out of the reach of the pow-wow we reckoned the duke's work in the printing offi
was going to make in that little town—then we could boom right along, if w
wanted to.

We laid low and kept still, and never shoved out till nearly ten o'clock; the
we slid by, pretty wide away from the town, and didn't hoist our lantern till w
was clear out of sight of it.

When Jim called me to take the watch at four in the morning, he says—

"Huck, does you reck'n we gwyne to run acrost any mo' kings on d
trip?"

"No," I says, "I reckon not."

"Well," says he, "dat's all right, den. I doan' mine one er two kings, b
dat's enough. Dis one's powerful drunk, en de duke ain' much better."

I found Jim had been trying to get him to talk French, so he could hear wh
it was like; but he said he had been in this country so long, and had so mue
trouble, he'd forgot it.

Chapter XXI

PRACTICING.

IT was after sun-up, now, but we went right on, and didn't tie up. The king and the duke turned out, by-and-by, looking pretty rusty; but after they'd jumped overboard and took a swim, it chippered them up a good deal. After breakfast the king he took a seat on a corner of the raft, and pulled off his boots and rolled up his britches, and let his legs dangle in the water, so as to be comfortable, and lit his pipe, and went to getting his Romeo and Juliet by heart. When he had got it pretty good, him and the duke begun to practice it together. The duke had to learn him over and over again, how to say every speech; and he made him sigh, and put his hand on his heart, and after while he said he done it pretty well; "only," he says, "you mustn't bellow out *Romeo!* that way, like a bull—you must say it soft, and sick, and languishy, so—R-o-o-meo! that is the idea; for Juliet's a dear sweet mere child of a girl, you know, and she don't bray like a jackass."

Well, next they got out a couple of long swords that the duke made out of oak laths, and begun to practice the sword-fight—the duke called himself Richard III.; and the way they laid on, and pranced around the raft was grand to see. But by-and-by the king tripped and fell overboard, and after that they

took a rest, and had a talk about all kinds of adventures they'd had in other
times along the river.

After dinner, the duke says:

"Well, Capet, we'll want to make this a first-class show, you know, so I
guess we'll add a little more to it. We want a little something to answer
encores with, anyway."

"What's onkores, Bilgewater?"

The duke told him, and then says:

"I'll answer by doing the Highland fling or the sailor's hornpipe; and you—
well, let me see—oh, I've got it—
you can do Hamlet's soliloquy."

"Hamlet's which?"

"Hamlet's soliloquy, you know,
the most celebrated thing in
Shakespeare. Ah, it's sublime,
sublime! Always fetches the
house. I haven't got it in the
book—I've only got one volume—
but I reckon I can piece it out
from memory. I'll just walk up
and down a minute, and see if I
can call it back from recollection's
vaults."

So he went to marching up
and down, thinking, and frowning horrible every now and then;
then he would hoist up his eyebrows; next he would squeeze his
hand on his forehead and stag-

HAMLET'S SOLILOQUY.

ger back and kind of moan; next he would sigh, and next he'd let on to drop
a tear. It was beautiful to see him. By-and-by he got it. He told us to give
attention. Then he strikes a most noble attitude, with one leg shoved forward,

l his arms stretched away up, and his head tilted back, looking up at the sky ;
l then he begins to rip and rave and grit his teeth ; and after that, all through
speech he howled, and spread around, and swelled up his chest, and just
ocked the spots out of any acting ever *I* see before. This is the speech—
earned it, easy enough, while he was learning it to the king :

> To be, or not to be ; that is the bare bodkin
> That makes calamity of so long life ;
> For who would fardels bear, till Birnam Wood do come to Dunsinane,
> But that the fear of something after death
> Murders the innocent sleep,
> Great nature's second course,
> And makes us rather sling the arrows of outrageous fortune
> Than fly to others that we know not of.
> There's the respect must give us pause :
> Wake Duncan with thy knocking ! I would thou couldst ;
> For who would bear the whips and scorns of time,
> The oppressor's wrong, the proud man's contumely,
> The law's delay, and the quietus which his pangs might take,
> In the dead waste and middle of the night, when churchyards yawn
> In customary suits of solemn black,
> But that the undiscovered country from whose bourne no traveler returns,
> Breathes forth contagion on the world,
> And thus the native hue of resolution, like the poor cat i' the adage,
> Is sicklied o'er with care,
> And all the clouds that lowered o'er our housetops,
> With this regard their currents turn awry,
> And lose the name of action.
> 'Tis a consummation devoutly to be wished. But soft you, the fair Ophelia :
> Ope not thy ponderous and marble jaws,
> But get thee to a nunnery—go !

Well, the old man he liked that speech, and he mighty soon got it so he could
it first rate. It seemed like he was just born for it ; and when he had his
nd in and was excited, it was perfectly lovely the way he would rip and tear
d rair up behind when he was getting it off.

The first chance we got, the duke he had some show bills printed ; and aft
that, for two or three days as we floated along, the raft was a most uncomm
lively place, for there warn't nothing but sword-fighting and rehearsing—as t
duke called it—going on all the time.   One morning, when we was pretty w
down the State of Arkansaw, we come in sight of a little one-horse town in a ℔
bend ; so we tied up about three-quarters of a mile above it, in the mouth of
crick which was shut in like a tunnel by the cypress trees, and all of us but J
took the canoe and went down there to see if there was any chance in that pla
for our show.

We struck it mighty lucky ; there was going to be a circus there that aft
noon, and the country people was already beginning to come in, in all kinds
old shackly wagons, and on horses.   The circus would leave before night, so o
show would have a pretty good chance.   The duke he hired the court house, a
we went around and stuck up our bills.   They read like this :

Shaksperean Revival ! ! !

Wonderful Attraction !

For One Night Only !

The world renowned tragedians,

David Garrick the younger, of Drury Lane Theatre, London,

and

Edmund Kean the elder, of the Royal Haymarket Theatre, White-

chapel, Pudding Lane, Piccadilly, London, and the

Royal Continental Theatres, in their sublime

Shaksperean Spectacle entitled

The Balcony Scene

in

Romeo and Juliet ! ! !

Romeo.... .... Mr. Garrick.

Juliet.. Mr. Kean.

Assisted by the whole strength of the company !

New costumes, new scenery, new appointments !

Also :
The thrilling, masterly, and blood-curdling
Broad-sword conflict
In Richard III. ! ! !

Richard III............................... Mr. Garrick.
Richmond .... Mr. Kean.

also :
(by special request,)
Hamlet's Immortal Soliloquy ! !
By the Illustrious Kean !
Done by him 300 consecutive nights in Paris !
For One Night Only,
On account of imperative European engagements !
Admission 25 cents ; children and servants, 10 cents.

Then we went loafing around the town.   The stores and houses was most all old
ackly dried-up frame concerns that hadn't ever been painted ; they was set up
ree or four foot above ground on stilts, so as to be out of reach of the water
en the river was overflowed.   The houses had little gardens around them, but
ey didn't seem to raise hardly anything in them but jimpson weeds, and sun-
wers, and ash-piles, and old curled-up boots and shoes, and pieces of bottles,
d rags, and played-out tin-ware.   The fences was made of different kinds of
ards, nailed on at different times ; and they leaned every which-way, and had
tes that didn't generly have but one hinge—a leather one.   Some of the fences
d been whitewashed, some time or another, but the duke said it was in
umbus's time, like enough.   There was generly hogs in the garden, and people
iving them out.

All the stores was along one street.   They had white-domestic awnings in
nt, and the country people hitched their horses to the awning-posts.
ere was empty dry-goods boxes under the awnings, and loafers roosting
them all day long, whittling them with their Barlow knives ; and chaw-
g tobacco, and gaping and yawning and stretching—a mighty ornery lot.
ey generly had on yellow straw hats most as wide as an umbrella, but
dn't wear no coats nor waistcoats ; they called one another Bill, and Buck,

and Hank, and Joe, and Andy, and talked lazy and drawly, and used co siderable many cuss-words. There was as many as one loafer leaning against every awning-post, and he most always had his hands in his britch

"GIMME A CHAW."

pockets, except when he fetch them out to lend a chaw of t bacco or scratch. What a bo was hearing amongst them, the time was—

"Gimme a chaw 'v toback Hank."

"Cain't—I hain't got but o chaw left. Ask Bill."

Maybe Bill he gives him chaw; maybe he lies and sa he ain't got none. Some them kinds of loafers never h a cent in the world, nor a ch of tobacco of their own. Th get all their chawing by borro ing—they say to a fellow, ' wisht you'd len' me a chaw, Jac I jist this minute give B Thompson the last chaw I had —which is a lie, pretty mu every time; it don't fool nobo

but a stranger; but Jack ain't no stranger, so he says—

"*You* give him a chaw, did you? so did your sister's cat's grandmother. Y pay me back the chaws you've awready borry'd off'n me, Lafe Buckner, then I loan you one or two ton of it, and won't charge you no back intrust, nuther."

"Well, I *did* pay you back some of it wunst."

"Yes, you did—'bout six chaws. You borry'd store tobacker and paid ba nigger-head."

Store tobacco is flat black plug, but these fellows mostly chaws the natural
f twisted. When they borrow a chaw, they don't generly cut it off with a
ife, but they set the plug in between their teeth, and gnaw with their teeth
l tug at the plug with their hands till they get it in two—then sometimes the
e that owns the tobacco looks mournful at it when it's handed back, and
s, sarcastic—

"Here, gimme the *chaw*, and you take the *plug*."

All the streets and lanes was just mud, they warn't nothing else *but* mud—
d as black as tar, and nigh about a foot deep in some places; and two or
ee inches deep in *all* the places. The hogs loafed and grunted around,
rywheres. You'd see a muddy sow and a litter of pigs come lazying along
e street and whollop herself right down in the way, where folks had to walk
und her, and she'd stretch out, and shut her eyes, and wave her ears, whilst
e pigs was milking her, and look as happy as if she was on salary. And
etty soon you'd hear a loafer sing out, "Hi! *so* boy! sick him, Tige!" and
ay the sow would go, squealing most horrible, with a dog or two swinging to
h ear, and three or four dozen more a-coming; and then you would see all the
fers get up and watch the thing out of sight, and laugh at the fun and
k grateful for the noise. Then they'd settle back again till there was a
g-fight. There couldn't anything wake them up all over, and make them
ppy all over, like a dog-fight—unless it might be putting turpentine on a stray
g and setting fire to him, or tying a tin pan to his tail and see him run himself
death.

On the river front some of the houses was sticking out over the bank, and
ey was bowed and bent, and about ready to tumble in. The people had
ved out of them. The bank was caved away under one corner of some
ers, and that corner was hanging over. People lived in them yet, but it
s dangersome, because sometimes a strip of land as wide as a house caves
at a time. Sometimes a belt of land a quarter of a mile deep will start in
d cave along and cave along till it all caves into the river in one summer.
ch a town as that has to be always moving back, and back, and back, because
e river's always gnawing at it.

The nearer it got to noon that day, the thicker and thicker was the wago
and horses in the streets, and more coming all the time. Families fetched th
dinners with them, from the country, and eat them in the wagons. The
was considerable whiskey drinking going on, and I seen three fights. By-ar
by somebody sings out—

"Here comes old Boggs !—in from the country for his little old month
drunk—here he comes, boys ! "

All the loafers looked glad—I reckoned they was used to having fun out
Boggs. One of them says—

"Wonder who he's a gwyne to chaw up this time. If he'd a chawed up
the men he's ben a gwyne to chaw up in the last twenty year, he'd have co
siderble ruputation, now."

Another one says, "I wisht old Boggs 'd threaten me, 'cuz then I'd know
warn't gwyne to die for a thousan' year."

Boggs comes a-tearing along on his horse, whooping and yelling like an Inju
and singing out—

"Cler the track, thar. I'm on the waw-path, and the price uv coffins is
gwyne to raise."

He was drunk, and weaving about in his saddle ; he was over fifty year o
and had a very red face. Everybody yelled at him, and laughed at him, a
sassed him, and he sassed back, and said he'd attend to them and lay them out
their regular turns, but he couldn't wait now, because he'd come to town to k
old Colonel Sherburn, and his motto was, "meat first, and spoon vittles to t
off on."

He see me, and rode up and says—

"Whar'd you come f'm, boy ? You prepared to die ?"

Then he rode on. I was scared ; but a man says—

"He don't mean nothing ; he's always a carryin' on like that, when h
drunk. He's the best-naturedest old fool in Arkansaw—never hurt nobod
drunk nor sober."

Boggs rode up before the biggest store in town and bent his head down so
could see under the curtain of the awning, and yells—

"Come out here, Sherburn ! Come out and meet the man you've swindled.
u're the houn' I'm after, and I'm a gwyne to have you, too !"

And so he went on, calling Sherburn everything he could lay his tongue to,
the whole street packed with people listening and laughing and going on.
-and-by a proud-looking man about fifty-five—and he was a heap the best
ssed man in that town, too—steps out of the store, and the crowd drops back
each side to let him come. He says to Boggs, mighty ca'm and slow—he says:
"I'm tired of this ; but I'll endure it till one o'clock. Till one o'clock, mind—

A LITTLE MONTHLY DRUNK.

longer. If you open your mouth against me only once, after that time, you
ı't travel so far but I will find you."

Then he turns and goes in. The crowd looked mighty sober ; nobody stirred,
d there warn't no more laughing. Boggs rode off blackguarding Sherburn
loud as he could yell, all down the street ; and pretty soon back he comes and
ps before the store, still keeping it up. Some men crowded around him
d tried to get him to shut up, but he wouldn't ; they told him it would be one
lock in about fifteen minutes, and so he *must* go home—he must go right
ay. But it didn't do no good. He cussed away, with all his might, and

throwed his hat down in the mud and rode over it, and pretty soon away he we a-raging down the street again, with his gray hair a-flying. Everybody t could get a chance at him tried their best to coax him off of his horse so t could lock him up and get him sober ; but it warn't no use—up the street would tear again, and give Sherburn another cussing. By-and-by somebody say

"Go for his daughter!—quick, go for his daughter ; sometimes he'll listen her. If anybody can persuade him, she can."

So somebody started on a run. I walked down street a ways, and stopp In about five or ten minutes, here comes Boggs again—but not on his horse. was a-reeling across the street towards me, bareheaded, with a friend on be sides of him aholt of his arms and hurrying him along. He was quiet, a looked uneasy ; and he warn't hanging back any, but was doing some of hurrying himself. Somebody sings out—

"Boggs !"

I looked over there to see who said it, and it was that Colonel Sherburn. was standing perfectly still, in the street, and had a pistol raised in his rig hand—not aiming it, but holding it out with the barrel tilted up towards the s The same second I see a young girl coming on the run, and two men with h Boggs and the men turned round, to see who called him, and when t see the pistol the men jumped to one side, and the pistol barrel co down slow and steady to a level—both barrels cocked. Boggs throws both of his hands, and says, "O Lord, don't shoot !" Bang ! goes first shot, and he staggers back clawing at the air—bang ! goes the second on and he tumbles backwards onto the ground, heavy and solid, with his ar spread out. That young girl screamed out, and comes rushing, and do she throws herself on her father, crying, and saying, "Oh, he's killed hi he's killed him !" The crowd closed up around them, and shouldered a jammed one another, with their necks stretched, trying to see, and people the inside trying to shove them back, and shouting, "Back, back ! give him a give him air !"

Colonel Sherburn he tossed his pistol onto the ground, and turned around his heels and walked off.

They took Boggs to a little drug store, the crowd pressing around, just the same, and the whole town following, and I rushed and got a good place at the window, where I was close to him and could see in. They laid him on the floor, and put one large Bible under his head, and opened another one and spread it on his breast—

THE DEATH OF BOGGS.

but they tore open his shirt first, and I seen where one of the bullets went in. He made about a dozen long gasps, his breast lifting the Bible up when he drawed in his breath, and letting it down again when he breathed it out—and after that he laid still; he was dead. Then they pulled his daughter away from him, screaming and crying, and took her off. She was about sixteen, and very sweet and gentle-looking, but awful pale and scared.

Well, pretty soon the whole town was there, squirming and crowding and pushing and shoving to get at the window and have a look, but people that had the places wouldn't give them up, and folks behind them was saying all the time, "Say, now, you've looked enough, you fellows ; taint right and 'taint fair, for you to stay thar all the time, and never give nobody a chance ; other folks has their rights as well as you."

There was considerable jawing back, so I slid out, thinking maybe there was going to be trouble. The streets was full, and everybody was excited. Everybody that seen the shooting was telling how it happened, and there was a big

crowd packed around each one of these fellows, stretching their necks a
listening. One long lanky man, with long hair and a big white fur stove-pi
hat on the back of his head, and a crooked-handled cane, marked out the pla
on the ground where Boggs stood, and where Sherburn stood, and the peop
following him around from one place to t'other and watching everything he do
and bobbing their heads to show they understood, and stooping a little a
resting their hands on their thighs to watch him mark the places on the grou
with his cane; and then he stood up straight and stiff where Sherburn h
stood, frowning and having his hat-brim down over his eyes, and sung o
"Boggs!" and then fetched his cane down slow to a level, and says "Bang
staggered backwards, says "Bang!" again, and fell down flat on his back. T
people that had seen the thing said he done it perfect; said it was just exac
the way it all happened. Then as much as a dozen people got out their bott
and treated him.

Well, by-and-by somebody said Sherburn ought to be lynched. In about
minute everybody was saying it; so away they went, mad and yelling, a
snatching down every clothes-line they come to, to do the hanging with.

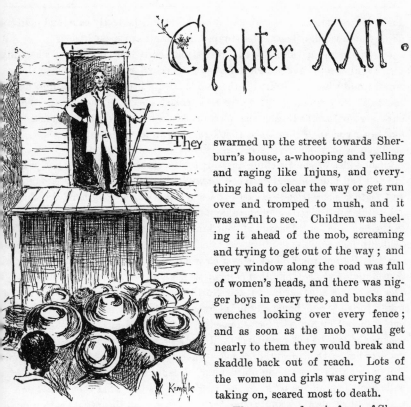

Chapter XXII

SHERBURN STEPS OUT.

They swarmed up the street towards Sherburn's house, a-whooping and yelling and raging like Injuns, and everything had to clear the way or get run over and tromped to mush, and it was awful to see. Children was heeling it ahead of the mob, screaming and trying to get out of the way; and every window along the road was full of women's heads, and there was nigger boys in every tree, and bucks and wenches looking over every fence; and as soon as the mob would get nearly to them they would break and skaddle back out of reach. Lots of the women and girls was crying and taking on, scared most to death.

They swarmed up in front of Sherburn's palings as thick as they could jam together, and you couldn't hear yourself think for the noise. It was a little twenty-foot yard. Some sung out "Tear down the fence! tear down the fence!" Then there was a racket of ripping and tearing and smashing, and down she goes, and the front wall of the crowd begins to roll in like a wave.

Just then Sherburn steps out on to the roof of his little front porch, with a

double-barrel gun in his hand, and takes his stand, perfectly ca'm and delibera
not saying a word. The racket stopped, and the wave sucked back.

Sherburn never said a word—just stood there, looking down. The stilln
was awful creepy and uncomfortable. Sherburn run his eye slow along t
crowd ; and wherever it struck, the people tried a little to outgaze him, but th
couldn't ; they dropped their eyes and looked sneaky. Then pretty soon Sh
burn sort of laughed ; not the pleasant kind, but the kind that makes you f
like when you are eating bread that's got sand in it.

Then he says, slow and scornful :

"The idea of *you* lynching anybody ! It's amusing. The idea of you thir
ing you had pluck enough to lynch a *man !* Because you re brave enough to
and feather poor friendless cast-out women that come along here, did that ma
you think you had grit enough to lay your hands on a *man ?* Why, a *man's* s
in the hands of ten thousand of your kind—as long as it's day-time and you're r
behind him.

"Do I know you ? I know you clear through. I was born and raised in t
South, and I've lived in the North ; so I know the average all around. T
average man's a coward. In the North he lets anybody walk over him th
wants to, and goes home and prays for a humble spirit to bear it. In the Sow
one man, all by himself, has stopped a stage full of men, in the day-time, a
robbed the lot. Your newspapers call you a brave people so much that you thi
you *are* braver than any other people—whereas you're just *as* brave, and no brav
Why don't your juries hang murderers? Because they're afraid the man's frier
will shoot them in the back, in the dark—and it's just what they *would* do

"So they always acquit ; and then a *man* goes in the night, with a hundr
masked cowards at his back, and lynches the rascal. Your mistake is, that y
didn't bring a man with you ; that's one mistake, and the other is that you did
come in the dark, and fetch your masks. You brought *part* of a man—Bu
Harkness, there—and if you hadn't had him to start you, you'd a taken it out
blowing.

"You didn't want to come. The average man don't like trouble and dang
You don't like trouble and danger. But if only *half* a man—like Buck Ha

s, there—shouts 'Lynch him, lynch him!' you're afraid to back down—
aid you'll be found out to be what you are—*cowards*—and so you raise a yell,
l hang yourselves onto that half-a-man's coat tail, and come raging up here,
earing what big things you're going to do. The pitifulest thing out is a
b; that's what an army is—a mob; they don't fight with courage that's born
them, but with courage that's borrowed from their mass, and from their
cers. But a mob without any *man* at the head of it, is *beneath* pitifulness.
w the thing for *you* to do, is to droop your tails and go home and crawl in a
e. If any real lynching's going to be done, it will be done in the dark,

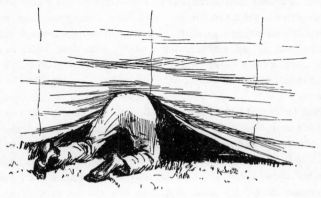

A DEAD HEAD.

uthern fashion; and when they come they'll bring their masks, and fetch a
n along. Now *leave*—and take your half-a-man with you"—tossing his gun
across his left arm and cocking it, when he says this.

The crowd washed back sudden, and then broke all apart and went tearing
every which way, and Buck Harkness he heeled it after them, looking toler-
e cheap. I could a staid, if I'd a wanted to, but I didn't want to.

I went to the circus, and loafed around the back side till the watchman went
, and then dived in under the tent. I had my twenty-dollar gold piece and
ne other money, but I reckoned I better save it, because there ain't no telling

THE ART OF HUCKLEBERRY FINN **211**

how soon you are going to need it, away from home and amongst strangers, th
way. You can't be too careful. I ain't opposed to spending money on circus
when there ain't no other way, but there ain't no use in *wasting* it on them.

It was a real bully circus. It was the splendidest sight that ever was, wh
they all come riding in, two and two, a gentleman and lady, side by side,
men just in their drawers and under-shirts, and no shoes nor stirrups, and rest
their hands on their thighs, easy and comfortable—there must a' been twenty
them—and every lady with a lovely complexion, and perfectly beautiful, a
looking just like a gang of real sure-enough queens, and dressed in clothes th
cost millions of dollars, and just littered with diamonds. It was a powerful f
sight; I never see anything so lovely. And then one by one they got up a
stood, and went a-weaving around the ring so gentle and wavy and graceful,
men looking ever so tall and airy and straight, with their heads bobbing a
skimming along, away up there under the tent-roof, and every lady's rose-le
dress flapping soft and silky around her hips, and she looking like the most lo
liest parasol.

And then faster and faster they went, all of them dancing, first one foot stu
out in the air and then the other, the horses leaning more and more, and
ring-master going round and round the centre-pole, cracking his whip a
shouting " hi !—hi ! " and the clown cracking jokes behind him ; and by-an
by all hands dropped the reins, and every lady put her knuckles on her hips a
every gentleman folded his arms, and then how the horses did lean over a
hump themselves ! And so, one after the other they all skipped off into the rii
and made the sweetest bow I ever see, and then scampered out, and everybc
clapped their hands and went just about wild.

Well, all through the circus they done the most astonishing things ; and
the time that clown carried on so it most killed the people. The ring-mas
couldn't ever say a word to him but he was back at him quick as a wink with
funniest things a body ever said ; and how he ever *could* think of so many
them, and so sudden and so pat, was what I couldn't noway understand. Wh
I couldn't a thought of them in a year. And by-and-by a drunk man tried
get into the ring—said he wanted to ride ; said he could ride as well as anybo

t ever was. They argued and tried to keep him out, but he wouldn't listen,
the whole show come to a standstill. Then the people begun to holler at
and make fun of him, and that made him mad, and he begun to rip and
r ; so that stirred up the people, and a lot of men begun to pile down off of
benches and swarm towards the ring, saying, " Knock him down ! throw
out ! " and one or two women begun to scream. So, then, the ring-master
made a little speech, and said he hoped there wouldn't be no disturbance, and
he man would promise he wouldn't make no more trouble, he would let him
e, if he thought he could stay on the horse. So everybody laughed and said all
ht, and the man got on.

e minute he was on, the
se begun to rip and tear
jump and cavort around,
h two circus men hanging
o his bridle trying to hold
n, and the drunk man
nging onto his neck, and
heels flying in the air every
up, and the whole crowd
people standing up shout-
and laughing till the tears
led down. And at last,
e enough, all the circus
n could do, the horse broke
se, and away he went like
very nation, round and
nd the ring, with that sot
ing down on him and hang-
to his neck, with first one
hanging most to the ground

HE SHED SEVENTEEN SUITS.

one side, and then t'other one on t'other side, and the people just crazy. It
rn't funny to me, though ; I was all of a tremble to see his danger. But

pretty soon he struggled up astraddle and grabbed the bridle, a-reeling this w
and that; and the next minute he sprung up and dropped the bridle and stoo
and the horse agoing like a house afire too. He just stood up there, a-saili
around as easy and comfortable as if he warn't ever drunk in his life—and th
he begun to pull off his clothes and sling them. He shed them so thick th
kind of clogged up the air, and altogether he shed seventeen suits. And th
there he was, slim and handsome, and dressed the gaudiest and prettiest y
ever saw, and he lit into that horse with his whip and made him fairly hum
and finally skipped off, and made his bow and danced off to the dressing-roo
and everybody just a-howling with pleasure and astonishment.

Then the ring-master he see how he had been fooled, and he *was* the sick
ring-master you ever see, I reckon. Why, it was one of his own men! He h
got up that joke all out of his own head, and never let on to nobody. Well
felt sheepish enough, to be took in so, but I wouldn't a been in that ring-ma
ter's place, not for a thousand dollars. I don't know; there may be bull
circuses than what that one was, but I never struck them yet. Anyways it w
plenty good enough for *me ;* and wherever I run across it, it can have all of *r*
custom, every time.

Well, that night we had *our* show; but there warn't only about twel
people there; just enough to pay expenses. And they laughed all the time, a
that made the duke mad; and everybody left, anyway, before the show was ov
but one boy which was asleep. So the duke said these Arkansaw lunkhea
couldn't come up to Shakspeare; what they wanted was low comedy—and m
be something ruther worse than low comedy, he reckoned. He said he cou
size their style. So next morning he got some big sheets of wrapping-paper a
some black paint, and drawed off some handbills and stuck them up all over t
village. The bills said :

AT THE COURT HOUSE!

FOR 3 NIGHTS ONLY!

The World-Renowned Tragedians

DAVID GARRICK THE YOUNGER!

AND

EDMUND KEAN THE ELDER!

Of the London and Continental

Theatres,

In their Thrilling Tragedy of

THE KING'S CAMELOPARD

OR

THE ROYAL NONESUCH!!!

Admission 50 *cents.*

Then at the bottom was the biggest line of all—which said :

LADIES AND CHILDREN NOT ADMITTED.

"There," says he, "if that line don't fetch them, I dont know Arkansaw!"

Chapter XXIII

TRAGEDY.

Well, all day him and the king was ha[rd]
at it, rigging up a stage, and a c[ur]
tain, and a row of candles for fo[ot]
lights ; and that night the hou[se]
was jam full of men in no ti[me.]
When the place couldn't hold [any]
more, the duke he quit tending d[oor]
and went around the back way a[nd]
come onto the stage and stood [up]
before the curtain, and made [a]
little speech, and praised up t[he]
tragedy, and said it was the m[ost]
thrillingest one that ever was ; a[nd]
so he went on a-bragging about [the]
tragedy and about Edmund Ke[an]
the Elder, which was to play [the]
main principal part in it ; and [at]
last when he'd got everybody's [ex]

pectations up high enough, he rolled up the curtain, and the next minute t[he]
king come a-prancing out on all fours, naked ; and he was painted all over, ri[ng]
streaked-and-striped, all sorts of colors, as splendid as a rainbow. And—[but]
never mind the rest of his outfit, it was just wild, but it was awful funny. T[he]
people most killed themselves laughing ; and when the king got done caperi[ng]
and capered off behind the scenes, they roared and clapped and stormed and ha[w]
hawed till he come back and done it over again ; and after that, they made h[im]

it another time.   Well, it would a made a cow laugh to see the shines that old
t cut.

Then the duke he lets the curtain down, and bows to the people, and says the
at tragedy will be performed only two nights more, on accounts of pressing
ndon engagements, where the seats is all sold aready for it in Drury Lane ;
then he makes them another bow, and says if he has succeeded in pleasing
m and instructing them, he will be deeply obleeged if they will mention it to
ir friends and get them to come and see it.

Twenty people sings out :

" What, is it over ?   Is that *all?* "

The duke says yes.   Then there was a fine time.   Everybody sings out " sold,"
rose up mad, and was agoing for that stage and them tragedians.   But a big
e-looking man jumps up on a bench, and shouts :

" Hold on !   Just a word, gentlemen."   They stopped to listen.   " We are
l—mighty badly sold.   But we don't want to be the laughing-stock of this
ole town, I reckon, and never hear the last of this thing as long as we live.

What we want, is to go out of here quiet, and talk this show up, and sell
rest of the town !   Then we'll all be in the same boat.   Ain't that sensible ? "
You bet it is !—the jedge is right !" everybody sings out.)   " All right, then
ot a word about any sell.   Go along home, and advise everybody to come and
the tragedy."

Next day you couldn't hear nothing around that town but how splendid that
w was.   House was jammed again, that night, and we sold this crowd the
ie way.   When me and the king and the duke got home to the raft, we all had
upper ; and by-and-by, about midnight, they made Jim and me back her out
float her down the middle of the river and fetch her in and hide her about
mile below town.

The third night the house was crammed again—and they warn't new-comers,
s time, but people that was at the show the other two nights.   I stood by
duke at the door, and I see that every man that went in had his pockets
ging, or something muffled up under his coat—and I see it warn't no per-
nery neither, not by a long sight.   I smelt sickly eggs by the barrel, and

rotten cabbages, and such things; and if I know the signs of a dead cat be
around, and I bet I do, there was sixty-four of them went in. I shoved

THEIR POCKETS BULGED.

there for a minute, but it was
various for me, I couldn't stand
Well, when the place couldn't hold
more people, the duke he give a fel
a quarter and told him to tend door
him a minute, and then he star
around for the stage door, I after hi
but the minute we turned the cor
and was in the dark, he says:

"Walk fast, now, till you get a
from the houses, and then shin for
raft like the dickens was after you!"

I done it, and he done the same.
struck the raft at the same time, an
less than two seconds we was glid
down stream, all dark and still,
edging towards the middle of the ri
nobody saying a word. I reckoned
poor king was in for a gaudy time
it with the audience; but nothing

the sort; pretty soon he crawls out from under the wigwam, and says:

"Well, how'd the old thing pan out this time, Duke?"

He hadn't been up town at all.

We never showed a light till we was about ten mile below that villa
Then we lit up and had a supper, and the king and the duke fairly laughed t
bones loose over the way they'd served them people. The duke says:

"Greenhorns, flatheads! *I* knew the first house would keep mum and
the rest of the town get roped in; and I knew they'd lay for us the third nig
and consider it was *their* turn now. Well, it *is* their turn, and I'd give so
thing to know how much they'd take for it. I *would* just like to know

y're putting in their opportunity. They can turn it into a picnic, if they
ıt to—they brought plenty provisions."

Them rapscallions took in four hundred and sixty-five dollars in that three
hts. I never see money hauled in by the wagon-load like that, before.

By-and-by, when they was asleep and snoring, Jim says :

"Don't it 'sprise you, de way dem kings carries on, Huck ? "

"No," I says, " it don't."

"Why don't it, Huck ? "

"Well, it don't, because it's in the breed. I reckon they're all alike."

"But, Huck, dese kings o' ourn is regular rapscallions ; dat's jist what dey
dey's reglar rapscallions."

"Well, that's what I'm a-saying ; all kings is mostly rapscallions, as fur as
an make out."

"Is dat so ? "

"You read about them once—you'll see. Look at Henry the Eight ;
's'n 's a Sunday-School Superintendent to *him*. And look at Charles Second,
t Louis Fourteen, and Louis Fifteen, and James Second, and Edward Second,
I Richard Third, and forty more ; besides all them Saxon heptarchies that
d to rip around so in old times and raise Cain. My, you ought to seen old
nry the Eight when he was in bloom. He *was* a blossom. He used to marry
ew wife every day, and chop off her head next morning. And he would do it
t as indifferent as if he was ordering up eggs. ' Fetch up Nell Gwynn,' he
s. They fetch her up. Next morning, ' Chop off her head !' And they
p it off. ' Fetch up Jane Shore,' he says ; and up she comes. Next morning
hop off her head '—and they chop it off. ' Ring up Fair Rosamun.' Fair
samun answers the bell. Next morning, ' Chop off her head.' And he made
ry one of them tell him a tale every night ; and he kept that up till he had
ged a thousand and one tales that way, and then he put them all in a book,
I called it Domesday Book—which was a good name and stated the case.
u don't know kings, Jim, but I know them ; and this old rip of ourn is one
the cleanest I've struck in history. Well, Henry he takes a notion he wants
get up some trouble with this country. How does he go at it—give notice ?

—give the country a show ? No. All of a sudden he heaves all the tea
Boston Harbor overboard, and whacks out a declaration of independence, a

dares them to come on. That v
his style—he never give anybod
chance. He had suspicions of
father, the Duke of Wellingt
Well, what did he do ?—ask him
show up ? Nc—drownded him
a butt of mamsey, like a cat. Sp
people left money laying arou
where he was—what did he d
He collared it. Spose he contrac
to do a thing; and you paid hi
and didn't set down there and
that he done it—what did he d
He always done the other thi
Spose he opened his mouth—w
then ? If he didn't shut it
powerful quick, he'd lose a lie, ev
time. That's the kind of a b
Henry was; and if we'd a had h
along 'stead of our kings, he'd

HENRY THE EIGHTH IN BOSTON HARBOR.

fooled that town a heap worse than ourn done. I don't say that ourn is laml
because they ain't, when you come right down to the cold facts; but they ai
nothing to *that* old ram, anyway. All I say is, kings is kings, and you got
make allowances. Take them all around, they're a mighty ornery lot. It's t
way they're raised."

"But dis one do *smell* so like de nation, Huck."

"Well, they all do, Jim. *We* can't help the way a king smells; hist
don't tell no way."

"Now de duke, he's a tolerble likely man, in some ways."

"Yes, a duke's different. But not very different. This one's a middli

d lot, for a duke. When he's drunk, there ain't no near-sighted man could
him from a king."

"Well, anyways, I doan' hanker for no mo' un um, Huck. Dese is all I
stan'."

"It's the way I feel, too, Jim. But we've got them on our hands, and
got to remember what they are, and make allowances. Sometimes I wish
could hear of a country that's out of kings."

What was the use to tell Jim these warn't real kings and dukes? It wouldn't
one no good; and besides, it was just as I said; you couldn't tell them from
real kind.

I went to sleep, and Jim didn't call me when it was my turn. He often done
t. When I waked up, just at day-break, he was setting there with his head
wn betwixt his knees, moaning and mourning to himself. I didn't take notice,
let on. I knowed what it was about. He was thinking about his wife and
children, away up yonder, and he was low and homesick; because he hadn't
r been away from home before in his life; and I do believe he cared just as
ich for his people as white folks does for their'n. It don't seem natural, but I
kon it's so. He was often moaning and mourning that way, nights, when he
lged I was asleep, and saying, " Po' little 'Lizabeth! po' little Johnny! its
ghty hard; I spec' I ain't ever gwyne to see you no mo', no mo'!" He was a
ghty good nigger, Jim was.

But this time I somehow got to talking to him about his wife and young ones;
d by-and-by he says:

"What makes me feel so bad dis time, 'uz bekase I hear sumpn over yonder
de bank like a whack, er a slam, while ago, en it mine me er de time I treat
little 'Lizabeth so ornery. She warn't on'y 'bout fo' year ole, en she tuck de
yarlet-fever, en had a powful rough spell; but she got well, en one day she was
tannin' aroun', en I says to her, I says:

"Shet de do'.'

"She never done it; jis' stood dah, kiner smilin' up at me. It make me
d; en I says agin, mighty loud, I says:

"'Doan' you hear me?—shet de do'!'

"She jis' stood de same way, kiner smilin' up.   I was a-bilin' !   I says :

" ' I lay I *make* you mine ! '

"En wid dat I fetch' her a slap side de head dat sont her a-sprawlin'.   De
went into de yuther room, en 'uz gone 'bout ten minutes ; en when I come ba
dah was dat do' a-stannin' open *yit*, en dat chile stannin' mos' right in
a-lookin' down and mournin', en de tears runnin' down.   My, but I *wuz* m
I was agwyne for de chile, but jis' den—it was a do' dat open innerds—jis' d
'long come de wind en slam it to, behine de chile, ker-*blam!*—en my lan',
chile never move' !   My breff mos' hop outer me ; en I feel so—so—I doan' kn
how I feel.   I crope out, all a-tremblin', en crope aroun' en open de do' easy
slow, en poke my head in behine de chile, sof' en still, en all uv a sudden, I s
pow ! jis' as loud as I could yell.   *She never budge !*   Oh, Huck, I bust
a-cryin' en grab her up in my arms, en say, ' Oh, de po' little thing ! de Lord G
Amighty fogive po' ole Jim, kaze he never gwyne to fogive hisself as long's
live ! '   Oh, she was plumb deef en dumb, Huck, plumb deef en dumb—en
ben a-treat'n her so ! "

Chapter XXIV.

Sick Arab — bu harmless when not out of his head

HARMLESS.

NEXT day, towards night, we laid up under a little willow tow-head out in the middle, where there was a village on each side of the river, and the duke and the king begun to lay out a plan for working them towns. Jim he spoke to the duke, and said he hoped it wouldn't take but a few hours, because it got mighty heavy and tiresome to him when he had to lay all day in the wigwam tied with the rope. You see, when we left him all alone we had to tie him, because if anybody happened on him all by himself and not tied, it wouldn't look much like he was a runaway nigger, you know. So the duke said was kind of hard to have to lay roped all day, and he'd cipher out some way to around it.

He was uncommon bright, the duke was, and he soon struck it. He dressed n up in King Lear's outfit—it was a long curtain-calico gown, and a white rse-hair wig and whiskers ; and then he took his theatre-paint and painted n's face and hands and ears and neck all over a dead dull solid blue, like a n that's been drownded nine days. Blamed if he warn't the horriblest looking rage I ever see. Then the duke took and wrote out a sign on a shingle so—

Sick Arab—but harmless when not out of his head.

And he nailed that shingle to a lath, and stood the lath up four or five foot
front of the wigwam.   Jim was satisfied.   He said it was a sight better th
laying tied a couple of years every day and trembling all over every time th
was a sound.   The duke told him to make himself free and easy, and if an
body ever come meddling around, he must hop out of the wigwam, and carry
a little, and fetch a howl or two like a wild beast, and he reckoned they wo
light out and leave him alone.   Which was sound enough judgment ; but y
take the average man, and he wouldn't wait for him to howl.   Why, he did
only look like he was dead, he looked considerable more than that.

These rapscallions wanted to try the Nonesuch again, because there was
much money in it, but they judged it wouldn't be safe, because maybe the ne
might a worked along down by this time.   They couldn't hit no project th
suited, exactly ; so at last the duke said he reckoned he'd lay off and work
brains an hour or two and see if he couldn't put up something on the Arkans
village; and the king he allowed he would drop over to t'other village, without a
plan, but just trust in Providence to lead him the profitable way—meaning t
devil, I reckon.   We had all bought store clothes where we stopped last; and n
the king put his'n on, and he told me to put mine on.   I done it, of course.   T
king's duds was all black, and he did look real swell and starchy.   I never know
how clothes could change a body before.   Why, before, he looked like t
orneriest old rip that ever was ; but now, when he'd take off his new white bea
and make a bow and do a smile, he looked that grand and good and pious th
you'd say he had walked right out of the ark, and maybe was old Levitic
himself.   Jim cleaned up the canoe, and I got my paddle ready.   Th
was a big steamboat laying at the shore away up under the point, about thr
mile above town—been there a couple of hours, taking on freight.   Says t
king :

"Seein' how I'm dressed, I reckon maybe I better arrive down from St. Lo
or Cincinnati, or some other big place.   Go for the steamboat, Hucklebern
we'll come down to the village on her."

I didn't have to be ordered twice, to go and take a steamboat ride.   I fetch

shore a half a mile above the village, and then went scooting along the bluff
ik in the easy water.   Pretty soon we come to a nice innocent-looking young
intry jake setting on a log swabbing the sweat off of his face, for it was
werful warm weather ; and he had a couple of big carpet-bags by him.

"Run her nose in shore," says the king.   I done it.   "Wher' you bound for,
ing man ?"

"For the steamboat ; going to Orleans."

"Git aboard," says the king.   "Hold on a minute, my servant 'll he'p you

ADOLPHUS.

th them bags.   Jump out and he'p the gentleman, Adolphus "—meaning
, I see.

I done so, and then we all three started on again.   The young chap was
ghty thankful ; said it was tough work toting his baggage such weather.
asked the king where he was going, and the king told him he'd come
wn the river and landed at the other village this morning, and now he was
ing up a few mile to see an old friend on a farm up there.   The young
low says :

"When I first see you, I says to myself, 'It's Mr. Wilks, sure, and he co[t] mighty near getting here in time.' But then I says again, 'No, I reckon ain't him, or else he wouldn't be paddling up the river.' You *ain't* him, you ?"

"No, my name's Blodgett—Elexander Blodgett—*Reverend* Elexan[e] Blodgett, I spose I must say, as I'm one o' the Lord's poor servants. [I] still I'm jist as able to be sorry for Mr. Wilks for not arriving in time, the same, if he's missed anything by it—which I hope he hasn't."

"Well, he don't miss any property by it, because he'll get that all rig[t] but he's missed seeing his brother Peter die—which he mayn't mind, nob[e] can tell as to that—but his brother would a give anything in this world see *him* before he died ; never talked about nothing else all these three wee[k] hadn't seen him since they was boys together—and hadn't ever seen brother William at all—that's the deef and dumb one—William ain't m[ore] than thirty or thirty-five. Peter and George was the only ones that come here ; George was the married brother ; him and his wife both died last ye[ar] Harvey and William's the only ones that's left now ; and, as I was saying, t[hey] haven't got here in time."

"Did anybody send 'em word ?"

"Oh, yes ; a mouth or two ago, when Peter was first took ; because Pe[ter] said then that he sorter felt like he warn't going to get well this ti[me.] You see, he was pretty old, and George's g'yirls was too young to be m[uch] company for him, except Mary Jane the red-headed one ; and so he [was] kinder lonesome after George and his wife died, and didn't seem to care m[uch] to live. He most desperately wanted to see Harvey—and William too, for t[hat] matter—because he was one of them kind that can't bear to make a will. [He] left a letter behind for Harvey, and said he'd told in it where his money [was] hid, and how he wanted the rest of the property divided up so George's g'y[irls] would be all right—for George didn't leave nothing. And that letter was [all] they could get him to put a pen to."

"Why do you reckon Harvey don't come ? Wher' does he live ?"

"Oh, he lives in England—Sheffield—preaches there—hasn't ever been in t[his]

ntry. He hasn't had any too much time—and besides he mightn't a got the
er at all, you know."

"Too bad, too bad he couldn't a lived to see his brothers, poor soul. You
ng to Orleans, you say?"

"Yes, but that ain't only a part of it. I'm going in a ship, next Wednesday,
Ryo Janeero, where my uncle lives."

"It's a pretty long journey. But it'll be lovely; I wisht I was agoing. Is
ry Jane the oldest? How old is the others?"

HE FAIRLY EMPTIED THAT YOUNG FELLOW.

"Mary Jane's nineteen, Susan's fifteen, and Joanna's about fourteen—that's
one that gives herself to good works and has a hare-lip."

"Poor things! to be left alone in the cold world so."

"Well, they could be worse off. Old Peter had friends, and they ain't going
let them come to no harm. There's Hobson, the Babtis' preacher; and
acon Lot Hovey, and Ben Rucker, and Abner Shackleford, and Levi Bell,
e lawyer; and Dr. Robinson, and their wives, and the widow Bartley, and—
ll, there's a lot of them; but these are the ones that Peter was thickest with,

and used to write about sometimes, when he wrote home ; so Harvey 'll kn⋯
where to look for friends when he get's here."

Well, the old man he went on asking questions till he just fairly empti⋯
that young fellow.   Blamed if he didn't inquire about everybody and everythi⋯
in that blessed town, and all about all the Wilkses ; and about Peter's business
which was a tanner ; and about George's—which was a carpenter ; and abc⋯
Harvey's—which was a dissentering minister ; and so on, and so on.   Then
says :

"What did you want to walk all the way up to the steamboat for ? "

"Because she's a big Orleans boat, and I was afeard she mightn't stop the⋯
When they're deep they won't stop for a hail.   A Cincinnati boat will, but tl⋯
is a St. Louis one."

"Was Peter Wilks well off ? "

"Oh, yes, pretty well off.   He had houses and land, and it's reckoned he l⋯
three or four thousand in cash hid up som'ers."

"When did you say he died ? "

"I didn't say, but it was last night."

"Funeral to-morrow, likely ? "

"Yes, 'bout the middle of the day."

"Well, it's all terrible sad ; but we've all got to go, one time or another.
what we want to do is to be prepared ; then we're all right."

"Yes, sir, it's the best way.   Ma used to always say that."

When we struck the boat, she was about done loading, and pretty soon s⋯
got off.   The king never said nothing about going aboard, so I lost my rid⋯
after all.   When the boat was gone, the king made me paddle up another m⋯
to a lonesome place, and then he got ashore, and says :

"Now hustle back, right off, and fetch the duke up here, and the n⋯
carpet-bags.   And if he's gone over to t'other side, go over there and git hi⋯
And tell him to git himself up regardless.   Shove along, now."

I see what *he* was up to ; but I never said nothing, of course.   When I g⋯
back with the duke, we hid the canoe and then they set down on a log, and t⋯
king told him everything, just like the young fellow had said it—every last wo⋯

it. And all the time he was a doing it, he tried to talk like an Englishman; d he done it pretty well too, for a slouch. I can't imitate him, and so I ain't oing to try to; but he really done it pretty good. Then he says:

"How are you on the deef and dumb, Bilgewater?"

The duke said, leave him alone for that; said he had played a deef and dumb rson on the histrionic boards. So then they waited for a steamboat.

About the middle of the afternoon a couple of little boats come along, but ey didn't come from high enough up the river; but at last there was a big one, d they hailed her. She sent out her yawl, and we went aboard, and she was om Cincinnati; and when they found we only wanted to go four or five mile, ey was booming mad, and give us cussing, and said they wouldn't nd us. But the king was ca'm. e says:

"If gentlemen kin afford to pay dollar a mile apiece, to be took and put off in a yawl, a steam- at kin afford to carry 'em, can't ?"

So they softened down and said was all right; and when we t to the village, they yawled us hore. About two dozen men cked down, when they see the wl a coming; and when the king ys—

"Kin any of you gentlemen l me wher' Mr. Peter Wilks ves?" they give a glance at one other, and nodded their heads, much as to say, "What d' I tell you?" Then one of them says, kind of soft d gentle:

"ALAS, OUR POOR BROTHER."

"I'm sorry, sir, but the best we can do is to tell you where he *did* li
yesterday evening."

Sudden as winking, the ornery old cretur went all to smash, and fell up agai
the man, and put his chin on his shoulder, and cried down his back, and says :

"Alas, alas, our poor brother—gone, and we never got to see him ; o
it's too, *too* hard !"

Then he turns around, blubbering, and makes a lot of idiotic signs to t
duke on his hands, and blamed if *he* didn't drop a carpet-bag and bust o
a-crying.   If they warn't the beatenest lot, them two frauds, that ever I struck

Well, the men gethered around, and sympathized with them, and said all so
of kind things to them, and carried their carpet-bags up the hill for them, a
let them lean on them and cry, and told the king all about his brother's la
moments, and the king he told it all over again on his hands to the duke, and bo
of them took on about that dead tanner like they'd lost the twelve disciple
Well, if ever I struck anything like it, I'm a nigger.   It was enough to ma
a body ashamed of the human race.

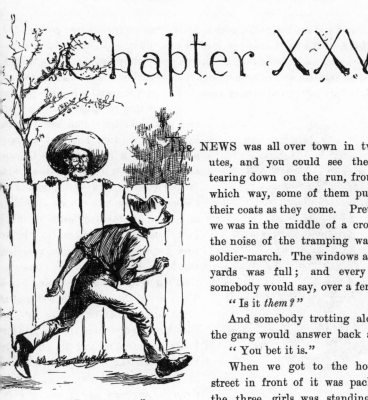

Chapter XXV

THE NEWS was all over town in two minutes, and you could see the people
tearing down on the run, from every
which way, some of them putting on
their coats as they come. Pretty soon
we was in the middle of a crowd, and
the noise of the tramping was like a
soldier-march. The windows and door-
yards was full; and every minute
somebody would say, over a fence:

"Is it *them?*"

And somebody trotting along with
the gang would answer back and say,

"You bet it is."

When we got to the house, the
street in front of it was packed, and
the three girls was standing in the
door. Mary Jane *was* red-headed,

"YOU BET IT IS."

but that don't make no difference, she was most awful beautiful, and her face
and her eyes was all lit up like glory, she was so glad her uncles was come. The
king he spread his arms, and Mary Jane she jumped for them, and the hare-lip
jumped for the duke, and there they *had* it! Everybody most, leastways women,
cried for joy to see them meet again at last and have such good times.

Then the king he hunched the duke, private—I see him do it—and then he

looked around and see the coffin, over in the corner on two chairs ; so then, hi
and the duke, with a hand across each other's shoulder, and t'other hand to the
eyes, walked slow and solemn over there, everybody dropping back to give the
room, and all the talk and noise stopping, people saying "Sh !" and all the me
taking their hats off and drooping their heads, so you could a heard a pin fal

LEAKING.

And when they got there, they bent ove
and looked in the coffin, and took on
sight, and then they bust out a cryin
so you could a heard them to Orleans
most ; and then they put their arm
around each other's necks, and hun
their chins over each other's shoulders
and then for three minutes, or mayb
four, I never see two men leak the wa
they done. And mind you, everybod
was doing the same ; and the place wa
that damp I never see anything like i
Then one of them got on one side of th
coffin, and t'other on t'other side, an
they kneeled down and rested their for
heads on the coffin, and let on to pra
all to theirselves. Well, when it com
to that, it worked the crowd like yo
never see anything like it, and so ever

body broke down and went to sobbing right out loud—the poor girls, too ; an
every woman, nearly, went up to the girls, without saying a word, and kisse
them, solemn, on the forehead, and then put their hand on their head, an
looked up towards the sky, with the tears running down, and then busted ou
and went off sobbing and swabbing, and give the next woman a show. I neve
see anything so disgusting.

Well, by-and-by the king he gets up and comes forward a little, and work
himself up and slobbers out a speech, all full of tears and flapdoodle about it

ing a sore trial for him and his poor brother to lose the diseased, and to miss
eing diseased alive, after the long journey of four thousand mile, but its a trial
at's sweetened and sanctified to us by this dear sympathy and these holy tears,
d so he thanks them out of his heart and out of his brother's heart, because
t of their mouths they can't, words being too weak and cold, and all that kind
rot and slush, till it was just sickening ; and then he blubbers out a pious
ody-goody Amen, and turns himself loose and goes to crying fit to bust.

And the minute the words was out of his mouth somebody over in the crowd
ruck up the doxolojer, and everybody joined in with all their might, and it just
armed you up and made you feel as good as church letting out.   Music *is* a
od thing ; and after all that soul-butter and hogwash, I never see it freshen up
ings so, and sound so honest and bully.

Then the king begins to work his jaw again, and says how him and his nieces
ould be glad if a few of the main principal friends of the family would take
pper here with them this evening, and help set up with the ashes of the dis-
sed ; and says if his poor brother laying yonder could speak, he knows who he
ould name, for they was names that was very dear to him, and mentioned often
his letters ; and so he will name the same, to-wit, as follows, vizz :—Rev. Mr.
obson, and Deacon Lot Hovey, and Mr. Ben Rucker, and Abner Shackleford,
d Levi Bell, and Dr. Robinson, and their wives, and the widow Bartley.

Rev. Hobson and Dr. Robinson was down to the end of the town, a-hunting
gether ; that is, I mean the doctor was shipping a sick man to t'other world,
d the preacher was pinting him right.   Lawyer Bell was away up to Louisville
a some business.   But the rest was on hand, and so they all come and shook
ands with the king and thanked him and talked to him; and then they shook
ands with the duke, and didn't say nothing but just kept a-smiling and bob-
ng their heads like a passel of sapheads whilst he made all sorts of signs with his
ands and said " Goo-goo—goo-goo-goo," all the time, like a baby that can't talk.

So the king he blatted along, and managed to inquire about pretty much
erybody and dog in town, by his name, and mentioned all sorts of little things
at happened one time or another in the town, or to George's family, or to
eter ; and he always let on that Peter wrote him the things, but that was a lie,

he got every blessed one of them out of that young flathead that we canoed up t
the steamboat.

Then Mary Jane she fetched the letter her father left behind, and the kin
he read it out loud and cried over it. It give the dwelling-house and thre
thousand dollars, gold, to the girls; and it give the tanyard (which was doing
good business), along with some other houses and land (worth about sevc
thousand), and three thousand dollars in gold to Harvey and William, and tol
where the six thousand cash was hid, down cellar. So these two frauds said they'
go and fetch it up, and have everything square and above-board; and told me t
come with a candle. We shut the cellar door behind us, and when they foun
the bag they spilt it out on the floor, and it was a lovely sight, all them yalle
boys. My, the way the king's eyes did shine! He slaps the duke on th
shoulder, and says:

"Oh, *this* ain't bully, nor noth'n! Oh, no, I reckon not! Why, Biljy,
beats the Nonesuch, *don't* it!"

The duke allowed it did. They pawed the yaller-boys, and sifted ther
through their fingers and let them jingle down on the floor; and the kin
says:

"It ain't no use talkin'; bein' brothers to a rich dead man, and represents
tives of furrin heirs that's got left, is the line for you and me, Bilge. Thish-ye
comes of trust'n to Providence. It's the best way, in the long run. I've trie
'em all, and ther' ain't no better way."

Most everybody would a been satisfied with the pile, and took it on trust; bu
no, they must count it. So they counts it, and it comes out four hundred an
fifteen dollars short. Says the king:

"Dern him, I wonder what he done with that four hunderd and fiftee
dollars?"

They worried over that a while, and ransacked all around for it. Then th
duke says:

"Well, he was a pretty sick man, and likely he made a mistake—I recko
that's the way of it. The best way's to let it go, and keep still about it. W
can spare it."

"Oh, shucks, yes, we can *spare* it. I don't k'yer noth'n 'bout that—it's
[th]e *count* I'm thinkin' about. We want to be awful square and open and above-

[bo]ard, here, you know. We
[w]ant to lug this h-yer money up
[st]airs and count it before every-
[b]ody—then ther' ain't noth'n
[su]spicious. But when the dead
[m]an says ther's six thous'n dol-
[la]rs, you know, we don't want
[to]——"

"Hold on," says the duke.
"Less make up the deffisit"—
[a]nd he begun to haul out yaller-
[b]oys out of his pocket.

"It's a most amaz'n' good idea,
[d]uke—you *have* got a rattlin'
[cl]ever head on you," says the
[k]ing. "Blest if the old None-
[su]ch ain't a heppin' us out agin"
—and *he* begun to haul out yaller-
[j]ackets and stack them up.

It most busted them, but they
[m]ade up the six thousand clean and clear.

MAKING UP THE "DEFFISIT."

"Say," says the duke, "I got another idea. Le's go up stairs and count this
[m]oney, and then take and *give it to the girls.*"

"Good land, duke, lemme hug you! It's the most dazzling idea 'at ever a
[m]an struck. You have cert'nly got the most astonishin' head I ever see. Oh,
[t]his is the boss dodge, ther' ain't no mistake 'bout it. Let 'em fetch along their
[su]spicions now, if they want to—this'll lay 'em out."

When we got up stairs, everybody gethered around the table, and the king he
[c]ounted it and stacked it up, three hundred dollars in a pile—twenty elegant
[li]ttle piles. Everybody looked hungry at it, and licked their chops. Then they

raked it into the bag again, and I see the king begin to swell himself up f
another speech. He says :

"Friends all, my poor brother that lays yonder, has done generous by the
that's left behind in the vale of sorrers. He has done generous by these-yer poo
little lambs that he loved and sheltered, and that's left fatherless and motherles
Yes, and we that knowed him, knows that he would a done *more* generous by 'e
if he hadn't ben afeard o' woundin' his dear William and me. Now, *wouldn*
he ? Ther' ain't no question 'bout it, in *my* mind. Well, then—what kind
brothers would it be, that 'd stand in his way at sech a time ? And what kin
o' uncles would it be that 'd rob—yes, *rob*—sech poor sweet lambs as these 'at h

GOING FOR HIM.

loved so, at sech a time ? If I kno
William—and I *think* I do—he
well, I'll jest ask him." He tur
around and begins to make a lot
signs to the duke with his hands
and the duke he looks at him stupi
and leather-headed a while, then a
of a sudden he seems to catch h
meaning, and jumps for the king
goo-gooing with all his might for joy
and hugs him about fifteen time
before he lets up. Then the kin
says, "I knowed it ; I reckon th
'll convince anybody the way *he* fee
about it. Here, Mary Jane, Susan
Joanner, take the money—take
all. It's the gift of him that lay
yonder, cold but joyful."

Mary Jane she went for hi
Susan and the hare-lip went for the duke, and then such another hugging an
kissing I never see yet. And everybody crowded up with the tears in the
eyes, and most shook the hands off of them frauds, saying all the time :

" You *dear* good souls !—how *lovely!*--how *could* you !"

Well, then, pretty soon all hands got to talking about the diseased again, and w good he was, and what a loss he was, and all that ; and before long a big n-jawed man worked himself in there from outside, and stood a listening and oking, and not saying anything ; and nobody saying anything to him either, cause the king was talking and they was all busy listening. The king was say-g—in the middle of something he'd started in on—

"—they bein' partickler friends o' the diseased. That's why they're invited here is evenin' ; but to-morrow we want *all* to come—everybody ; for he respected erybody, he liked everybody, and so it's fitten that his funeral orgiess h'd be public."

And so he went a-mooning on and on, liking to hear himself talk, and every tle while he fetched in his funeral orgies again, till the duke he couldn't stand no more ; so he writes on a little scrap of paper, " *obsequies,* you old fool," and lds it up and goes to goo-gooing and reaching it over people's heads to him. he king he reads it, and puts it in his pocket, and says :

" Poor William, afflicted as he is, his *heart's* aluz right. Asks me to invite erybody to come to the funeral—wants me to make 'em all welcome. But he edn't a worried—it was jest what I was at."

Then he weaves along again, perfectly ca'm, and goes to dropping in his neral orgies again every now and then, just like he done before. And when he ne it the third time, he says :

" I say orgies, not because it's the common term, because it ain't—obsequies in' the common term—but because orgies is the right term. Obsequies ain't ed in England no more, now—it's gone out. We say orgies now, in England. rgies is better, because it means the thing you're after, more exact. It's a word at's made up out'n the Greek *orgo,* outside, open, abroad ; and the Hebrew *esum,* to plant, cover up ; hence in*ter.* So, you see, funeral orgies is an open er iblic funeral."

He was the *worst* I ever struck. Well, the iron-jawed man he laughed right his face. Everybody was shocked. Everybody says, " Why *doctor !* " and bner Shackleford says :

" Why, Robinson, hain't you heard the news ? This is Harvey Wilks."

The king he smiled eager, and shoved out his flapper, and says :

"*Is* it my poor brother's dear good friend and physician ? I——"

"Keep your hands off of me !" says the doctor. "*You* talk like an Englishman—*don't* you ? It's the worse imitation I ever heard. *You* Peter Wilks's brother. You're a fraud, that's what you are !"

Well, how they all took on ! They crowded around the doctor, and tried to quiet him down, and tried to explain to him and tell him how Harvey'd showed in forty ways that he *was* Harvey, and knowed everybody by name, and the names of the very dogs, and begged and *begged* him not to hurt Harvey's feelings and the poor girls' feelings, and all that ; but it warn't no use, he stormed right along, and said any man that pretended to be an Englishman and couldn't imitate the lingo no better than what he did, was a fraud and a liar. The poor girls was hanging to the king and crying ; and all of a sudden the doctor ups and turns on them. He says :

THE DOCTOR.

"I was your father's friend, and I'm your friend ; and I warn you *as* a friend, and an honest one, that wants to protect you and keep you out of harm and trouble, to turn your backs on that scoundrel, and have nothing to do with him, the ignorant tramp, with his idiotic Greek and Hebrew as he calls it. He is the thinnest kind of an impostor—has come here with a lot of empty names and facts which he has picked up somewheres, and you take them for *proofs*, and are helped to fool yourselves by these foolish friends here, who ought to know better. Mary Jane Wilks, you know me for your friend, and for your unselfish friend, too. Now listen to me ; turn this pitiful rascal out—I *beg* you to do it. Will you ?"

Mary Jane straightened herself up, and my, but she was handsome ! She
ys :

"*Here* is my answer." She hove up the bag of money and put it in the
ng's hands, and says, "Take this six thousand dollars, and invest for me and
y sisters any way you want to, and don't give us no receipt for it."

Then she put her arm around the king on one side, and Susan and the hare-
done the same on the other. Everybody clapped their hands and stomped on
e floor like a perfect storm, whilst the king held up his head and smiled proud.
ie doctor says :

"All right, I wash *my* hands of the matter. But I warn you all that a time's
ming when you're going to feel sick whenever you think of this day"—and
ay he went.

"All right, doctor," says the king, kinder mocking him, "we'll try and get
n to send for you"—which made them all laugh, and they said it was a prime
od hit.

THE BAG OF MONEY.

Chapter XXVI

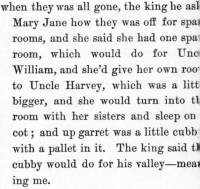

THE CUBBY.

ell when they was all gone, the king he ask
Mary Jane how they was off for spar
rooms, and she said she had one spar
room, which would do for Unc
William, and she'd give her own roo
to Uncle Harvey, which was a litt
bigger, and she would turn into th
room with her sisters and sleep on
cot; and up garret was a little cubb
with a pallet in it. The king said th
cubby would do for his valley—mear
ing me.

So Mary Jane took us up, an
she showed them their room
which was plain but nice. She sa
she'd have her frocks and a lot
other traps took out of her room
they was in Uncle Harvey's way, b

he said they warn't. The frocks was hung along the wall, and before them w
a curtain made out of calico that hung down to the floor. There was an old ha
trunk in one corner, and a guitar box in another, and all sorts of little knic
knacks and jimcracks around, like girls brisken up a room with. The king said
was all the more homely and more pleasanter for these fixings, and so don't di
turb them. The duke's room was pretty small, but plenty good enough, and
was my cubby.

That night they had a big supper, and all them men and women was ther

d I stood behind the king and the duke's chairs and waited on them, and the
ggers waited on the rest. Mary Jane she set at the head of the table, with
1san along side of her, and said how bad the biscuits was, and how mean the

eserves was, and how ornery and
ugh the fried chickens was—and
1 that kind of rot, the way
omen always do for to force out
mpliments; and the people all
nowed everything was tip-top,
d said so—said "How *do* you
t biscuits to brown so nice?"
d "Where, for the land's sake
'd you get these amaz'n pick-
s?" and all that kind of hum-
1g talky-talk, just the way
ople always does at a supper,
u know.

And when it was all done, me
d the hare-lip had supper in the
tchen off of the leavings, whilst
e others was helping the niggers
ean up the things. The hare-lip
e got to pumping me about

SUPPER WITH THE HARE-LIP.

ngland, and blest if I didn't think the ice was getting mighty thin, sometimes.
1e says :

"Did you ever see the king?"

"Who? William Fourth? Well, I bet I have—he goes to our church." I
nowed he was dead years ago, but I never let on. So when I says he goes to
r church, she says :

"What—regular?"

"Yes—regular. His pew's right over opposite ourn—on 'tother side the
1lpit."

"I thought he lived in London?"

"Well, he does. Where *would* he live?"

"But I thought *you* lived in Sheffield?"

I see I was up a stump. I had to let on to get choked with a chicken bon
so as to get time to think how to get down again. Then I says:

"I mean he goes to our church regular when he's in Sheffield. That's onl
in the summer-time, when he comes there to take the sea baths."

"Why, how you talk—Sheffield ain't on the sea."

"Well, who said it was?"

"Why, you did."

"I *didn't,* nuther."

"You did!"

"I didn't."

"You did."

"I never said nothing of the kind."

"Well, what *did* you say, then?"

"Said he come to take the sea *baths*—that's what I said."

"Well, then! how's he going to take the sea baths if it ain't on the sea?"

"Looky here," I says; "did you ever see any Congress water?"

"Yes."

"Well, did you have to go to Congress to get it?"

"Why, no."

"Well, neither does William Fourth have to go to the sea to get a sea bath.

"How does he get it, then?"

"Gets it the way people down here gets Congress-water—in barrels. There i
the palace at Sheffield they've got furnaces, and he wants his water hot. The
can't bile that amount of water away off there at the sea. They haven't got n
conveniences for it."

"Oh, I see, now. You might a said that in the first place and save
time."

When she said that, I see I was out of the woods again, and so I was comfort
able and glad. Next, she says:

"Do you go to church, too?"

"Yes—regular."

"Where do you set?"

"Why, in our pew."

"*Whose* pew?"

"Why, *ourn*—your Uncle Harvey's."

"His'n? What does *he* want with a pew?"

"Wants it to set in. What did you *reckon* he wanted with it?"

"Why, I thought he'd be in the pulpit."

Rot him, I forgot he was a preacher. I see I was up a stump again, so I ayed another chicken bone and got another think. Then I says:

"Blame it, do you suppose there ain't but one preacher to a church?"

"Why, what do they want with more?"

"What!—to preach before a king? I never see such a girl as you. They on't have no less than seventeen."

"Seventeen! My land! Why, I wouldn't set out such a string as that, ot if I *never* got to glory. It must take 'em a week."

"Shucks, they don't *all* of 'em preach the same day—only *one* of 'em."

"Well, then, what does the rest of 'em do?"

"Oh, nothing much. Loll around, pass the plate—and one thing or another. ut mainly they don't do nothing."

"Well, then, what are they *for?*"

"Why, they're for *style*. Don't you know nothing?"

"Well, I don't *want* to know no such foolishness as that. How is servants eated in England? Do they treat 'em better 'n we treat our niggers?"

"*No!* A servant ain't nobody there. They treat them worse than dogs."

"Don't they give 'em holidays, the way we do, Christmas and New Year's eek, and Fourth of July?"

"Oh, just listen! A body could tell *you* hain't ever been to England, that. Why, Hare-l—why, Joanna, they never see a holiday from year's d to year's end; never go to the circus, nor theatre, nor nigger shows, nor wheres."

"Nor church ?"

"Nor church."

"But *you* always went to church."

Well, I was gone up again. I forgot I was the old man's servant. But ne
minute I whirled in on a kir
of an explanation how a valle
was different from a comm
servant, and *had* to go
church whether he want
to or not, and set with t
family, on account of i
being the law. But I didr
do it pretty good, and wher
got done I see she warı
satisfied. She says :

"HONEST INJUN."

"Honest injun, no
hain't you been telling me
lot of lies ?"

"Honest injun," says I.

"None of it at all ?"

"None of it at all. Not
lie in it," says I.

"Lay your hand on tl
book and say it."

I see it warn't nothing b
a dictionary, so I laid my hand on it and said it. So then she looked a lit
better satisfied, and says :

"Well, then, I'll believe some of it ; but I hope to gracious if I'll believe t
rest."

"What is it you won't believe, Joe ?" says Mary Jane, stepping in wi
Susan behind her. "It ain't right nor kind for you to talk so to him, and hi
a stranger and so far from his people. How would you like to be treated so ?

"That's always your way, Maim—always sailing in to help somebody before ey're hurt. I hain't done nothing to him. He's told some stretchers, I ckon ; and I said I wouldn't swallow it all ; and that's every bit and grain I d say. I reckon he can stand a little thing like that, can't he ? "

"I don't care whether 'twas little or whether 'twas big, he's here in our house d a stranger, and it wasn't good of you to say it. If you was in his place, it uld make you feel ashamed ; and so you oughtn't to say a thing to another rson that will make *them* feel ashamed."

"Why, Maim, he said—— "

"It don't make no difference what he *said*—that ain't the thing. The thing for you to treat him *kind*, and not be saying things to make him remember he n't in his own country and amongst his own folks."

I says to myself, *this* is a girl that I'm letting that old reptile rob her of her oney !

Then Susan *she* waltzed in ; and if you'll believe me, she did give Hare-lip rk from the tomb !

Says I to myself, And this is *another* one that I'm letting him rob her of her oney !

Then Mary Jane she took another inning, and went in sweet and lovely again— iich was her way—but when she got done there warn't hardly anything left o' or Hare-lip. So she hollered.

"All right, then," says the other girls, "you just ask his pardon."

She done it, too. And she done it beautiful. She done it so beautiful it was od to hear ; and I wished I could tell her a thousand lies, so she could do it ain.

I says to myself, this is *another* one that I'm letting him rob her of her ney. And when she got through, they all jest laid theirselves out to make me el at home and know I was amongst friends. I felt so ornery and low down d mean, that I says to myself, My mind's made up ; I'll hive that money for em or bust.

So then I lit out—for bed, I said, meaning some time or another. When I t by myself, I went to thinking the thing over. I says to myself, shall I go to that doctor, private, and blow on these frauds? No—that won't do. I might tell who told him; then the king and the duke would make it warm for me. Shall I go, private, and tell Mary Jane? No—I dasn't do it. Her face would give them a hint, sure; they've got the money, and they'd slide right out and get away with it. If she was to fetch in help, I'd get mixed up in the business, before it was done with, I judge. No, there ain't no good way but one.

THE DUKE LOOKS UNDER THE BED.

I got to steal that money, somehow; and I got to steal it some way that they won't suspicion that I done it. They've got a good thing, here; and they ain't agoing to leave till they've played this family and this town for all they're worth, so I'll find a chance time enough. I'll steal it, and hide it; and by-and-by, when I'm away down the river, I'll write a letter and tell Mary Jane where it's hid. But I better hive it to-night, if I can, because the doctor maybe hasn't let up so much as he lets on he has; he might scare them out of here, yet.

So, thinks I, I'll go and search them rooms. Up stairs the hall was dark, but

und the duke's room, and started to paw around it with my hands; but I
ollected it wouldn't be much like the king to let anybody else take care of
t money but his own self; so then I went to his room and begun to paw
und there. But I see I couldn't do nothing without a candle, and I dasn't
t one, of course. So I judged I'd got to do the other thing—lay for them,
eavesdrop. About that time, I hears their footsteps coming, and was going
kip under the bed; I reached for it, but it wasn't where I thought it would
but I touched the curtain that hid Mary Jane's frocks, so I jumped in
ind that and snuggled in amongst the gowns, and stood there perfectly

They come in and shut the door; and the first thing the duke done was to
down and look under the bed. Then I was glad I hadn't found the bed
en I wanted it. And yet, you know, it's kind of natural to hide under
bed when you are up to anything private. They sets down, then, and the
g says:

"Well, what is it? and cut it middlin' short, because it's better for us to be
n there a whoopin'-up the mournin', than up here givin' 'em a chance to talk
over."

"Well, this is it, Capet. I ain't easy; I ain't comfortable. That doctor
s on my mind. I wanted to know your plans. I've got a notion, and I think
a sound one."

"What is it, duke?"

"That we better glide out of this, before three in the morning, and clip it
n the river with what we've got. Specially, seeing we got it so easy—*given*
k to us, flung at our heads, as you may say, when of course we allowed to have
teal it back. I'm for knocking off and lighting out."

That made me feel pretty bad. About an hour or two ago, it would a been a
le different, but now it made me feel bad and disappointed. The king rips
and says:

"What! And not sell out the rest o' the property? March off like a pas-
o' fools and leave eight or nine thous'n' dollars' worth o' property layin' around
sufferin' to be scooped in?—and all good salable stuff, too."

The duke he grumbled; said the bag of gold was enough, and he didn't wa
to go no deeper—didn't want to rob a lot of orphans of *everything* they had.

"Why, how you talk!" says the king. "We shan't rob 'em of nothing
all but jest this money. The people that *buys* the property is the suff're
because as soon's it's found out 'at we didn't own it—which won't be long af
we've slid—the sale won't be valid, and it'll all go back to the estate. These-
orphans 'll git their house back agin, and that's enough for *them;* they're you
and spry, and k'n easy earn a livin'. *They* ain't agoing to suffer. Why, j
think—there's thous'n's and thous'n's that ain't nigh so well off. Bless you, t
ain't got noth'n to complain of."

Well, the king he talked him blind; so at last he give in, and said all rig
but said he believed it was blame foolishness to stay, and that doctor hangi
over them. But the king says:

"Cuss the doctor! What do we k'yer for *him?* Hain't we got all the fo
in town on our side? and ain't that a big enough majority in any town?"

So they got ready to go down stairs again. The duke says:

"I don't think we put that money in a good place."

That cheered me up. I'd begun to think I warn't going to get a hint of
kind to help me. The king says:

"Why?"

"Because Mary Jane 'll be in mourning from this out; and first you kn
the nigger that does up the rooms will get an order to box these duds up a
put 'em away; and do you reckon a nigger can run across money and not borr
some of it?"

"Your head's level, agin, duke," says the king; and he come a fumbling und
the curtain two or three foot from where I was. I stuck tight to the wall, a
kept mighty still, though quivery; and I wondered what them fellows would
to me if they catched me; and I tried to think what I'd better do if they
catch me. But the king he got the bag before I could think more than ab
a half a thought, and he never suspicioned I was around. They took a
shoved the bag through a rip in the straw tick that was under the feather b
and crammed it in a foot or two amongst the straw and said it was all right, n

ause a nigger only makes up the feather bed, and don't turn over the straw

k only about twice a year,
l so it warn't in no danger
getting stole, now.

But I knowed better. I
l it out of there before
y was half-way down
irs. I groped along up to
cubby, and hid it there
I could get a chance to
better. I judged I better
e it outside of the house
newheres, because if they
ssed it they would give
house a good ransacking.
knowed that very well.
en I turned in, with my
thes all on ; but I couldn't
gone to sleep, if I'd a
nted to, I was in such a

Kemble .

HUCK TAKES THE MONEY.

eat to get through with the business. By-and-by I heard the king and the
ke come up ; so I rolled off of my pallet and laid with my chin at the top of
ladder and waited to see if anything was going to happen. But nothing
l.

So I held on till all the late sounds had quit and the early ones hadn't begun,
; ; and then I slipped down the ladder.

Chapter XXVII.

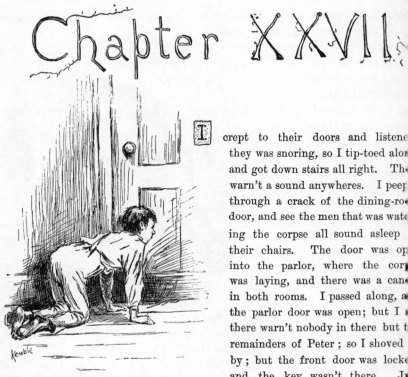

A CRACK IN THE DINING-ROOM DOOR.

I crept to their doors and listened; they was snoring, so I tip-toed along and got down stairs all right. There warn't a sound anywheres. I peeped through a crack of the dining-room door, and see the men that was watching the corpse all sound asleep in their chairs. The door was open into the parlor, where the corpse was laying, and there was a candle in both rooms. I passed along, and the parlor door was open; but I see there warn't nobody in there but the remainders of Peter; so I shoved by; but the front door was locked, and the key wasn't there. Just then I heard somebody coming down the stairs, back behind me. I run in the parlor, and took a swift look around, and the only place I see to hide the bag was in the coffin. The lid was shoved along about a foot, showing the dead man's face down in there, with a wet cloth over it, and his shroud on. I tucked the money-bag in under the lid, just down beyond where his hands was crossed, which made me creep, they was so cold, and then I run back across the room and in behind the door.

The person coming was Mary Jane. She went to the coffin, very soft, and

eeled down and looked in ; then she put up her handkerchief and I see she
gun to cry, though I couldn't hear her, and her back was to me. I slid out,
d as I passed the dining-room I thought I'd make sure them watchers
dn't seen me ; so I looked through the crack and everything was all right.
ey hadn't stirred.

I slipped up to bed, feeling ruther blue, on accounts of the thing playing
t that way after I had took so much trouble and run so much resk about it.
ys I, if it could stay where it is, all right ; because when we get down the
er a hundred mile or two, I could write back to Mary Jane, and she could
g him up again and get it ; but that ain't the thing that's going to happen;
e thing that's going to happen is, the money 'll be found when they come to
ew on the lid. Then the king 'll get it again, and it 'll be a long day before
gives anybody another chance to smouch it from him. Of course I *wanted*
slide down and get it out of there, but I dasn't try it. Every minute it was
tting earlier, now, and pretty soon some of them watchers would begin to stir,
d I might get catched—catched with six thousand dollars in my hands that
body hadn't hired me to take care of. I don't wish to be mixed up in no such
siness as that, I says to myself.

When I got down stairs in the morning, the parlor was shut up, and the
tchers was gone. There warn't nobody around but the family and the widow
rtley and our tribe. I watched their faces to see if anything had been happen-
g, but I couldn't tell.

Towards the middle of the day the undertaker come, with his man, and they
the coffin in the middle of the room on a couple of chairs, and then set all
r chairs in rows, and borrowed more from the neighbors till the hall and the
rlor and the dining-room was full. I see the coffin lid was the way it was
fore, but I dasn't go to look in under it, with folks around.

Then the people begun to flock in, and the beats and the girls took seats in
e front row at the head of the coffin, and for a half an hour the people filed
ound slow, in single rank, and looked down at the dead man's face a minute,
d some dropped in a tear, and it was all very still and solemn, only the girls
d the beats holding handkerchiefs to their eyes and keeping their heads bent,

and sobbing a little.   There warn't no other sound but the scraping of the f
on the floor, and blowing noses—because people always blows them more a
funeral than they do at other places except church.

When the place was packed full, the undertaker he slid around in his bla

THE UNDERTAKER.

gloves with his softy soothering ways, putting on t
last touches, and getting people and things all sh
shape and comfortable, and making no more sou
than a cat. He never spoke ; he moved peo
around, he squeezed in late ones, he opened
passage-ways, and done it all with nods, and sig
with his hands. Then he took his place over agai
the wall. He was the softest, glidingest, stealthi
man I ever see ; and there warn't no more smile
him than there is to a ham.

They had borrowed a melodeum—a sick one ; a
when everything was ready, a young woman
down and worked it, and it was pretty skreeky a
colicky, and everybody joined in and sung, a
Peter was the only one that had a good thing,
cording to my notion. Then the Reverend Hobs
opened up, slow and solemn, and begun to tal
and straight off the most outrageous row busted
in the cellar a body ever heard; it was only one d
but he made a most powerful racket, and he kept

up, right along; the parson he had to stand there, over the coffin, and wait—y
couldn't hear yourself think. It was right down awkward, and nobody did
seem to know what to do.   But pretty soon they see that long-legged undertak
make a sign to the preacher as much as to say, " Don't you worry—just depe
on me." Then he stooped down and begun to glide along the wall, just
shoulders showing over the people's heads. So he glided along, and the pow-w
and racket getting more and more outrageous all the time ; and at last, when
had gone around two sides of the room, he disappears down cellar. Then,

out two seconds we heard a whack, and the dog he finished up with a most
amazing howl or two, and then everything was dead still, and the parson begun
his solemn talk where he left off. In a minute or two here comes this undertaker's back and shoulders gliding along the wall again; and so he glided, and
glided, around three sides of the room, and then rose up, and shaded his mouth
with his hands, and stretched his neck out towards the preacher, over the people's
heads, and says, in a kind of a coarse whisper, *"He had a rat!"* Then he droop-

ed down and glided along
the wall again to his place.
You could see it was a great
satisfaction to the people,
because naturally they wanted to know. A little thing
like that don't cost nothing,
and it's just the little things
that makes a man to be looked up to and liked. There
warn't no more popular man
in town than what that
undertaker was.

Well, the funeral sermon
was very good, but pison

"HE HAD A RAT!"

long and tiresome; and then the king he shoved in and got off some of his usual
rubbage, and at last the job was through, and the undertaker begun to sneak up
on the coffin with his screw-driver. I was in a sweat then, and watched him
pretty keen. But he never meddled at all; just slid the lid along, as soft as
mush, and screwed it down tight and fast. So there I was! I didn't know
whether the money was in there, or not. So, says I, spose somebody has hogged
that bag on the sly?—now how do *I* know whether to write to Mary Jane or not?
Spose she dug him up and didn't find nothing—what would she think of me?
Blame it, I says, I might get hunted up and jailed; I'd better lay low and keep
dark, and not write at all; the thing's awful mixed, now; trying to better it, I've

worsened it a hundred times, and I wish to goodness I'd just let it alone, d
fetch the whole business !

They buried him, and we come back home, and I went to watching fac
again—I couldn't help it, and I couldn't rest easy.   But nothing come of it ; t
faces didn't tell me nothing.

The king he visited around, in the evening, and sweetened every body up, a
made himself ever so friendly; and he give out the idea that his congregration ov
in England would be in a sweat about him, so he must hurry and settle up t
estate right away, and leave for home.   He was very sorry he was so pushe
and so was everybody; they wished he could stay longer, but they said they cou
see it couldn't be done.   And he said of course him and William would take t
girls home with them ; and that pleased everybody too, because then the gi
would be well fixed, and amongst their own relations ; and it pleased the gir
too—tickled them so they clean forgot they ever had a trouble in the world; and to
him to sell out as quick as he wanted to, they would be ready.   Them poor thin
was that glad and happy it made my heart ache to see them getting fooled and li
to so, but I didn't see no safe way for me to chip in and change the general tur

Well, blamed if the king didn't bill the house and the niggers and all t
property for auction straight off—sale two days after the funeral ; but anybo
could buy private beforehand if they wanted to.

So the next day after the funeral, along about noontime, the girls' joy got t
first jolt ; a couple of nigger traders come along, and the king sold them t
niggers reasonable, for three-day drafts as they called it, and away they wer
the two sons up the river to Memphis, and their mother down the river
Orleans.   I thought them poor girls and them niggers would break their hear
for grief ; they cried around each other, and took on so it most made me dov
sick to see it.   The girls said they hadn't ever dreamed of seeing the fami
separated or sold away from the town.   I can't ever get it out of my memor
the sight of them poor miserable girls and niggers hanging around each othe
necks and crying ; and I reckon I couldn't a stood it all but would a had to bu
out and tell on our gang if I hadn't knowed the sale warn't no account and t
niggers would be back home in a week or two.

The thing made a big stir in the town, too, and a good many come out flat-
ted and said it was scandalous to separate the mother and the children that

y. It injured the frauds
me; but the old fool he
lled right along, spite of
the duke could say or do,
d I tell you the duke was
werful uneasy.

Next day was auction day.
out broad-day in the morn-
g, the king and the duke
me up in the garret and
ke me up, and I see by
eir look that there was
uble. The king says:

"Was you in my room
ght before last?"

"No, your majesty"—
ich was the way I always
lled him when nobody but
r gang warn't around.

"Was you in there yister-
y er last night?"

"No, your majesty."

"WAS YOU IN MY ROOM?"

"Honor bright, now—no lies."

"Honor bright, your majesty, I'm telling you the truth. I hain't been anear
ur room since Miss Mary Jane took you and the duke and showed it to
u."

The duke says:

"Have you seen anybody else go in there?"

"No, your grace, not as I remember, I believe."

"Stop and think."

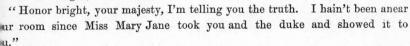

I studied a while, and see my chance, then I says :

" Well, I see the niggers go in there several times."

Both of them give a little jump ; and looked like they hadn't ever expected i
and then like they *had*. Then the duke says :

" What, *all* of them ? "

" No—leastways not all at once. That is, I don't think I ever see them a
come *out* at once but just one time."

" Hello—when was that ? "

" It was the day we had the funeral. In the morning. It warn't ear
because I overslept. I was just starting down the ladder, and I s
them."

" Well, go on, *go* on—what did they do ? How'd they act ? "

" They didn't do nothing. And they didn't act anyway, much, as fur as I se
They tip-toed away; so I seen, easy enough, that they'd shoved in there to
up your majesty's room, or something, sposing you was up; and found you war
up, and so they was hoping to slide out of the way of trouble without waking y
up, if they hadn't already waked you up."

" Great guns, *this* is a go ! " says the king ; and both of them looked pret
sick, and tolerable silly. They stood there a thinking and scratching their hea
a minute, and then the duke he bust into a kind of a little raspy chuckle, a
says :

" It does beat all, how neat the niggers played their hand. They let on
be *sorry* they was going out of this region ! and I believed they *was* sorry. A
so did you, and so did everybody. Don't ever tell *me* any more that a nigger ai
got any histrionic talent. Why, the way they played that thing, it would f
anybody. In my opinion there's a fortune in 'em. If I had capital and
theatre, I wouldn't want a better lay out than that—and here we've gone and s
'em for a song. Yes, and ain't privileged to sing the song, yet. Say, where
that song ?—that draft."

" In the bank for to be collected. Where *would* it be ? "

" Well, *that's* all right then, thank goodness."

Says I, kind of timid-like :

" Is something gone wrong ? "

The king whirls on me and rips out :

" None o' your business !   You keep your head shet, and mind y'r own
airs—if you got any.   Long as you're in this town, don't you forgit *that*, you
ar ? "   Then he says to the duke, " We got to jest swaller it, and say noth'n :
m's the word for *us*."

As they was starting down the ladder, the duke he chuckles again, and
ys :

" Quick sales *and* small profits !   It's a good business—yes."

The king snarls around on him and says ,

" I was trying to do for the best, in sellin' 'm out so quick.   If the profits has

JAWING.

rned out to be none, lackin' considable, and none to carry, is it my fault any
ore'n it's yourn ? "

" Well, *they'd* be in this house yet, and we *wouldn't* if I could a got my
vice listened to."

The king sassed back, as much as was safe for him, and then swapped around
d lit into *me* again.   He give me down the banks for not coming and *telling*
m I see the niggers come out of his room acting that way—said any fool would

a *knowed* something was up.   And then waltzed in and cussed *himself* a whil
and said it all come of him not laying late and taking his natural rest that mor
ing, and he'd be blamed if he'd ever do it again.   So they went off a jawing; a
I felt dreadful glad I'd worked it all off onto the niggers and yet hadn't done t
niggers no harm by it.

Chapter XXVIII

IN TROUBLE.

By and-by it was getting-up time; so I come down the ladder and started for down stairs, but as I come to the girls' room, the door was open, and I see Mary Jane setting by her old hair trunk, which was open and she'd been packing things in it—getting ready to go to England. But she had stopped now, with a folded gown in her lap, and had her face in her hands, crying. I felt awful bad to see it; of course anybody would. I went in there, and says:

"Miss Mary Jane, you can't abear to see people in trouble, and *I* can't—most always. Tell me about it."

So she done it. And it was the niggers—I just expected it. She said the beautiful trip to England was most out spoiled for her; she didn't know *how* she was ever going to be happy there, owing the mother and the children warn't ever going to see each other no more—and then busted out bitterer than ever, and flung up her hands, and

78

" Oh, dear, dear, to think they ain't *ever* going to see each other any more !

" But they *will*—and inside of two weeks—and I *know* it !" says I.

Laws it was out before I could think !—and before I could budge, she throw her arms around my neck, and told me to say it *again*, say it *again*, say it *again*

I see I had spoke too sudden, and said too much, and was in a close place.
asked her to let me think a minute ; and she set there, very impatie
and excited, and handsome, but looking kind of happy and eased-up, lil
a person that's had a tooth pulled out. So I went to studying it ou
I says to myself, I reckon a body that ups and tells the truth when i
is in a tight place, is taking considerable many resks, though I ain't had i
experience, and can't say for certain ; but it looks so to me, anyway ; and y
here's a case where I'm blest if it don't look to me like the truth is bette
and actuly *safer*, than a lie. I must lay it by in my mind, and think it ov
some time or other, it's so kind of strange and unregular. I never see nothi
like it. Well, I says to myself at last, I'm agoing to chance it ; I'll up and t
the truth this time, though it does seem most like setting down on a kag
powder and touching it off just to see where you'll go to. Then I says :

" Miss Mary Jane, is there any place out of town a little ways, where ye
could go and stay three or four days ?"

" Yes—Mr. Lothrop's. Why ?"

" Never mind why, yet. If I'll tell you how I know the niggers will see ea
other again—inside of two weeks—here in this house—and *prove* how I know
—will you go to Mr. Lothrop's and stay four days ?"

" Four days !" she says ; " I'll stay a year !"

" All right," I says, " I don't want nothing more out of *you* than just yo
word—I druther have it than another man's kiss-the-Bible." She smiled, a
reddened up very sweet, and I says, " If you don't mind it, I'll shut the door
and bolt it."

Then I come back and set down again, and says :

" Don't you holler. Just set still, and take it like a man. I got to tell t
truth, and you want to brace up, Miss Mary, because it's a bad kind, and going
be hard to take, but there ain't no help for it. These uncles of yourn ain't

cles at all—they're a couples of frauds—regular dead-beats. There, now we're
er the worst of it—you can stand the rest middling easy."

It jolted her up like everything, of course ; but I was over the shoal water
w, so I went right along, her eyes a blazing higher and higher all the time,
d told her every blame thing, from where we first struck that young fool going
to the steamboat, clear through to where she flung herself onto the king's
east at the front door and he kissed her sixteen or seventeen times—and then
she jumps, with her face afire like sunset, and says :

"The brute ! Come—don't waste a minute—
t a *second*—we'll have them tarred and
athered, and flung in the river ! "

Says I :

"Cert'nly. But do you mean, *before* you go
Mr. Lothrop's, or——"

"Oh," she says, "what am I *thinking* about ! "
e says, and set right down again. "Don't mind
hat I said—please don't—you *won't*, now, *will*
u ?" Laying her silky hand on mind in that
nd of a way that I said I would die first. "I
ver thought, I was so stirred up," she says ;
now go on, and I won't do so any more. You tell
e what to do, and whatever you say, I'll do it."

"Well," I says, "it's a rough gang, them two
auds, and I'm fixed so I got to travel with them
while longer, whether I want to or not—I
uther not tell you why—and if you was to blow

INDIGNATION.

them this town would get me out of their claws, and *I*'d be all right, but
ere'd be another person that you don't know about who'd be in big trouble. Well,
e got to save *him*, hain't we ? Of course. Well, then, we won't blow on them."

Saying them words put a good idea in my head. I see how maybe I could
t me and Jim rid of the frauds ; get them jailed here, and then leave. But
didn't want to run the raft in day-time, without anybody aboard to answer

questions but me ; so I didn't want the plan to begin working till pretty la
to-night.　I says :

"Miss Mary Jane, I'll tell you what we'll do—and you won't have to st
at Mr. Lothrop's so long, nuther.　How fur is it ?"

"A little short of four miles—right out in the country, back here."

"Well, that'll answer.　Now you go along out there, and lay low till nine
half-past, to-night, and then get them to fetch you home again—tell them you'
thought of something.　If you get here before eleven, put a candle in this windo
and if I don't turn up, wait *till* eleven, and *then* if I don't turn up it means I'
gone, and out of the way, and safe.　Then you come out and spread the ne
around, and get these beats jailed."

"Good," she says, "I'll do it."

"And if it just happens so that I don't get away, but get took up along wi
them, you must up and say I told you the whole thing beforehand, and you mu
stand by me all you can."

"Stand by you, indeed I will.　They sha'n't touch a hair of your head !" s
says, and I see her nostrils spread and her eyes snap when she said it, too.

"If I get away, I sha'n't be here," I says, "to prove these rapscallions ai

HOW TO FIND THEM.

your uncles, and I couldn't do it if
was here.　I could swear they was be
and bummers, that's all ; though tha
worth something.　Well, there's othe
can do that better than what I can
and they're people that ain't going to
doubted as quick as I'd be.　I'll tell y
how to find them.　Gimme a pencil a
a piece of paper.　There—'*Royal Non
such, Bricksville.*'　Put it away, a
don't lose it.　When the court wants
find out something about these two, l
them send up to Bricksville and s

they've got the men that played the Royal Nonesuch, and ask for some witness

-why, you'll have that entire town down here before you can hardly wink, Miss Mary. And they'll come a-biling, too."

I judged we had got everything fixed about right, now. So I says :

"Just let the auction go right along, and don't worry. Nobody don't have pay for the things they buy till a whole day after the auction, on accounts of the short notice, and they ain't going out of this till they get that money—and the way we've fixed it the sale ain't going to count, and they ain't going to *get* no money. It's just like the way it was with the niggers—it warn't no sale, and the niggers will be back before long. Why, they can't collect the money for the *niggers*, yet—they're in the worst kind of a fix, Miss Mary."

"Well," she says, "I'll run down to breakfast now, and then I'll start straight for Mr. Lothrop's."

"'Deed, *that* ain't the ticket, Miss Mary Jane," I says, "by no manner of means ; go *before* breakfast."

"Why ?"

"What did you reckon I wanted you to go at all for, Miss Mary ?"

"Well, I never thought—and come to think, I don't know. What was it ?"

"Why, it's because you ain't one of these leather-face people. I don't want no better book that what your face is. A body can set down and read it off like coarse print. Do you reckon you can go and face your uncles, when they come to kiss you good-morning, and never——"

"There, there, don't ! Yes, I'll go before breakfast—I'll be glad to. And leave my sisters with them ?"

"Yes—never mind about them. They've got to stand it yet a while. They might suspicion something if all of you was to go. I don't want you to see them, nor your sisters, nor nobody in this town—if a neighbor was to ask how is your uncles this morning, your face would tell something. No, you go right along, Miss Mary Jane, and I'll fix it with all of them. I'll tell Miss Susan to give your love to your uncles and say you've went away for a few hours for to get a little rest and change, or to see a friend, and you'll be back to-night or early in the morning."

"Gone to see a friend is all right, but I won't have my love given to them."

"Well, then, it sha'n't be." It was well enough to tell *her* so—no harm in it.

It was only a little thing to do, and no trouble ; and it's the little things th
smoothes people's roads the most, down here below ; it would make Mary Ja
comfortable, and it wouldn't cost nothing. Then I says : "There's one mo
thing—that bag of money."

"Well, they've got that ; and it makes me feel pretty silly to think *how* the
got it."

"No, you're out, there. They hain't got it."

"Why, who's got it ?"

"I wish I knowed, but I don't. I *had* it, because I stole it from them : an
I stole it to give to you ; and I know where I hid it, but I'm afraid it ain
there no more. I'm awful sorry, Miss Mary Jane, I'm just as sorry as I can be
but I done the best I could ; I did, honest. I come nigh getting caught, and
had to shove it into the first place I come to, and run—and it warn't a goo
place."

"Oh, stop blaming yourself—it's too bad to do it, and I won't allow it—yo
couldn't help it ; it wasn't you fault. Where did you hide it ?"

I didn't want to set her to thinking about her troubles again ; and I couldn
seem to get my mouth to tell her what would make her see that corpse laying i

HE WROTE.

the coffin with that bag of money on his stomach. So for a minute I didn't sa
nothing—then I says :

"I'd ruther not *tell* you where I put it, Miss Mary Jane, if you don't min
letting me off ; but I'll write it for you on a piece of paper, and you can read i
along the road to Mr. Lothrop's, if you want to. Do you reckon that'll do ?"

"Oh, yes."

So I wrote: "I put it in the coffin. It was in there when you was crying ᵻere, away in the night. I was behind the door, and I was mighty sorry for ᵒu, Miss Mary Jane."

It made my eyes water a little, to remember her crying there all by herself ᵻ the night, and them devils laying there right under her own roof, shaming ₑr and robbing her ; and when I folded it up and give it to her, I see the water ᵻme into her eyes, too ; and she shook me by the hand, hard, and says :

"*Good*-bye—I'm going to do everything just as you've told me ; and if I ᵒn't ever see you again, I sha'n't ever forget you, and I'll think of you a many ᵻd a many a time, and I'll *pray* for you, too !"—and she was gone.

Pray for me ! I reckoned if she knowed me she'd take a job that was more ₑarer her size. But I bet she done it, just the same—she was just that kind. ᵻe had the grit to pray for Judus if she took the notion—there warn't no back-ᵒwn to her, I judge. You may say what you want to, but in my opinion she ᵻd more sand in her than any girl I ever see ; in my opinion she was just full of ᵻnd. It sounds like flattery, but it ain't no flattery. And when it comes to ₑauty—and goodness too—she lays over them all. I hain't ever seen her since ᵻat time that I see her go out of that door ; no, I hain't ever seen her since, ᵻt I reckon I've thought of her a many and a many a million times, and of her ᵻying she would pray for me ; and if ever I'd a thought it would do any good ᵒr me to pray for *her*, blamed if I wouldn't a done it or bust.

Well, Mary Jane she lit out the back way, I reckon ; because nobody see ₑr go. When I struck Susan and the hare-lip, I says :

"What's the name of them people over on t'other side of the river that you. ll goes to see sometimes ?"

They says :

"There's several ; but it's the Proctors, mainly."

"That's the name," I says ; "I most forgot it. Well, Miss Mary Jane she ᵻld me to tell you she's gone over there in a dreadful hurry—one of them's ᵼk."

"Which one ?"

"I don't know ; leastways I kinder forget ; but I think it's——"

"Sakes alive, I hope it ain't *Hanner?*"

"I'm sorry to say it," I says, "but Hanner's the very one."

"My goodness—and she so well only last week! Is she took bad?"

"It ain't no name for it. They set up with her all night, Miss Mary Jane said, and they don't think she'll last many hours."

"Only think of that, now! What's the matter with her!"

I couldn't think of anything reasonable, right off that way, so I says:

"Mumps."

"Mumps your granny! They don't set up with people that's got the mumps."

"They don't, don't they? You better bet they do with *these* mumps. These mumps is different. It's a new kind, Miss Mary Jane said."

"How's it a new kind?"

"Because it's mixed up with other things."

"What other things?"

"Well, measles, and whooping-cough, and erysiplas, and consumption, and yaller janders, and brain fever, and I don't know what all."

"My land! And they call it the *mumps?*"

"That's what Miss Mary Jane said."

"Well, what in the nation do they call it th mumps for?"

"Why, because it *is* the mumps. That's what it starts with."

HANNER WITH THE MUMPS.

"Well, ther' ain't no sense in it. A body might stump his toe, and take pison and fall down the well, and break his neck, and bust his brains out, and some body come along and ask what killed him, and some numskull up and say, 'Why he stumped his *toe.*' Would ther' be any sense in that? *No.* And ther' ain' no sense in *this*, nuther. Is it ketching?"

"Is it *ketching?* Why, how you talk. Is a *harrow* catching?—in the dark t you don't hitch onto one tooth, you're bound to on another, ain't you? And ou can't get away with that tooth without fetching the whole harrow along, an you? Well, these kind of mumps is a kind of a harrow, as you may say— nd it ain't no slouch of a harrow, nuther, you come to get it hitched on ood."

"Well, it's awful, *I* think," says the hare-lip. "I'll go to Uncle Harvey nd——"

"Oh, yes," I says, "I *would*. Of *course* I would. I wouldn't lose no time."

"Well, why wouldn't you?"

"Just look at it a minute, and maybe you can see. Hain't your uncles bleeged to get along home to England as fast as they can? And do you reckon hey'd be mean enough to go off and leave you to go all that journey by your-elves? *You* know they'll wait for you. So fur, so good. Your uncle Harvey's a reacher, ain't he? Very well, then; is a *preacher* going to deceive a steamboat lerk? is he going to deceive a *ship clerk?*—so as to get them to let Miss Mary ane go aboard? Now *you* know he ain't. What *will* he do, then? Why, he'll ay, 'It's a great pity, but my church matters has got to get along the best way they an; for my niece has been exposed to the dreadful pluribus-unum mumps, and o it's my bounden duty to set down here and wait the three months it takes to now on her if she's got it.' But never mind, if you think it's best to tell your ncle Harvey——"

"Shucks, and stay fooling around here when we could all be having good imes in England whilst we was waiting to find out whether Mary Jane's got it or ot? Why, you talk like a muggins."

"Well, anyway, maybe you better tell some of the neighbors."

"Listen at that, now. You do beat all, for natural stupidity. Can't you ee that *they'd* go and tell? Ther' ain't no way but just to not tell anybody at *all*."

"Well, maybe you're right—yes, I judge you *are* right."

"But I reckon we ought to tell Uncle Harvey she's gone out a while, anyway, o he wont be uneasy about her?"

"Yes, Miss Mary Jane she wanted you to do that. She says, 'Tell them to ;ive Uncle Harvey and William my love and a kiss, and say I've run over the river

to see Mr.—Mr.—what *is* the name of that rich family your uncle Peter use
to think so much of ?—I mean the one that——"

"Why, you must mean the Apthorps, ain't it ?"

THE AUCTION.

"Of course; bother the:
kind of names, a body can
ever seem to remember then
half the time, somehov
Yes, she said, say she has ru
over for to ask the Apthor]
to be sure and come to th
auction and buy this hous
because she allowed her un
cle Peter would ruther the
had it than anybody else
and she's going to stick t
them till they say they'
come, and then, if she ain'
too tired, she's comin
home ; and if she is, she'
be home in the morning any
way. She said, don't sa
nothing about the Proctor:
but only about the Apthor]
—which'll be perfectly tru
because she *is* going there to speak about their buying the house; I know i
because she told me so, herself."

"All right," they said, and cleared out to lay for their uncles, and give ther
the love and the kisses, and tell them the message.

Everything was all right now. The girls wouldn't say nothing because the
wanted to go to England ; and the king and the duke would ruther Mary Jar
was off working for the auction than around in reach of Doctor Robinson. I fe
very good ; I judged I had done it pretty neat—I reckoned Tom Sawyer couldn

done it no neater himself.   Of course he would a throwed more style into it,
but I can't do that very handy, not being brung up to it.

Well, they held the auction in the public square, along towards the end of the
afternoon, and it strung along, and strung along, and the old man he was on
hand and looking his level pisonest, up there longside of the auctioneer, and
chipping in a little Scripture, now and then, or a little goody-goody saying, of
some kind, and the duke he was around goo-gooing for sympathy all he knowed
how, and just spreading himself generly.

But by-and-by the thing dragged through, and everything was sold.   Everything but a little old trifling lot in the graveyard.   So they'd got to work *that*
off—I never see such a girafft as the king was for wanting to swallow *everything*.
Well, whilst they was at it, a steamboat landed, and in about two minutes up
comes a crowd a whooping and yelling and laughing and carrying on, and singing
out :

"*Here's* your opposition line ! here's your two sets o' heirs to old Peter Wilks
—and you pays your money and you takes your choice !"

Chapter XXIX.

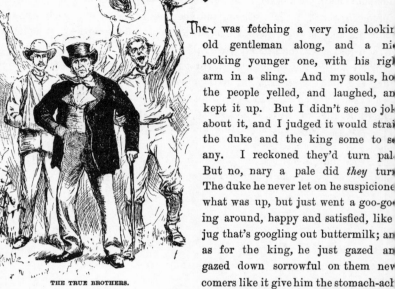

THE TRUE BROTHERS.

They was fetching a very nice lookin old gentleman along, and a ni looking younger one, with his rigl arm in a sling. And my souls, ho the people yelled, and laughed, an kept it up. But I didn't see no jok about it, and I judged it would strai the duke and the king some to se any. I reckoned they'd turn pal But no, nary a pale did *they* tur The duke he never let on he suspicione what was up, but just went a goo-go ing around, happy and satisfied, like jug that's googling out buttermilk; an as for the king, he just gazed an gazed down sorrowful on them new comers like it give him the stomach-ach in his very heart to think there could be such frauds and rascals in th world. Oh, he done it admirable. Lots of the principal people gethered aroun the king, to let him see they was on his side. That old gentleman that ha just come looked all puzzled to death. Pretty soon he begun to speak, an I see, straight off, he pronounced *like* an Englishman, not the king's wa; though the king's *was* pretty good, for an imitation. I can't give the old gent words, nor I can't imitate him; but he turned around to the crowd, and say; about like this :

"This is a surprise to me which I wasn't looking for; and I'll acknowledg

ndid and frank, I ain't very well fixed to meet it and answer it; for my brother
id me has had misfortunes, he's broke his arm, and our baggage got put off at a
wn above here, last night in the night by a mistake. I am Peter Wilks's
other Harvey, and this is his brother Willian, which can't hear nor speak—and
n't even make signs to amount to much, now 't he's only got one hand to work
em with. We are who we say we are; and in a day or two, when I get the
ggage, I can prove it. But, up till then, I won't say nothing more, but go to
e hotel and wait."

So him and the new dummy started off; and the king he laughs, and blethers
it:

"Broke his arm—*very* likely *ain't* it? —and very convenient, too, for a fraud
at's got to make signs, and hain't learnt how. Lost their baggage! That's
ighty good! —and mighty ingenious—under the *circumstances!* "

So he laughed again; and so did everybody else, except three or four, or
aybe half a dozen. One of these was that doctor; another one was a sharp
oking gentleman, with a carpet-bag of the old-fashioned kind made out of car-
t-stuff, that had just come off of the steamboat and was talking to him in a low
ice, and glancing towards the king now and then and nodding their heads—it
as Levi Bell, the lawyer that was gone up to Louisville; and another one was a
g rough husky that come along and listened to all the old gentleman said, and
as listening to the king now. And when the king got done, this husky up
id says:

"Say, looky here; if you are Harvey Wilks, when'd you come to this town?"

"The day before the funeral, friend," says the king.

"But what time o' day?"

"In the evenin'—'bout an hour er two before sundown."

"*How'd* you come?"

"I come down on the *Susan Powell*, from Cincinnati."

"Well, then, how'd you come to be up at the Pint in the *mornin'*—in a
anoe?"

"I warn't up at the Pint in the mornin'."

"It's a lie."

Several of them jumped for him and begged him not to talk that way
an old man and a preacher.

"Preacher be hanged, he's a fraud and a liar.   He was up at the Pi
that mornin'.   I live up there, don't I ?   Well, I was up there, and he was
there.   I *see* him there.   I
come in a canoe, along with Ti
Collins and a boy."

The doctor he up and say
"Would you know the b
again if you was to see hir
Hines ? "

"I reckon I would, but
don't know.   Why, yonder I
is, now.   I know him perfect
easy."

It was me he pointed a
The doctor says :

"Neighbors, I don't kno
whether the new couple is frau
or not ; but if *these* two air
frauds, I am an idiot, that's a
I think it's our duty to see th
they don't get away from he
till we've looked into this thin

THE DOCTOR LEADS HUCK.

Come along, Hines ; come along, the rest of you.   We'll take these fellows to t
tavern and affront them with t'other couple, and I reckon we'll find out *som
thing* before we get through."

It was nuts for the crowd, though maybe not for the king's friends ; so we a
started.   It was about sundown.   The doctor he led me along by the hand, an
was plenty kind enough, but he never let *go* my hand.

We all got in a big room in the hotel, and lit up some candles, and fetched i
the new couple.   First, the doctor says :

" I don't wish to be too hard on these two men, but *I* think they're frauds, d they may have complices that we don't know nothing about. If they have, n't the complices get away with that bag of gold Peter Wilks left ? It ain't likely. If these men ain't frauds, they won't object to sending for that money d letting us keep it till they prove they're all right—ain't that so ? "

Everybody agreed to that. So I judged they had our gang in a pretty tight ace, right at the outstart. But the king he only looked sorrowful, and says :

" Gentlemen, I wish the money was there, for I ain't got no disposition to row anything in the way of a fair, open, out-and-out investigation o' this sable business ; but alas, the money ain't there ; you k'n send and see, if you nt to."

" Where is it, then ? "

" Well, when my niece give it to me to keep for her, I took and hid it inside the straw tick o' my bed, not wishin' to bank it for the few days we'd be here, d considerin' the bed a safe place, we not bein' used to niggers, and suppos'n' n honest, like servants in England. The niggers stole it the very next mornin' ter I had went down stairs ; and when I sold 'em, I hadn't missed the money t, so they got clean away with it. My servant here k'n tell you 'bout it gentle- en."

The doctor and several said " Shucks ! " and I see nobody didn't altogether be- ve him. One man asked me if I see the niggers steal it. I said no, but I see em sneaking out of the room and hustling away, and I never thought nothing, ly I reckoned they was afraid they had waked up my master and was trying to t away before he made trouble with them. That was all they asked me. Then e doctor whirls on me and says :

" Are *you* English too ? "

I says yes ; and him and some others laughed, and said, " Stuff ! "

Well, then they sailed in on the general investigation, and there we had it, up d down, hour in, hour out, and nobody never said a word about supper, nor er seemed to think about it—and so they kept it up, and kept it up ; and it as the worst mixed-up thing you ever see. They made the king tell his yarn, d they made the old gentleman tell his'n ; and anybody but a lot of prejudiced

chuckleheads would a *seen* that the old gentleman was spinning truth and t'oth
one lies. And by-and-by they had me up to tell what I knowed. The king
give me a left-handed look out of the corner of his eye, and so I knowed enou;
to talk on the right side. I begun to tell about Sheffield, and how we lived ther
and all about the English Wilkses, and so on ; but I didn't get pretty fur till t
doctor begun to laugh; and Levi Bell, the lawyer, says :

"Set down, my boy, I wouldn't strain myself, if I was you. I reckon y
ain't used to lying, it don't seem to come handy ; what you want is practic
You do it pretty awkward."

I didn't care nothing for the compliment, but I was glad to be let o
anyway.

The doctor he started to say something, and turns and says :

"If you'd been in town at first, Levi Bell——"

The king broke in and reached out his hand, and says :

"Why, is this my poor dead brother's old friend that he's wrote so often about?

The lawyer and him shook hands, and the lawyer smiled and looked please
and they talked right along a while, and then got to one side and talked low
and at last the lawyer speaks up and says :

"That'll fix it. I'll take the order and send it, along with your brother'
and then they'll know it's all right."

So they got some paper and a pen, and the king he set down and twisted b
head to one side, and chawed his tongue, and scrawled off something ; and the
they give the pen to the duke—and then for the first time, the duke looked sic
But he took the pen and wrote. So then the lawyer turns to the new old gentl
man and says :

"You and your brother please write a line or two and sign your names."

The old gentleman wrote, but nobody couldn't read it. The lawyer look
powerful astonished, and says :

"Well, it beats *me*"—and snaked a lot of old letters out of his pocket, an
examined them, and then examined the old man's writing, and then *them* agair
and then says : "These old letters is from Harvey Wilks ; and here's *these* two
handwritings, and anybody can see *they* didn't write them" (the king and th

ke looked sold and foolish, I tell you, to see how the lawyer had took them in),
nd here's *this* old gentleman's handwriting, and anybody can tell, easy enough,
didn't write them—fact is, the scratches he makes **ain't** properly *writing*,
all.   Now here's some letters
m——"

The new old gentleman says:
" If you please, let me explain.
body can read my hand but my
other there—so he copies for me.
's *his* hand you've got there,
t mine."

" *Well !* " says the lawyer, "this
a state of things.   I've got some
William's letters too; so if you'll
t him to write a line or so we
n com——"

THE DUKE WROTE.

" He *can't* write with his left hand," says the old gentleman.   " If he could
e his right hand, you would see that he wrote his own letters and mine too.
ok at both, please—they're by the same hand."

The lawyer done it, and says :

" I believe it's so—and if it ain't so, there's a heap stronger resemblance than
I noticed before, anyway.   Well, well, well ! I thought we was right on the track
a slution, but it's gone to grass, partly.   But anyway, *one* thing is proved—
ese two ain't either of 'em Wilkses "—and he wagged his head towards the king
d the duke.

Well, what do you think ?—that muleheaded old fool wouldn't give in *then!*
deed he wouldn't.   Said it warn't no fair test.   Said his brother William was
e cussedest joker in the world, and hadn't *tried* to write—*he* see William was
ing to play one of his jokes the minute he put the pen to paper.   And so he
armed up and went warbling and warbling right along, till he was actuly be-
nning to believe what he was saying, *himself*—but pretty soon the new old
entleman broke in, and says :

" I've thought of something. Is there anybody here that helped to lay o
my br—helped to lay out the late Peter Wilks for burying ? "

" Yes," says somebody, " me and Ab Turner done it.   We're both here."

Then the old man turns towards the king, and says :

" Peraps this gentleman can tell me what was tatooed on his breast ? "

Blamed if the king didn't have to brace up mighty quick, or he'd
squshed down like a bluff bank that the river has cut under, it took him so su
den—and mind you, it was a thing that was calculated to make most *anybo*
sqush to get fetched such a solid one as that without any notice—because how w
he going to know what was tatooed on the man? He whitened a little; he could
help it ; and it was mighty still in there, and everybody bending a little forwar
and gazing at him.   Says I to myself, *Now* he'll throw up the sponge—there ai
no more use.   Well, did he?   A body can't hardly believe it, but he didn't.
reckon he thought he'd keep the thing up till he tired them people out, so they
thin out, and him and the duke could break loose and get away.   Anyway, he s
there, and pretty soon he begun to smile, and says :

" Mf !   It's a *very* tough question, *ain't* it !   *Yes,* sir, I k'n tell you wha
tatooed on his breast.   It's jest a small, thin, blue arrow—that's what it is ; a
if you don't look clost, you can't see it.   *Now* what do you say—hey? "

Well, *I* never see anything like that old blister for clean out-and-out cheek.

The new old gentleman turns brisk towards Ab Turner and his pard, and I
eye lights up like he judged he'd got the king *this* time, and says :

" There—you've heard what he said !   Was there any such mark on Pet
Wilks's breast ? "

Both of them spoke up and says :

" We didn't see no such mark."

" Good ! " says the old gentleman.   " Now, what you *did* see on b
breast was a small dim P, and a B (which is an initial he dropped when he w
young), and a W, with dashes between them, so : P—B—W "—and he mark
them that way on a piece of paper.   " Come—ain't that what you saw? "

Both of them spoke up again, and says :

" No, we *didn't*.   We never seen any marks at all."

Well, everybody *was* in a state of mind, now ; and they sings out :

"The whole *bilin'* of 'm 's frauds ! Le's duck 'em ! le's drown 'em ! le's
[l]e 'em on a rail !" and everybody was whooping at once, and there was a rat-
[i]ng pow-wow. But the lawyer he jumps on the table and yells, and says :

"Gentlemen—gentle*men !* Hear
[m]e just a word—just a *single* word—
[if] you PLEASE! There's one way yet
[—]let's go and dig up the corpse and
[loo]k."

That took them.

"Hooray!" they all shouted, and
[wa]s starting right off ; but the lawyer
[an]d the doctor sung out :

"Hold on, hold on ! Collar all
[th]ese four men and the boy, and
[fet]ch *them* along, too !"

"We'll do it !" they all shouted:
[and if] we don't find them marks
[we]'ll lynch the whole gang !"

I *was* scared, now, I tell you.
[Bu]t there warn't no getting away,
[yo]u know. They gripped us all, and
[m]arched us right along, straight for

[th]e graveyard, which was a mile and a half down the river, and the whole town
[at] our heels, for we made noise enough, and it was only nine in the evening.

As we went by our house I wished I hadn't sent Mary Jane out of town ; be-
[ca]use now if I could tip her the wink, she'd light out and save me, and blow on
[ou]r dead-beats.

Well, we swarmed along down the river road, just carrying on like wild-cats ;
[an]d to make it more scary, the sky was darking up, and the lightning beginning
[to] wink and flitter, and the wind to shiver amongst the leaves. This was the
[m]ost awful trouble and most dangersome I ever was in; and I was kinder stunned ;

everything was going so different from what I had allowed for ; stead of bei
fixed so I could take my own time, if I wanted to, and see all the fun, and ha
Mary Jane at my back to save me and set me free when the close-fit come, he
was nothing in the world betwixt me and sudden death but just them tatc
marks. If they didn't find them—

I couldn't bear to think about it ; and yet, somehow, I couldn't think abo
nothing else. It got darker and darker, and it was a beautiful time to give t
crowd the slip; but that big husky had me by the wrist—Hines—and a bo
might as well try to give Goliar the slip. He dragged me right along, he was
excited; and I had to run to keep up.

When they got there they swarmed into the graveyard and washed over it li
an overflow. And when they got to the grave, they found they had about
hundred times as many shovels as they wanted, but nobody hadn't thought
fetch a lantern. But they sailed into digging, anyway, by the flicker of t
lightning, and sent a man to the nearest house a half a mile off, to borrow one.

So they dug and dug, like everything ; and it got awful dark, and the ra
started, and the wind swished and swushed along, and the lightning come brisk
and brisker, and the thunder boomed; but them people never took no notice
it, they was so full of this business; and one minute you could see everything ar
every face in that big crowd, and the shovelfuls of dirt sailing up out of the grav
and the next second the dark wiped it all out, and you couldn't see nothing at a

At last they got out the coffin, and begun to unscrew the lid, and the
such another crowding, and shouldering, and shoving as there was, to scroug
in and get a sight, you never see ; and in the dark, that way, it was awfu
Hines he hurt my wrist dreadful, pulling and tugging so, and I reckon he clea
forgot I was in the world, he was so excited and panting.

All of a sudden the lightning let go a perfect sluice of white glare, and som
body sings out :

" By the living jingo, here's the bag of gold on his breast ! "

Hines let out a whoop, like everybody else, and dropped my wrist and give
big surge to bust his way in and get a look, and the way I lit out and shinne
for the road in the dark, there ain't nobody can tell.

I had the road all to myself, and I fairly flew—leastways I had it all to myself
ept the solid dark, and the now and-then glares, and the buzzing of the rain,
l the thrashing of the wind, and the splitting of the thunder; and sure as you
born I did clip it along!

When I struck the town, I see there warn't nobody out in the storm, so I
er hunted for no back streets, but humped it straight through the main one;
l when I begun to get towards our house I aimed my eye and set it. No light
re; the house all dark—which made me feel sorry and disappointed, I didn't
w why. But at last, just as I was sailing by, *flash* comes the light in Mary
e's window! and my heart swelled up sudden, like to bust; and the same
ond the house and all was behind me in the dark, and wasn't ever going to be
ore me no more in this world. She *was* the best girl I ever see, and had the
st sand.

The minute I was far enough above the town to see I could make the tow-
d, I begun to look sharp for a boat to borrow; and the first time the lightning
wed me one that wasn't chained, I snatched it and shoved. It was a canoe,
l warn't fastened with nothing but a rope. The towhead was a rattling big
tance off, away out there in the middle of the river, but I didn't lose no time;
l when I struck the raft at last, I was so fagged I would a just laid down
blow and gasp if I could afforded it. But I didn't. As I sprung aboard
ung out:

"Out with you Jim, and set her loose! Glory be to goodness, we're shut
hem!"

Jim lit out, and was a coming for me with both arms spread, he was so
l of joy; but when I glimpsed him in the lightning, my heart shot up in my
uth, and I went overboard backwards; for I forgot he was old King Lear
l a drownded A-rab all in one, and it most scared the livers and lights out
me. But Jim fished me out, and was going to hug me and bless me, and
on, he was so glad I was back and we was shut of the king and the duke,
I says:

"Not now—have it for breakfast, have it for breakfast! Cut loose and let
slide!"

So, in two seconds, away we went, a sliding down the river, and it *did* se

"JIM LET OUT."

so good to be free again a
all by ourselves on the
river and nobody to bot
us. I had to skip aroun
bit, and jump up and cra
my heels a few times, I could
help it; but about the th
crack, I noticed a sound tha
knowed mighty well—and h
my breath and listened a
waited—and sure enough, wh
the next flash busted out o
the water, here they come
and just a laying to their o
and making their skiff hu
It was the king and the duk

So I wilted right down o
the planks, then, and give u
and it was all I could do
keep from crying.

Chapter XXX

When they got aboard, the king went for me, and shook me by the collar, and says:

"Tryin' to give us the slip, was ye, you pup! Tired of our company —hey?"

I says:

"No, your majesty, we warn't— *please* don't, your majesty!"

"Quick, then, and tell us what *was* your idea, or I'll shake the insides out o' you!"

THE KING SHAKES HUCK.

"Honest, I'll tell you everything, just as it happened, your majesty. The man that had aholt of me was very good to me, and kept saying he had a boy about as big as me that died last year, and he was sorry to see a boy in such a dangerous fix; and when they was all took by surprise by finding the gold, and made a rush for the coffin, he lets go of me and whispers, 'Heel it, now, or they'll hang ye, sure!' and I lit out. It didn't seem no good for *me* to stay—I couldn't do nothing, and I didn't want to be hung if I could get away. So I never stopped running till I found the canoe; and when I got here I told Jim to hurry, or they'd catch me and hang me yet, and said I was afeard you and the duke wasn't alive, now, and

I was awful sorry, and so was Jim, and was awful glad when we see you com
you may ask Jim if I didn't."

Jim said it was so ; and the king told him to shut up, and said, " Oh,
it's *mighty* likely !" and shook me up again, and said he reckoned he'd drov
me. But the duke says :

"Leggo the boy, you old idiot ! Would *you* a done any different ? Did
inquire around for *him*, when you got loose ? *I* don't remember it."

So the king let go of me, and begun to cuss that town and everybody in
But the duke says :

"You better a blame sight give *yourself* a good cussing, for you're the
that's entitled to it most. You hain't done a thing, from the start, that 1
any sense in it, except coming out so cool and cheeky with that imaginary b
arrow mark. That *was* bright—it was right down bully ; and it was the th
that saved us. For if it hadn't been for that, they'd a jailed us till them Engl
men's baggage come—and then—the penitentiary, you bet ! But that trick t
'em to the graveyard, and the gold done us a still bigger kindness ; for if
excited fools hadn't let go all holts and made that rush to get a look, we'd a slep
our cravats to-night—cravats warranted to *wear*, too—longer than *we'd* need 'e

They was still a minute—thinking—then the king says, kind of absc
minded like :

"Mf ! And we reckoned the *niggers* stole it !"

That made me squirm !

"Yes," says the duke, kinder slow, and deliberate, and sarcastic, " *We* di
After about a half a minute, the king drawls out :

"Leastways—*I* did."

The duke says, the same way :

"On the contrary—*I* did."

The king kind of ruffles up, and says :

"Looky here, Bilgewater, what'r you referrin' to ? "

The duke says, pretty brisk :

"When it comes to that, maybe you'll let me ask, what was *you* ref
ring to ?"

"Shucks!" says the king, very sarcastic; "but *I* don't know—maybe you
s asleep, and didn't know what you was about."

The duke bristles right up, now, and says:

"Oh, let *up* on this cussed nonsense—do you take me for a blame' fool?
n't you reckon *I* know who hid that money in that coffin?"

"*Yes,* sir! I know you *do* know—because you done it yourself!"

"It's a lie!"—and the duke went for him. The king sings out:

THE DUKE WENT FOR HIM.

"Take y'r hands off!—leggo my throat!—I take it all back!"

The duke says:

"Well, you just own up, first, that you *did* hide that money there, intending
give me the slip one of these days, and come back and dig it up, and have it
to yourself."

"Wait jest a minute, duke—answer me this one question, honest and fair;
you didn't put the money there, say it, and I'll b'lieve you, and take back
rything I said."

"You old scoundrel, I didn't, and you know I didn't. There, now!"

"Well, then, I b'lieve you. But answer me only jest this one more—now

don't git mad ; didn't you have it in your *mind* to hook the money a
hide it ? "

The duke never said nothing for a little bit ; then he says :

"Well—I don't care if I *did*, I didn't *do* it, anyway.   But you not only l
it in mind to do it, but you *done* it."

" I wisht I may never die if I done it, duke, and that's honest.   I won't sa
warn't *goin'* to do it, because I *was ;* but you—I mean somebody—got in ah
o' me."

"It's a lie !   You done it, and you got to *say* you done it, or—— "

The king begun to gurgle, and then he gasps out :

" 'Nough !—*I own up !* "

I was very glad to hear him say that, it made me feel much more easier th
what I was feeling before.   So the duke took his hands off, and says :

"If you ever deny it again, I'll drown you.   It's *well* for you to set there a
blubber like a baby—it's fitten for you, after the way you've acted.   I never
such an old ostrich for wanting to gobble everything—and I a trusting you all t
time, like you was my own father.   You ought to been ashamed of yourself
stand by and hear it saddled onto a lot of poor niggers and you never say a wc
for 'em.   It makes me feel ridiculous to think I was soft enough to *believe* tl
rubbage.   Cuss you, I can see, now, why you was so anxious to make up t
deffesit—you wanted to get what money I'd got out of the Nonesuch and c
thing or another, and scoop it *all !* "

The king says, timid, and still a snuffling :

"Why, duke, it was you that said make up the deffersit, it war
me."

"Dry up !   I don't want to hear no more *out* of you !" says the duke.   "A
now you see what you *got* by it.   They've got all their own money back, and
of *ourn* but a shekel or two, *besides.*   G'long to bed—and don't you deffersit
no more deffersits, long 's *you* live ! "

So the king sneaked into the wigwam, and took to his bottle for comfort ; a
before long the duke tackled *his* bottle ; and so in about a half an hour they v
as thick as thieves again, and the tighter they got, the lovinger they got ; a

nt off a snoring in each other's arms. They both got powerful mellow, but I
ticed the king didn't get mellow enough to forget to remember to not deny
ut hiding the money-bag again. That made me feel easy and satisfied. Of
rse when they got to snoring, we had a long gabble, and I told Jim every-
ng.

Chapter XXXI

SPANISH MOSS.

We dasn't stop again at any town, days and days; kept right alo down the river. We was down sou in the warm weather, now, and mighty long ways from home. begun to come to trees with Spani moss on them, hanging down fr the limbs like long gray beards. was the first I ever see it growin and it made the woods look soler and dismal. So now the frau reckoned they was out of dang and they begun to work the villag again.

First they done a lecture temperance; but they didn't ma enough for them both to drunk on. Then in another villa they started a dancing school; but they didn't know no more how to dance th a kangaroo does; so the first prance they made, the general public jumped and pranced them out of town. Another time they tried a go at yellocutio but they didn't yellocute long till the audience got up and give them a solid g cussing and made them skip out. They tackled missionarying, and mesmeriz ing, and doctoring, and telling fortunes, and a little of everything; but th couldn't seem to have no luck. So at last they got just about dead broke, a

l around the raft, as she floated along, thinking, and thinking, and never
ing nothing, by the half a day at a time, and dreadful blue and desperate.

And at last they took a change, and begun to lay their heads together in the
ʒwam and talk low and confidential two or three hours at a time. Jim and
got uneasy. We didn't like the look of it. We judged they was studying
some kind of worse deviltry than ever. We turned it over and over, and at
t we made up our minds they was going to break into somebody's house or
re, or was going into the counterfeit-money business, or something. So then
was pretty scared, and made up an agreement that we wouldn't have nothing
the world to do with such actions, and if we ever got the least show we would
e them the cold shake, and clear out and leave them behind. Well, early one
rning we hid the raft in a good safe place about two mile below a little bit of
habby village, named Pikesville, and the king he went ashore, and told us all
stay hid whilst he went up to town and smelt around to see if anybody had got
ʳ wind of the Royal Nonesuch there yet. ("House to rob, you *mean*," says I to
self; "and when you get through robbing it you'll come back here and won-
ʳ what's become of me and Jim and the raft—and you'll have to take it out in
ndering.") And he said if he warn't back by midday, the duke and me would
ɔw it was all right, and we was to come along.

So we staid where we was. The duke he fretted and sweated around, and
ʒ in a mighty sour way. He scolded us for everything, and we couldn't seem
do nothing right; he found fault with every little thing. Something was
ʳewing, sure. I was good and glad when midday come and no king; we could
ʳe a change, anyway—and maybe a chance for *the* change, on top of it. So
and the duke went up to the village, and hunted around there for the king,
ɩ by-and-by we found him in the back room of a little low doggery, very tight,
ɩ a lot of loafers bullyragging him for sport, and he a cussing and threatening
h all his might, and so tight he couldn't walk, and couldn't do nothing to
m. The duke he begun to abuse him for an old fool, and the king begun to
ʒ back; and the minute they was fairly at it, I lit out, and shook the reefs out
ny hind legs, and spun down the river road like a deer—for I see our chance;
ɩ I made up my mind that it would be a long day before they ever see me and

Jim again.   I got down there all out of breath but loaded up with joy, and su
out—

"Set her loose, Jim, we're all right, now ! "

But there warn't no answer, and nobody come out of the wigwam.   Jim v
gone !   I set up a shout—and then another—and then another one ; and run t
way and that in the woods, whooping and screeching ; but it warn't no use—
Jim was gone.   Then I set down and cried ; I couldn't help it.   But I could
set still long.   Pretty soon I went out on the road, trying to think what I bet
do, and I run across a boy walking, and asked him if he'd seen a strange nigg
dressed so and so, and he says :

"Yes."

"Whereabouts ? " says I.

"Down to Silas Phelps's place, two mile below here.   He's a runaway nigg
and they've got him.   Was you looking for him ? "

"You bet I ain't !   I run across him in the woods about an hour or two a
and he said if I hollered he'd cut my livers out—and told me to lay down a
stay where I was ; and I done it.   Been there ever since ; afeard to come out."

"Well," he says, " you needn't be afeard no more, becuz they've got hi
He run off f'm down South, som'ers."

"It's a good job they got him."

"Well, I *reckon !*   There's two hunderd dollars reward on him.   It's l
picking up money out'n the road."

"Yes, it is—and *I* could a had it if I'd been big enough ; I see him *fir*
Who nailed him ? "

"It was an old fellow—a stranger—and he sold out his chance in him
forty dollars, becuz he's got to go up the river and can't wait.   Think o' th
now !   You bet *I'd* wait, if it was seven year."

"That's me, every time," says I.   " But maybe his chance ain't worth
more than that, if he'll sell it so cheap.   Maybe there's something ain't strai;
about it."

"But it *is*, though—straight as a string.   I see the handbill myself.   It t
all about him, to a dot—paints him like a picture, and tells the plantation h

m, below Newr*leans.* No-sirree-*bob*, they ain't no trouble 'bout *that* specu-
ion, you bet you. Say, gimme a chaw tobacker, won't ye ?"

I didn't have none, so he left. I went to the raft, and set down in the
gwam to think. But I couldn't come to nothing. I thought till I wore my head
e, but I couldn't see no way
t of the trouble. After all
s long journey, and after
we'd done for them scoun-
els, here was it all come to
thing, everything all busted
and ruined, because they
ild have the heart to serve
n such a trick as that, and
ke him a slave again all his
e, and amongst strangers,
, for forty dirty dollars.

Once I said to myself it
uld be a thousand times
tter for Jim to be a slave
home where his family
s, as long as he'd *got* to be
lave, and so I'd better
ite a letter to Tom Sawyer
l tell him to tell Miss
atson where he was. But
oon give up that notion,

" WHO NAILED HIM ? "

two things : she'd be mad and disgusted at his rascality and ungratefulness
leaving her, and so she'd sell him straight down the river again ; and if she
n't, everybody naturally despises an ungrateful nigger, and they'd make
n feel it all the time, and so he'd feel ornery and disgraced. And then think of
! It would get all around, that Huck Finn helped a nigger to get his
edom ; and if I was to ever see anybody from that town again, I'd be ready to

get down and lick his boots for shame. That's just the way : a person doe
low-down thing, and then he don't want to take no consequences of it. Thir
as long as he can hide it, it ain't no disgrace. That was my fix exactly. 1
more I studied about this, the more my conscience went to grinding me, and 1
more wicked and low-down and ornery I got to feeling. And at last, when it
me all of a sudden that here was the plain hand of Providence slapping me
the face and letting me know my wickedness was being watched all the time fr
up there in heaven, whilst I was stealing a poor old woman's nigger that had
ever done me no harm, and now was showing me there's One that's always on 1
lookout, and ain't agoing to allow no such miserable doings to go only just so
and no further, I most dropped in my tracks I was so scared. Well, I tried 1
best I could to kinder soften it up somehow for myself, by saying I was brung
wicked, and so I warn't so much to blame ; but something inside of me kept s
ing, " There was the Sunday school, you could a gone to it ; and if you'd a d(
it they'd a learnt you, there, that people that acts as I'd been acting about t
nigger goes to everlasting fire."

It made me shiver. And I about made up my mind to pray ; and see i
couldn't try to quit being the kind of a boy I was, and be better. So I knee
down. But the words wouldn't come. Why wouldn't they ? It warn't no i
to try and hide it from Him. Nor from *me,* neither. I knowed very well w
they wouldn't come. It was because my heart warn't right ; it was because
warn't square ; is was because I was playing double. I was letting *on* to give
sin, but away inside of me I was holding on to the biggest one of all. I 1
trying to make my mouth *say* I would do the right thing and the clean thin
and go and write to that nigger's owner and tell where he was ; but deep do
in me I knowed it was a lie—and He knowed it. You can't pray a lie—I fou
that out.

So I was full of trouble, full as I could be ; and didn't know what to do.
last I had an idea ; and I says, I'll go and write the letter—and *then* see if I (
pray. Why, it was astonishing, the way I felt as light as a feather, right strai;
off, and my troubles all gone. So I got a piece of paper and a pencil, all g
and excited, and set down and wrote :

Miss Watson your runaway nigger Jim is down here two mile below Pikesville and Mr.
elps has got him and he will give him up for the reward if you send.   HUCK FINN.

I felt good and all washed clean of sin for the first time I had ever felt so in
life, and I knowed I could pray now.   But I didn't do it straight off, but

THINKING.

d the paper down and set
re thinking—thinking how
od it was all this happened
and how near I come to
ng lost and going to hell.
d went on thinking.   And
t to thinking over our trip
wn the river; and I see
m before me, all the time,
the day, and in the night-
e, sometimes moonlight,
metimes storms, and we a
ating along, talking, and
ging, and laughing.   But
nehow I couldn't seem to
ike no places to harden me
ainst him, but only the
her kind.   I'd see him
nding my watch on top of
'n, stead of calling me, so I could go on sleeping; and see him how glad he
s when I come back out of the fog; and when I come to him again in the
amp, up there where the feud was; and such-like times; and would always
l me honey, and pet me, and do everything he could think of for me, and how
od he always was; and at last I struck the time I saved him by telling the men
had small-pox aboard, and he was so grateful, and said I was the best friend
Jim ever had in the world, and the *only* one he's got now; and then l
ppened to look around, and see that paper.

It was a close place. I took it up, and held it in my hand. I was trembling, because I'd got to decide, forever, betwixt two things, and knowed it. I studied a minute, sort of holding my breath, and then says myself :

" All right, then, I'll *go* to hell "—and tore it up.

It was awful thoughts, and awful words, but they was said. And I let the stay said ; and never thought no more about reforming. I shoved the wh thing out of my head ; and said I would take up wickedness again, which w in my line, being brung up to it, and the other warn't. And for a starter would go to work and steal Jim out of slavery again ; and if I could think anything worse, I would do that, too; because as long as I was in, and in good, I might as well go the whole hog.

Then I set to thinking over how to get at it, and turned over considerab many ways in my mind ; and at last fixed up a plan that suited me. So then took the bearings of a woody island that was down the river a piece, and as so as it was fairly dark I crept out with my raft and went for it, and hid it the and then turned in. I slept the night through, and got up before it was ligh and had my breakfast, and put on my store clothes, and tied up some others a one thing or another in a bundle, and took the canoe and cleared for sho I landed below where I judged was Phelps's place, and hid my bundle in t woods, and then filled up the canoe with water, and loaded rocks into her a sunk her where I could find her again when I wanted her, about a quarter of mile below a little steam sawmill that was on the bank.

Then I struck up the road, and when I passed the mill I see a sign on " Phelps's Sawmill," and when I come to the farm-houses, two or three hundr yards further along, I kept my eyes peeled, but didn't see nobody around, thou it was good daylight, now. But I didn't mind, because I didn't want to s nobody just yet—I only wanted to get the lay of the land. According to r plan, I was going to turn up there from the village, not from below. So I ju took a look, and shoved along, straight for town. Well, the very first man I se when I got there, was the duke. He was sticking up a bill for the Royal Nom such—three-night performance—like that other time. *They* had the chee

em frauds ! I was right on him, before I could shirk. He looked astonished,
d says :

"Hel-*lo !* Where'd *you* come from ?" Then he says, kind of glad and eager,
Where's the raft ?—got her in a good place ?"

I says :

"Why, that's just what I was agoing to ask your grace."

Then he didn't look so joyful—and says :

"What was your idea for asking *me ?* " he says.

"Well," I says, "when I see the king in that doggery yesterday, I says to my-
f, we can't get him home for hours, till he's soberer ; so I went a loafing
ound town to put in the time, and wait. A man up and offered me ten cents
help him pull a skiff over the river and back to fetch a sheep, and so I went
ong ; but when we was dragging him to the boat, and the man left me aholt of
e rope and went behind him to shove him along, he was too strong for me, and
ked loose and run, and we after him. We didn't have no dog, and so we had
chase him all over the country till we tired him out. We never got him till
rk, then we fetched him over, and I started down for the raft. When I got
ere and see it was gone, I says to myself, 'they've got into trouble and had to
ve ; and they've took my nigger, which is the only nigger I've got in the world,
d now I'm in a strange country, and ain't got no property no more, nor noth-
g, and no way to make my living ;' so I set down and cried. I slept in the
ods all night. But what *did* become of the raft then ?—and Jim, poor Jim !"

"Blamed if *I* know—that is, what's become of the raft. That old fool had
ade a trade and got forty dollars, and when we found him in the doggery the
afers had matched half dollars with him and got every cent but what he'd spent
r whisky ; and when I got him home late last night and found the raft gone,
 said, 'That little rascal has stole our raft and shook us, and run off down the
er.'"

"I wouldn't shake my *nigger*, would I ?—the only nigger I had in the world,
d the only property."

"We never thought of that. Fact is, I reckon we'd come to consider him
r nigger ; yes, we did consider him so—goodness knows we had trouble enough

for him.   So when we see the raft was gone, and we flat broke, there warn't an
thing for it but to try the Royal Nonesuch another shake.   And I've pegg

HE GAVE HIM TEN CENTS.

along ever since, dry as a powd
horn.   Where's that ten cent
Give it here."

I had considerable money,
I give him ten cents, but begg
him to spend it for something
eat, and give me some, becau
it was all the money I had, and
hadn't had nothing to eat sir
yesterday.   He never said not
ing.   The next minute
whirls on me and says :

"Do you reckon that nigg
would blow on us ?   We'd sk
him if he done that !"

"How can he blow ?   Hair
he run off ?"

"No !   That old fool so
him, and   never divided wi
me, and the money's gone."

"*Sold* him ?"   I says, a
begun to cry ;   "why, he was *my* nigger, and that was my money.   Where
he ?—I want my nigger."

"Well, you can't *get* your nigger, that's all—so dry up your blubberin
Looky here—do you think *you'd* venture to blow on us ?   Blamed if I think I
trust you.   Why, if you *was* to blow on us——"

He stopped, but I never see the duke look so ugly out of his eyes before.
went on a-whimpering, and says :

"I don't want to blow on nobody ; and I ain't got no time to blow, nohow.
got to turn out and find my nigger."

He looked kinder bothered, and stood there with his bills fluttering on his arm, thinking, and wrinkling up his forehead. At last he says :

"I'll tell you something. We got to be here three days. If you'll promise you won't blow, and won't let the nigger blow, I'll tell you where to find him."

So I promised, and he says :

"A farmer by the name of Silas Ph——" and then he stopped. You see he started to tell me the truth ; but when he stopped, that way, and begun to study and think again, I reckoned he was changing his mind. And so he was. He

STRIKING FOR THE BACK COUNTRY.

wouldn't trust me ; he wanted to make sure of having me out of the way the whole three days. So pretty soon he says : "The man that bought him is named Abram Foster—Abram G. Foster—and he lives forty mile back here in the country, on the road to Lafayette."

"All right," I says, "I can walk it in three days. And I'll start this very afternoon."

"No you won't, you'll start *now*; and don't you lose any time about it, neither, nor do any gabbling by the way. Just keep a tight tongue in your head and move right along, and then you won't get into trouble with *us*, d'ye hear ? "

That was the order I wanted, and that was the one I played for. I wanted t be left free to work my plans.

"So clear out," he says; "and you can tell Mr. Foster whatever you want t Maybe you can get him to believe that Jim *is* your nigger—some idiots don require documents—leastways I've heard there's such down South here. An when you tell him the handbill and the reward's bogus, maybe he'll believe yo when you explain to him what the idea was for getting 'em out. Go 'long, now and tell him anything you want to; but mind you don't work your jaw an *between* here and there."

So I left, and struck for the back country. I didn't look around, but kinder felt like he was watching me. But I knowed I could tire him out at that I went straight out in the country as much as a mile, before I stopped; then doubled back through the woods towards Phelps's. I reckoned I better start i on my plan straight off, without fooling around, because I wanted to stop Jim' mouth till these fellows could get away. I didn't want no trouble with thei kind. I'd seen all I wanted to of them, and wanted to get entirely shut o them.

Chapter XXXII

STILL AND SUNDAY LIKE.

When I got there it was all still and Sunday-like, and hot and sunshiny—the hands was gone to the fields ; and there was them kind of faint dronings of bugs and flies in the air that makes it seem so lonesome and like everybody's dead and gone ; and if a breeze fans along and quivers the leaves, it makes you feel mournful, because you feel like it's spirits whispering—spirits that's been dead ever so many years—and you always think they're talking about *you*. As a general thing it makes a body wish *he* was dead, too, and done with it all.

Phelps's was one of these little one-horse cotton plantations ; and they all look alike. A rail fence round a two-acre yard ; a stile, made out of logs sawed off and up-ended, in steps, like barrels of a different length, to climb over the fence with, and for the women to stand on when they are going to jump onto a horse ; some sickly grass-patches in the big yard, but mostly it was bare and smooth, like an old hat with the nap rubbed off ; big double log house for the white folks—hewed logs, with the chinks stopped up with mud or mortar, and these mud-stripes been whitewashed some time or another ; round-log kitchen, with a big broad, open but roofed passage joining it to the house ; log smoke-house

back of the kitchen ; three little log nigger-cabins in a row t'other side the smok
house ; one little hut all by itself away down against the back fence, and some ou
buildings down a piece the other side ; ash-hopper, and big kettle to bile soap in, t
the little hut ; bench by the kitchen door, with bucket of water and a gourd ; houn
asleep there, in the sun ; more hounds asleep, round about ; about three shad
trees away off in a corner ; some currant bushes and gooseberry bushes in one plac
by the fence ; outside of the fence a garden and a water-melon patch ; then th
cotton fields begins ; and after the fields, the woods.

I went around and clumb over the back stile by the ash-hopper, and started fo
the kitchen. When I got a little ways, I heard the dim hum of a spinning-whee
wailing along up and sinking along down again ; and then I knowed for certai
I wished I was dead—for that *is* the lonesomest sound in the whole world.

I went right along, not fixing up any particular plan, but just trusting to Provi
dence to put the right words in my mouth when the time come ; for I'd notice
that Providence always did put the right words in my mouth, if I left it alone.

When I got half-way, first one hound and then another got up and went fo
me, and of course I stopped and faced them, and kept still.   And such anothe
pow-wow as they made ! In a quarter of a minute I was a kind of a hub of
wheel, as you may say—spokes made out of dogs—circle of fifteen of them packe
together around me, with their necks and noses stretched up towards me, a bark
ing and howling ; and more a coming ; you could see them sailing over fence
and around corners from everywheres.

A nigger woman come tearing out of the kitchen with a rolling-pin in her hand
singing out, " Begone ! *you* Tige ! you Spot ! begone, sah ! " and she fetched firs
one and then another of them a clip and sent him howling, and then the rest fol
lowed ; and the next second, half of them come back, wagging their tails aroun
me and making friends with me.   There ain't no harm in a hound, nohow.

And behind the woman comes a little nigger girl and two little nigger boys
without anything on but tow-linen shirts, and they hung onto their mother'
gown, and peeped out from behind her at me, bashful, the way they always do
And here comes the white woman running from the house, about forty-five or fifty
year old, bareheaded, and her spinning-stick in her hand ; and behind her come

er little white children, acting the same way the little niggers was doing.   She

as smiling all over so she could hardly stand—and says :

"It's *you*, at last !—*ain't* it ?"

I out with a " Yes'm," before I thought.

She grabbed me and hugged me tight ; and then gripped me by both hands

nd shook and shook ; and the
ars come in her eyes, and run
own over ; and she couldn't
em to hug and shake enough,
nd kept saying, " You don't
ok as much like your mother
s I reckoned you would, but
w sakes, I don't care for that,
'm *so* glad to see you ! Dear,
ear, it does seem like I could
at you up !   Childern, it's your
ousin Tom !—tell him howdy."

But they ducked their heads,
nd put their fingers in their
nouths, and hid behind her. So
he run on :

" Lize, hurry up and get him
hot breakfast, right away—or
lid you get your breakfast on the
oat ?"

SHE HUGGED HIM TIGHT.

I said I had got it on the boat.   So then she started for the house, leading me
y the hand, and the children tagging after. When we got there, she set me down
n a split-bottomed chair, and set herself down on a little low stool in front of me,
olding both of my hands, and says :

" Now I can have a *good* look at you ; and laws-a-me, I've been hungry for it
many and a many a time, all these long years, and it's come at last ! We been
expecting you a couple of days and more. What's kep' you ?—boat get aground ?"

" Yes'm —she——"

" Don't say yes'm—say Aunt Sally.   Where'd she get aground ? "

I didn't rightly know what to say, because I didn't know whether the boa would be coming up the river or down.   But I go a good deal on instinct ; an my instinct said she would be coming up—from down towards Orleans.   Tha did'nt help me much, though ; for I didn't know the names of bars down that wa I see I'd got to invent a bar, or forget the name of the one we got aground on or—   Now I struck an idea, and fetched it out :

" It warn't the grounding—that didn't keep us back but a little.   We blowe out a cylinder-head."

" Good gracious ! anybody hurt ? "

" No'm.   Killed a nigger."

" Well, it's lucky ; because sometimes people do get hurt.   Two years ag last Christmas, your uncle Silas was coming up from Newrleans on the old *Lall Rook*, and she blowed out a cylinder-head and crippled a man.   And I think h died afterwards.   He was a Babtist.   Your uncle Silas knowed a family in Bato Rouge that knowed his people very well.   Yes, I remember, now he *did* di Mortification set in, and they had to amputate him.   But it didn't save him.   Ye it was mortification—that was it.   He turned blue all over, and died in the hop of a glorious resurrection.   They say he was a sight to look at.   Your uncle been up to the town every day to fetch you.   And he's gone again, not more' an hour ago ; he'll be back any minute, now.   You must a met him on the road didn't you ?—oldish man, with a——"

" No, I didn't see nobody, Aunt Sally.   The boat landed just at daylight, an I left my baggage on the wharf-boat and went looking around the town and ou a piece in the country, to put in the time and not get here too soon ; and so come down the back way."

" Who'd you give the baggage to ? "

" Nobody."

" Why, child, it'll be stole ! "

" Not where *I* hid it I reckon it won't," I says.

" How'd you get your breakfast so early on the boat ? "

It was kinder thin ice, but I says :

" The captain see me standing around, and told me I better have something to
eat before I went ashore ; so he took me in the texas to the officers' lunch, and
give me all I wanted."

I was getting so uneasy I couldn't listen good.   I had my mind on the
children all the time ; I wanted to get them out to one side, and pump them a
little, and find out who I was.   But I couldn't get no show, Mrs. Phelps kept it
up and run on so.   Pretty soon she made the cold chills streak all down my back,
because she says :

" But here we're a running on this way, and you hain't told me a word
about Sis, nor any of them.   Now I'll rest my works a little, and you start up
yourn ; just tell me *everything*—tell me all about 'm all—every one of 'm ; and
how they are, and what they're doing, and what they told you to tell me ; and
every last thing you can think of."

Well, I see I was up a stump—and up it good.   Providence had stood by me this
far, all right, but I was hard and tight aground, now.   I see it warn't a bit of use
to try to go ahead—I'd *got* to throw up my hand.   So I says to myself, here's
another place where I got to resk the truth.   I opened my mouth to begin ; but
she grabbed me and hustled me in behind the bed, and says :

" Here he comes ! stick your head down lower—there, that'll do ; you can't be
seen, now.   Don't you let on you're here.   I'll play a joke on him.   Childern,
don't you say a word."

I see I was in a fix, now.   But it warn't no use to worry ; there warn't nothing
to do but just hold still, and try and be ready to stand from under when the
lightning struck.

I had just one little glimpse of the old gentleman when he come in, then the
bed hid him.   Mrs. Phelps she jumps for him and says :

" Has he come ? "

" No," says her husband.

" Good-*ness* gracious ! " she says, " what in the world *can* have become of him ? "

" I can't imagine," says the old gentleman ; " and I must say, it makes me
dreadful uneasy."

" Uneasy !" she says, " I'm ready to go distracted ! He *must* a come ; an
you've missed him along the road. I *know* it's so—something *tells* me so."

" Why Sally, I *couldn't* miss him along the road—*you* know that."

" But oh, dear, dear, what *will* Sis say ! He must a come ! You must
missed him. He——"

" Oh, don't distress me any more'n I'm already distressed. I don't kno
what in the world to make of it. I'm at my wit's end, and I don't mind a
knowledging 't I'm right down scared. But there's no hope that he's come ; f
he *couldn't* come and me miss him. Sally, it's terrible—just terrible—something
happened to the boat, sure ! "

" Why, Silas ! Look yonder !—up the road !—ain't that somebody coming ?

He sprung to the window at the head of the bed, and that give Mrs. Phelps th
chance she wanted. She stooped down quick, at the foot of the bed, and give m
a pull, and out I come ; and when he turned back from the window, there sh
stood, a-beaming and a-smiling like a house afire, and I standing pretty mee
and sweaty alongside. The old gentleman stared, and says :

" Why, who's that ? "

" Who do you reckon 't is ? "

" I haint no idea. Who *is* it ? "

" It's *Tom Sawyer !* "

By jings, I most slumped though the floor. But there warn't no time to swa
knives ; the old man grabbed me by the hand and shook, and kept on shaking
and all the time, how the woman did dance around and laugh and cry ; and the
how they both did fire off questions about Sid, and Mary, and the rest of th
tribe.

But if they was joyful, it warn't nothing to what I was ; for it was like bein
born again, I was so glad to find out who I was. Well, they froze to me for tw
hours ; and at last when my chin was so tired it couldn't hardly go, any more,
had told them more about my family—I mean the Sawyer family—than eve
happened to any six Sawyer families. And I explained all about how we blowe
out a cylinder-head at the mouth of White River and it took us three days to fi
it. Which was all right, and worked first rate ; because *they* didn't know but

hat it would take three days to fix it. If I'd a called it a bolt-head it would done just as well.

Now I was feeling pretty comfortable all down one side, and pretty uncomfortable all up he other. Being Tom Sawyer as easy and comfortable; and stayed easy and comfortable ll by-and-by I hear a steamboat oughing along down the river— hen I says to myself, spose Tom awyer come down on that boat? —and spose he steps in here, any inute, and sings out my hame efore I can throw him a wink keep quiet? Well, I couldn't ave it that way—it wouldn't do all. I must go up the road nd waylay him. So I told the olks I reckoned I would go up the town and fetch down my

"WHO DO YOU RECKON IT IS?"

aggage. The old gentleman was for going along with me, but I said no, I could rive the horse myself, and I druther he wouldn't take no trouble about me.

Chapter XXXIII

"IT WAS TOM SAWYER."

So I started for town, in the wagon, an when I was half-way I see a wagon con ing, and sure enough it was Tom Saw yer, and I stopped and waited till I come along. I says "Hold on!" an it stopped alongside, and his mout opened up like a trunk, and staid so and he swallowed two or three time like a person that's got a dry throa and then says:

"I hain't ever done you no harm You know that. So then, what yo want to come back and ha'nt *me* for?"

I says:

"I hain't come back—I hain't bee *gone.*"

When he heard my voice, it righted him up some, but he warn't quite sati fied yet. He says:

"Don't you play nothing on me, because I wouldn't on you. Honest inju now, you ain't a ghost?"

"Honest injun, I ain't," I says.

"Well—I—I—well, that ought to settle it, of course; but I can't someho seem to understand it, no way. Looky here, warn't you ever murdered *at all?*

"No. I warn't ever murdered at all—I played it on them. You come here and feel of me if you don't believe me."

So he done it ; and it satisfied him ; and he was that glad to see me again, he dn't know what to do. And he wanted to know all about it right off ; because was a grand adventure, and mysterious, and so it hit him where he lived. But said, leave it alone till by-and-by ; and told his driver to wait, and we drove off little piece, and I told him the kind of a fix I was in, and what did he reckon e better do ? He said, let him alone a minute, and don't disturb him. So he ought and thought, and pretty soon he says :

"It's all right, I've got it. Take my trunk in your wagon, and let on it's ur'n ; and you turn back and fool along slow, so as to get to the house about the me you ought to ; and I'll go towards town a piece, and take a fresh start, and t there a quarter or a half an hour after you ; and you needn't let on to know e, at first."

I says :

" All right ; but wait a minute. There's one more thing—a thing that *no-dy* don't know but me. And that is, there's a nigger here that I'm a trying to eal out of slavery—and his name is *Jim*—old Miss Watson's Jim."

He says :

" What ! Why Jim is——"

He stopped and went to studying. I says :

"*I* know what you'll say. You'll say it's dirty low-down business ; but what it is ?—*I*'m low down ; and I'm agoing to steal him, and I want you to keep um and not let on. Will you ?"

His eye lit up, and he says :

" I'll *help* you steal him ! "

Well, I let go all holts then, like I was shot. It was the most astonishing eech I ever heard—and I'm bound to say Tom Sawyer fell, considerable, in my timation. Only I couldn't believe it. Tom Sawyer a *nigger stealer !*

" Oh, shucks," I says, " you're joking."

" I ain't joking, either."

" Well, then," I says, " joking or no joking, if you hear anything said about runaway nigger, don't forget to remember that *you* don't know nothing about im, and *I* don't know nothing about him."

Then we took the trunk and put it in my wagon, and he drove off his way
and I drove mine. But of course I forgot all about driving slow, on accounts c
being glad and full of thinking ; so I got home a heap too quick for that lengt
of a trip. The old gentleman was at the door, and he says :

" Why, this is wonderful. Who ever would a thought it was in that mare t
do it. I wish we'd a timed her. And she hain't sweated a hair—not a hai.
It's wonderful. Why, I wouldn't take a hunderd dollars for that horse now;
wouldn't, honest ; and yet I'd a sold her for fifteen before, and thought 'twa
all she was worth."

That's all he said. He was the innocentest, best old soul I ever see. But
warn't surprising ; because he warn't only just a farmer, he was a preacher, to
and had a little one-horse log church down back of the plantation, which l
built it himself at his own expense, for a church and school-house, and neve
charged nothing for his preaching, and it was worth it, too. There was plent
other farmer-preachers like that, and done the same way, down South.

In about half an hour Tom's wagon drove up to the front stile, and Au
Sally she see it through the window because it was only about fifty yards, an
says :

" Why, there's somebody come ! I wonder who 'tis ? Why, I do believe it
a stranger. Jimmy " (that's one of the children), " run and tell Lize to put o
another plate for dinner."

Everybody made a rush for the front door, because, of course, a stranger don
come *every* year, and so he lays over the yaller fever, for interest, when he do
come. Tom was over the stile and starting for the house ; the wagon was spir
ning up the road for the village, and we was all bunched in the front door. To
had his store clothes on, and an audience—and that was always nuts for To
Sawyer. In them circumstances it warn't no trouble to him to throw in a
amount of style that was suitable. He warn't a boy to meeky along up that yar
like a sheep ; no, he come ca'm and important, like the ram. When he g
afront of us, he lifts his hat ever so gracious and dainty, like it was the lid of
box that had butterflies asleep in it and he didn't want to disturb them, and says

" Mr. Archibald Nichols, I presume ? "

"No, my boy," says the old gentleman, "I'm sorry to say 't your driver has
ceived you; Nichols's place is down a matter of three mile more. Come in,
me in."

Tom he took a look back over his shoulder, and says, "Too late—he's out of
ght."

"Yes, he's gone, my son, and you
ust come in and eat your dinner
ith us; and then we'll hitch up and
ke you down to Nichols's."

"Oh, I *can't* make you so much
ouble; I couldn't think of it. I'll
alk—I don't mind the distance."

"But we won't *let* you walk—it
ouldn't be Southern hospitality to
o it. Come right in."

"Oh, *do*," says Aunt Sally; "it
n't a bit of trouble to us, not a bit
the world. You *must* stay. It's a
ng, dusty three mile, and we *can't*
t you walk. And besides, I've al-
ady told 'em to put on another
late, when I see you coming; so you
ustn't disappoint us. Come right in, and make yourself at home."

"MR. ARCHIBALD NICHOLS, I PRESUME?"

So Tom he thanked them very hearty and handsome, and let himself be per-
aaded, and come in; and when he was in, he said he was a stranger from Hicks-
lle, Ohio, and his name was William Thompson—and he made another bow.

Well, he run on, and on, and on, making up stuff about Hicksville and every-
ody in it he could invent, and I getting a little nervous, and wondering how
ais was going to help me out of my scrape; and at last, still talking along, he
ached over and kissed Aunt Sally right on the mouth, and then settled back
gain in his chair, comfortable, and was going on talking; but she jumped up
ad wiped it off with the back of her hand, and says:

" You owdacious puppy ! "

He looked kind of hurt, and says :

" I'm surprised at you, m'am."

" You're s'rp— Why, what do you reckon *I* am ? I've a good notion to ta
and—say, what do you mean by kissing me ? "

He looked kind of humble, and says :

" I didn't mean nothing, m'am. I didn't mean no harm. I—I—thoug
you'd like it."

" Why, you born fool ! " She took up the spinning-stick, and it looked li
it was all she could do to keep from giving him a crack with it. " What ma
you think I'd like it ? "

" Well, I don't know. Only, they—they—told me you would."

"*They* told you I would. Whoever told you 's *another* lunatic. I nev
heard the beat of it. Who's *they* ? "

" Why—everybody. They all said so, m'am."

It was all she could do to hold in ; and her eyes snapped, and her finge
worked like she wanted to scratch him ; and she says :

" Who's ' everybody ? ' Out with their names—or ther'll be an idiot short.'

He got up and looked distressed, and fumbled his hat, and says :

" I'm sorry, and I warn't expecting it. They told me to. They all told n
to. They all said kiss her ; and said she'll like it. They all said it—every on
of them. But I'm sorry, m'am, and I won't do it no more—I won't, honest."

" You won't, won't you ? Well, I sh'd *reckon* you won't ! "

" No'm, I'm honest about it ; I won't ever do it again. Till you ask me."

" Till I *ask* you ! Well, I never see the beat of it in my born days ! I l
you'll be the Methusalem-numskull of creation before ever *I* ask you—or t
likes of you."

" Well," he says, " it does surprise me so. I can't make it out, someho
They said you would, and I thought you would. But—" He stopped and look
around slow, like he wished he could run across a friendly eye, somewhere's ; a
fetched up on the old gentleman's, and says, " Didn't *you* think she'd like me
kiss her, sir ? "

" Why, no, I—I—well, no, I b'lieve I didn't."

Then he looks on around, the same way, to me—and says :

" Tom, didn't *you* think Aunt Sally 'd open out her arms and say, ' Sid wyer——' "

" My land !" she says, breaking in and jumping for him, " you impudent ung rascal, to fool a body so—" and was going to hug him, but he fended her f, and says :

" No, not till you've asked me, first."

So she didn't lose no time, but asked him ; and hugged him and kissed him, er and over again, and then turned him over to the old man, and he took what s left. And after they got a little quiet again, she says :

" Why, dear me, I never see such a surprise. We warn't looking for *you*, at , but only Tom. Sis never wrote to me about anybody coming but him."

" It's because it warn't *intended* for any of us to come but Tom," he says ; but I begged and begged, and at the last minute she let me come, too ; so, com- g down the river, me and Tom thought it would be a first-rate surprise for him come here to the house first, and for me to by-and-by tag along and drop in d let on to be a stranger. But it was a mistake, Aunt Sally. This ain't no althy place for a stranger to come."

" No—not impudent whelps, Sid. You ought to had your jaws boxed; I hain't en so put out since I don't know when. But I don't care, I don't mind the rms—I'd be willing to stand a thousand such jokes to have you here. Well, to ink of that performance ! I don't deny it, I was most putrified with astonish- ent when you give me that smack."

We had dinner out in that broad open passage betwixt the house and the tchen ; and there was things enough on that table for seven families—and all t, too ; none of your flabby tough meat that's laid in a cupboard in a damp llar all night and tastes like a hunk of old cold cannibal in the morning. Uncle las he asked a pretty long blessing over it, but it was worth it ; and it didn't ol it a bit, neither, the way I've seen them kind of interruptions do, lots of times.

There was a considerable good deal of talk, all the afternoon, and me and Tom as on the lookout all the time, but it warn't no use, they didn't happen to say nothing about any runaway nigger, and we was afraid to try to work up to But at supper, at night, one of the little boys says :

"Pa, mayn't Tom and Sid and me go to the show ?"

"No," says the old man, "I reckon there ain't going to be any; and y couldn't go if there was ; because the runaway nigger told Burton and me

A PRETTY LONG BLESSING.

about that scandalous show, and Burton said he would tell the people; so I reck they've drove the owdacious loafers out of town before this time."

So there it was !—but *I* couldn't help it.   Tom and me was to sleep in t same room and bed ; so, being tired, we bid good-night and went up to bed, rig after supper, and clumb out of the window and down the lightning-rod, ar shoved for the town ; for I didn't believe anybody was going to give the king ar the duke a hint, and so, if I didn't hurry up and give them one they'd get in trouble sure.

On the road Tom he told me all about how it was reckoned I was murdere and how pap disappeared, pretty soon, and didn t come back no more, and wh a stir there was when Jim run away ; and I told Tom all about our Royal Non such rapscallions, and as much of the raft-voyage as I had time to ; and as v

uck into the town and up through the middle of it—it was as much as half-
er eight, then—here comes a raging rush of people, with torches, and an awful
ooping and yelling, and banging tin pans and blowing horns ; and we jumped
one side to let them go by; and as they went by, I see they had the king and
e duke astraddle of a rail—that is, I knowed it *was* the king and the duke,
ugh they was all over tar and feathers, and didn't look like nothing in the
rld that was human—just looked like a couple of monstrous big soldier-plumes.
ll, it made me sick to see it ; and I was sorry for them poor pitiful rascals, it

TRAVELLING BY RAIL.

med like I couldn't ever feel any hardness against them any more in the
rld.   It was a dreadful thing to see.   Human beings *can* be awful cruel to one
other.

We see we was too late—couldn't do no good.   We asked some stragglers
ut it, and they said everybody went to the show looking very innocent ; and
l low and kept dark till the poor old king was in the middle of his cavortings
the stage ; then somebody give a signal, and the house rose up and went for
m.

So we poked along back home, and I warn't feeling so brash as I was before.

but kind of ornery, and humble, and to blame, somehow—though *I* hadn't d
nothing. But that's always the way; it don't make no difference whet
you do right or wrong, a person's conscience ain't got no sense, and just goes
him *anyway*. If I had a yaller dog that didn't know no more than a perso
conscience does, I would pison him. It takes up more room than all the rest
a person's insides, and yet ain't no good, nohow. Tom Sawyer he says the sar

Chapter XXXIV

VITTLES.

We stopped talking, and got to thinking. By-and-by Tom says :

"Looky here, Huck, what fools we are, to not think of it before ! I bet I know where Jim is."

"No ! Where ?"

"In that hut down by the ash-hopper. Why, looky here. When we was at dinner, didn't you see a nigger man go in there with some vittles ?"

"Yes."

"What did you think the vittles was for ?"

"For a dog."

"So'd I. Well, it wasn't for a dog."

"Why ?"

"Because part of it was watermelon."

"So it was—I noticed it. Well, it does beat all, that I never thought about dog not eating watermelon. It shows how a body can see and don't see at the same time."

"Well, the nigger unlocked the padlock when he went in, and he locked it again when he come out. He fetched uncle a key, about the time we got up from table—same key, I bet. Watermelon shows man, lock shows prisoner ; and ain't likely there's two prisoners on such a little plantation, and where t people's all so kind and good. Jim's the prisoner. All right—I'm glad we fou it out detective fashion ; I wouldn't give shucks for any other way. Now y work your mind and study out a plan to steal Jim, and I will study out one, to and we'll take the one we like the best."

What a head for just a boy to have ! If I had Tom Sawyer's head, I would trade it off to be a duke, nor mate of a steamboat, nor clown in a circus, nor not ing I can think of. I went to thinking out a plan, but only just to be doi something ; I knowed very well where the right plan was going to come fro Pretty soon, Tom says :

" Ready ? "

" Yes," I says.

" All right—bring it out."

" My plan is this," I says. " We can easy find out if it's Jim in there. Th get up my canoe to-morrow night, and fetch my raft over from the island. Th the first dark night that comes, steal the key out of the old man's britches, aft he goes to bed, and shove off down the river on the raft, with Jim, hiding da times and running nights, the way me and Jim used to do before. Wouldn't th plan work ? "

" *Work?* Why cert'nly, it would work, like rats a fighting. But it's too blan simple ; there ain't nothing *to* it. What's the good of a plan that ain't no mo trouble than that ? It's as mild as goose-milk. Why, Huck, it wouldn't ma no more talk than breaking into a soap factory."

I never said nothing, because I warn't expecting nothing different ; but knowed mighty well that whenever he got *his* plan ready it wouldn't have none them objections to it.

And it didn't. He told me what it was, and I see in a minute it was wor fifteen of mine, for style, and would make Jim just as free a man as mine woul and maybe get us all killed besides. So I was satisfied, and said we would wa in on it. I needn't tell what it was, here, because I knowed it wouldn't stay t way it was. I knowed he would be changing it around, every which way, as

nt along, and heaving in new bullinesses wherever he got a chance.   And that
what he done.

  Well, one thing was dead sure ; and that was, that Tom Sawyer was in earnest
d was actly going to help steal that nigger out of slavery.   That was the thing
at was too many for me.   Here was a boy that was respectable, and well brung
; and had a character to lose ; and folks at home that had characters ; and he
s bright and not leather-headed ; and knowing and not ignorant ; and not
an, but kind ; and yet here he was, without any more pride, or rightness, or
ling, than to stoop to this business, and make himself a shame, and his family
hame, before everybody.   I *couldn't* understand it, no way at all.   It was out-
geous, and I knowed I ought to just up and tell him so ; and so be his true
end, and let him quit the thing right where he was, and save himself.   And I
d start to tell him ; but he shut me up, and says :

  " Don't you reckon I know what I'm about ?   Don't I generly know what I'm
out ? "

  " Yes."

  " Didn't I *say* I was going to help steal the nigger ? "

  " Yes."

  " *Well* then."

That's all he said, and that's all I said.   It warn't no use to say any more ;
cause when he said he'd do a thing, he always done it.   But *I* couldn't
ake out how he was willing to go into this thing ; so I just let it go, and
ver bothered no more about it.   If he was bound to have it so, *I* couldn't
lp it.

  When we got home, the house was all dark and still ; so we went on down to
e hut by the ash hopper, for to examine it.   We went through the yard, so as
see what the hounds would do.   They knowed us, and didn't make no more
ise than country dogs is always doing when anything comes by in the night.
hen we got to the cabin, we took a look at the front and the two sides ; and on
e side I warn't acquainted with—which was the north side—we found a square
ndow-hole, up tolerable high, with just one stout board nailed across it.   I
ys :

"Here's the ticket.   This hole's big enough for Jim to get through, if
wrench off the board."

Tom says :

"It's as simple as tit-tat-toe, three-in-a-row, and as easy as playing hooky.
should *hope* we can find a way that's a little more complicated than *that*, Hu
Finn."

A SIMPLE JOB.

"Well   then,"   I   sa
"how'll it do to saw him o
the way I done before I w
murdered, that time ?"

"That's   more   *like*,"
says. "It's real mysterious, a
troublesome,   and   good,"
says ; "but I bet we can fi
a way that's twice as lor
There ain't no hurry; le's ke
on looking around."

Betwixt the hut and t
fence, on the back side, was
lean-to, that joined the hut
the eaves, and was made out
plank.   It was as long as t
hut, but narrow—only abo
six foot wide. The door to
was at the south end, and w
padlocked.   Tom he went
the soap kettle, and search

around and fetched back the iron thing they lift the lid with ; so he took it a
prized out one of the staples.   The chain fell down, and we opened the d
and went in, and shut it, and struck a match, and see the shed was only built agai
the cabin and hadn't no connection with it ; and there warn't no floor to the she
nor nothing in it but some old rusty played-out hoes, and spades, and picks, a

rippled plow. The match went out, and so did we, and shoved in the staple
ain, and the door was locked as good as ever. Tom was joyful. He says :

" Now we're all right. We'll *dig* him out. It'll take about a week ! "

Then we started for the house, and I went in the back door—you only have to
ll a buckskin latch-string, they don't fasten the doors—but that warn't roman-
al enough for Tom Sawyer : no way would do him but he must climb up the
htning-rod. But after he got up half-way about three times, and missed fire
l fell every time, and the last time most busted his brains out, he thought he'd
t to give it up ; but after he was rested, he allowed he would give her one more
n for luck, and this time he made the trip.

In the morning we was up at break of day, and down to the nigger cabins to
; the dogs and make friends with the nigger that fed Jim—if it *was* Jim that
s being fed. The niggers was just getting through breakfast and starting for
e fields ; and Jim's nigger was piling up a tin pan with bread and meat and
ngs ; and whilst the others was leaving, the key come from the house.

This nigger had a good-natured, chuckle-headed face, and his wool was all tied
in little bunches with thread. That was to keep witches off. He said the
:ches was pestering him awful, these nights, and making him see all kinds of
ange things, and hear all kinds of strange words and noises, and he didn't be-
ve he was ever witched so long, before, in his life. He got so worked up, and
t to runinng on so about his troubles, he forgot all about what he'd been agoing
do. So Tom says :

" What's the vittles for ? Going to feed the dogs ? "

The nigger kind of smiled around graduly over his face, like when you heave
rickbat in a mud puddle, and he says :

" Yes, Mars Sid, *a* dog. Cur'us dog, too. Does you want to go en look at
?"

" Yes."

I hunched Tom, and whispers :

" You going, right here in the day-break ? *That* warn't the plan."

" No, it warn't—but it's the plan *now*."

So, drat him, we went along, but I didn't like it much. When we got in,

we couldn't hardly see anything, it was so dark ; but Jim was there, sure enoug
and could see us ; and he sings out :

"Why, *Huck!* En good *lan'!* ain' dat Misto Tom ?"

I just knowed how it would be ; I just expected it. *I* didn't know nothing
do ; and if I had, I couldn't a done it ; because that nigger busted in and says :

"Why, de gracious sakes ! do he know you genlmen ?"

We could see pretty well, now. Tom he looked at the nigger, steady an
kind of wondering, and says :

"Does *who* know us ?"

"Why, dish-yer runaway nigger."

"I don't reckon he does ; but what put that into your head ?"

"What *put* it dar ? Didn' he jis' dis minute sing out like he knowed you ?

Tom says, in a puzzled-up kind of way :

"Well, that's mighty curious. *Who* sung out ? *When* did he sing out ? *Wh*
did he sing out ?" And turns to me, perfectly c'am, and says, "Did *you* he
anybody sing out ?"

Of course there warn't nothing to be said but the one thing ; so I says :

"No ; *I* ain't heard nobody say nothing."

Then he turns to Jim, and looks him over like he never see him before ; an
says :

"Did you sing out ?"

"No, sah," says Jim ; "*I* hain't said nothing, sah."

"Not a word ?"

"No, sah, I hain't said a word."

"Did you ever see us before ?"

"No, sah ; not as *I* knows on."

So Tom turns to the nigger, which was looking wild and distressed, and say
kind of severe :

"What do you reckon's the matter with you, anyway ? What made yo
think somebody sung out ?"

"Oh, it's de dad-blame' witches, sah, en I wisht I was dead, I do. Dey
awluz at it, sah, en dey do mos' kill me, dey sk'yers me so. Please to dor

l nobody 'bout it sah, er ole Mars Silas he'll scole me; 'kase he say dey
n't no witches. I jis' wish to goodness he was heah now—*den* what would he
y! I jis' bet he couldn' fine no way to git aroun' it *dis* time. But it's awluz
so; people dat's *sot*, stays sot; dey won't look into nothn' en fine it out
deyselves, en when *you* fine it out en tell um 'bout it, dey doan' b'lieve you."

Tom give him a dime, and
d we wouldn't tell no-
dy; and told him to buy
ne more thread to tie up his
ol with; and then looks at
n, and says:

"I wonder if Uncle Silas
going to hang this nigger.
I was to catch a nigger that
s ungrateful enough to run
ay, *I* wouldn't give him up,
hang him." And whilst
e nigger stepped to the
or to look at the dime and
e it to see if it was good,
whispers to Jim, and says:
"Don't ever let on to know
And if you hear any dig-
g going on nights, it's us:
're going to set you free."

WITCHES.

Jim only had time to grab us by the hand and squeeze it, then the nigger
ne back, and we said we'd come again some time if the nigger wanted us to;
l he said he would, more particular if it was dark, because the witches went
him mostly in the dark, and it was good to have folks around then.

Chapter XXXV

GETTING WOOD.

It would be most an hour, yet, breakfast, so we left, and stru down into the woods; because T said we got to have *some* light see how to dig by, and a lante makes too much, and might get into trouble; what we must h was a lot of them rotten chu that's called fox-fire and just ma a soft kind of a glow when you them in a dark place. We fetch an armful and hid it in the wee and set down to rest, and Tom sa kind of dissatisfied:

"Blame it, this whole thing just as easy and awkard as it be. And so it makes it so rot difficult to get up a difficult pl There ain't no watchman to drugged—now there *ought* to be a watchman. There ain't even a dog to giv sleeping-mixture to. And there's Jim chained by one leg, with a ten-foot cha to the leg of his bed: why, all you got to do is to lift up the bedstead and slip the chain. And Uncle Silas he trusts everybody; sends the key to the punk headed nigger, and don't send nobody to watch the nigger. Jim could a got of that window hole before this, only there wouldn't be no use trying to tra

h a ten-foot chain on his leg. Why, drat it, Huck, it's the stupidest arrange-
nt I ever see. You got to invent *all* the difficulties. Well, we can't help it,
got to do the best we can with the materials we've got. Anyhow, there's one
ng—there's more honor in getting him out through a lot of difficulties and
igers, where there warn't one of them furnished to you by the people who it
s their duty to furnish them, and you had to contrive them all out of your own
id. Now look at just that one thing of the lantern. When you come down
the cold facts, we simply got to *let on* that a lantern's resky. Why, we could
rk with a torchlight procession if we wanted to, *I* believe. Now, whilst I
nk of it, we got to hunt up something to make a saw out of, the first chance
get."

"What do we want of a saw ? "

"What do we *want* of it ? Hain't we got to saw the leg of Jim's bed off, so
to get the chain loose ? "

"Why, you just said a body could lift up the bedstead and slip the
iin off."

"Well, if that ain't just like you, Huck Finn. You *can* get up the infant-
ooliest ways of going at a thing. Why, hain't you ever read any books at
?—Baron Trenck, nor Casanova, nor Benvenuto Chelleeny, nor Henri IV.,
none of them heroes ? Whoever heard of getting a prisoner loose in such an
-maidy way as that ? No ; the way all the best authorities does, is to saw the
l-leg in two, and leave it just so, and swallow the sawdust, so it can't be found,
l put some dirt and grease around the sawed place so the very keenest seneskal
't see no sign of it's being sawed, and thinks the bed-leg is perfectly sound.
en, the night you're ready, fetch the leg a kick, down she goes ; slip off your
in, and there you are. Nothing to do but hitch your rope-ladder to the battle-
nts, shin down it, break your leg in the moat—because a rope-ladder is
eteen foot too short, you know—and there's your horses and your trusty vassles,
l they scoop you up and fling you across a saddle and away you go, to your
ive Langudoc, or Navarre, or wherever it is. It's gaudy, Huck. I wish there
a moat to this cabin. If we get time, the night of the escape, we'll dig
."

I says :

" What do we want of a moat, when we're going to snake him out from und
the cabin ?"

But he never heard me. He had forgot me and everything else. He had h
chin in his hand, thinking. Pretty soon, he sighs, and shakes his head ; the
sighs again, and says :

" No, it wouldn't do—there ain't necessity enough for it."

" For what ?" I says.

" Why, to saw Jim's leg off," he says.

" Good land !" I says, " why, there ain't *no* necessity for it. And wh
would you want to saw his l
off for, anyway ?"

" Well, some of the be
authorities has done it. Th
couldn't get the chain off,
they just cut their hand off, a
shoved. And a leg would
better still. But we got to
that go. There ain't necess
enough in this case ; and besid
Jim's a nigger and would
understand the reasons for
and how it's the custom in F
rope ; so we'll let it go. B
there's one thing—he can hav
rope-ladder ; we can tear up
sheets and make him a roj
ladder easy enough. And
can send it to him in a pie ;

ONE OF THE BEST AUTHORITIES.

mostly done that way. And I've et worse pies."

" Why, Tom Sawyer, how you talk," I says ; " Jim ain't got no use for a roj
ladder."

" He *has* got use for it. How *you* talk, you better say ; you don't know hing about it. He's *got* to have a rope ladder ; they all do."

" What in the nation can he *do* with it ? "

" *Do* with it ? He can hide it in his bed, can't he ? That's what they all ; and *he's* got to, too. Huck, you don't ever seem to want to do anything t's regular ; you want to be starting something fresh all the time. Spose he 't do nothing with it ? ain't it there in his bed, for a clew, after he's gone ? don't you reckon they'll want clews ? Of course they will. And you ldn't leave them any ? That would be a *pretty* howdy-do, *wouldn't* it ! I er heard of such a thing."

" Well," I says, "if it's in the regulations, and he's got to have it, all right, him have it ; because I don't wish to go back on no regulations ; but there's thing, Tom Sawyer—if we go to tearing up our sheets to make Jim a rope-der, we're going to get into trouble with Aunt Sally, just as sure as you're n. Now, the way I look at it, a hickry-bark ladder don't cost nothing, and 't waste nothing, and is just as good to load up a pie with, and hide in a straw , as any rag ladder you can start ; and as for Jim, he ain't had no experience, so *he* don't care what kind of a——"

" Oh, shucks, Huck Finn, if I was as ignorant as you, I'd keep still—that's at *I'd* do. Who ever heard of a state prisoner escaping by a hickry-bark der ? Why, it's perfectly ridiculous."

" Well, all right, Tom, fix it your own way ; but if you'll take my advice, 'll let me borrow a sheet off of the clothes-line."

He said that would do. And that give him another idea, and he says :

" Borrow a shirt, too."

" What do we want of a shirt, Tom ? "

" Want it for Jim to keep a journal on."

" Journal your granny—*Jim* can't write."

" Spose he *can't* write—he can make marks on the shirt, can't he, if we ke him a pen out of an old pewter spoon or a piece of an old iron barrel-hoop ? "

" Why, Tom, we can pull a feather out of a goose and make him a better one ; d quicker, too."

"*Prisoners* don't have geese running around the donjon-keep to pull pens of, you muggins. They *always* make their pens out of the hardest, toughe troublesomest piece of old brass candlestick or something like that they can their hands on ; and it takes them weeks and weeks, and months and mon to file it out, too, because they've got to do it by rubbing it on the wall. T wouldn't use a goose-quill if they had it. It ain't regular."

"Well, then, what'll we make him the ink out of ?"

"Many makes it out of iron-rust and tears ; but that's the common sort women ; the best authorities uses their own blood. Jim can do that ; and when wants to send any little common ordinary mysterious message to let the world kn where he's captivated, he can write it on the bottom of a tin plate with a fork throw it out of the window. The Iron Mask always done that, and it's a bla good way, too."

"Jim ain't got no tin plates. They feed him in a pan."

"That ain't anything ; we can get him some."

"Can't nobody *read* his plates."

"That ain't got nothing to *do* with it, Huck Finn. All *he's* got to do is write on the plate and throw it out. You don't *have* to be able to read it. W half the time you can't read anything a prisoner writes on a tin plate, or a where else."

"Well, then, what's the sense in wasting the plates ?"

"Why, blame it all, it ain't the *prisoner's* plates."

"But it's *somebody's* plates, ain't it ?"

"Well, spos'n it is ? What does the *prisoner* care whose—— "

He broke off there, because we heard the breakfast-horn blowing. So cleared out for the house.

Along during that morning I borrowed a sheet and a white shirt off of clothes-line ; and I found an old sack and put them in it, and we went down got the fox-fire, and put that in too. I called it borrowing, because that what pap always called it ; but Tom said it warn't borrowing, it was steali He said we was representing prisoners ; and prisoners don't care how they ge thing so they get it, and nobody don't blame them for it, either. It ain't me in a prisoner to steal the thing he needs to get away with, Tom said ; it's

s right ; and so, as long as
e was representing a pris-
er, we had a perfect right
steal anything on this
ace we had the least use
r, to get ourselves out of
ison with. He said if we
arn't prisoners it would be
very different thing, and
body but a mean ornery
rson would steal when he
arn't a prisoner.   So we
lowed we would steal every-
ing there was that come
andy.   And yet he made a
ighty fuss, one day, after
at, when I stole a water-
elon out of the nigger patch
d eat it ; and he made me
and give the niggers a
me, without telling them
hat it was for.   Tom said
at what he meant was, we

THE BREAKFAST-HORN.

uld steal anything we *needed*.   Well, I says, I needed the watermelon.   But
e said I didn't need it to get out of prison with, there's where the difference
as.   He said if I'd a wanted it to hide a knife in, and smuggle it to Jim to kill
e seneskal with, it would a been all right.   So I let it go at that, though I
uldn't see no advantage in my representing a prisoner, if I got to set down and
aw over a lot of gold-leaf distinctions like that, every time I see a chance to hog
watermelon.

Well, as I was saying, we waited that morning till everybody was settled

down to business, and nobody in sight around the yard ; then Tom he carried tl
sack into the lean-to whilst I stood off a piece to keep watch.   By-and-by h
come out, and we went and set down on the wood-pile, to talk.   He says :

"Everything's all right, now, except tools ; and that's easy fixed."

"Tools ?" I says.

"Yes."

"Tools for what ?"

"Why, to dig with.   We ain't agoing to *gnaw* him out, are we ?"

"Ain't them old crippled picks and things in there good enough to dig
nigger out with ?" I says.

He turns on me looking pitying enough to make a body cry, and says :

"Huck Finn, did you *ever* hear of a prisoner having picks and shovels, and a
the modern conveniences in his wardrobe to dig himself out with ?   Now I war
to ask you—if you got any reasonableness in you at all—what kind of a sho
would *that* give him to be a hero ?   Why, they might as well lend him the key
and done with it.   Picks and shovels—why they wouldn't furnish 'em to
king."

"Well, then," I says, "if we don't want the picks and shovels, what do w
want ?"

"A couple of case-knives."

"To dig the foundations out from under that cabin with ?"

"Yes."

"Confound it, it's foolish, Tom."

"It don't make no difference how foolish it is, it's the *right* way—and it's th
regular way.   And there ain't no *other* way, that ever *I* heard of, and I've rea
all the books that gives any information about these things.   They always di
out with a case-knife—and not through dirt, mind you ; generly it's throug
solid rock.   And it takes them weeks and weeks and weeks, and for ever an
ever.   Why, look at one of them prisoners in the bottom dungeon of the Castl
Deef, in the harbor of Marseilles, that dug himself out that way ; how long wa
he at it, you reckon ?"

"I don't know."

" Well, guess."

" I don't know. A month and a half ? "

" *Thirty-seven year*—and he come out in China. *That's* the kind. I wish e bottom of *this* fortress was solid rock."

" *Jim* don't know nobody in China."

" What's *that* got to do with it ? Neither did that other fellow. But you're ways a-wandering off on a side issue. Why can't you stick to the main point ? "

" All right—*I* don't care where he mes out, so he *comes* out; and Jim n't, either, I reckon. But there's one ing, anyway—Jim's too old to be dug t with a case-knife. He won't last."

" Yes he will *last*, too. You don't ckon it's going to take thirty-seven ars to dig out through a *dirt* founda- on, do you ? "

" How long will it take, Tom ? "

" Well, we can't resk being as long we ought to, because it mayn't take ry long for Uncle Silas to hear from wn there by New Orleans. He'll hear m ain't from there. Then his next ove will be to advertise Jim, or some- ing like that. So we can't resk being long digging him out as we ought to. y rights I reckon we ought to be a uple of years; but we can't. Things eing so uncertain, what I recommend is

SMOUCHING THE KNIVES.

iis : that we really dig right in, as quick as we can ; and after that, we can *let* , to ourselves, that we was at it thirty-seven years. Then we can snatch him t and rush him away the first time there's an alarm. Yes, I reckon that'll be e best way "

"Now, there's *sense* in that," I says. "Letting on don't cost nothing; letting on ain't no trouble ; and if it's any object, I don't mind letting on we was at it a hundred and fifty year. It wouldn't strain me none, after I got my hand in. So I'll mosey along now, and smouch a couple of case-knives."

"Smouch three," he says ; "we want one to make a saw out of."

"Tom, if it ain't unregular and irreligious to sejest it," I says, "there's a old rusty saw-blade around yonder sticking under the weatherboarding behind the smoke-house."

He looked kind of weary and discouraged-like, and says :

"It ain't no use to try to learn you nothing, Huck. Run along and smouch the knives—three of them." So I done it.

Chapter XXXVI

GOING DOWN THE LIGHTNING-ROD.

As soon as we reckoned everybody was asleep, that night, we went down the lightning-rod, and shut ourselves up in the lean-to, and got out our pile of fox-fire, and went to work. We cleared everything out of the way, about four or five foot along the middle of the bottom log. Tom said he was right behind Jim's bed now, and we'd dig in under it, and when we got through there couldn't nobody in the cabin ever know there was any hole there, because Jim's counterpin hung down most to the ground, and you'd have to raise it up and look under to see the hole. So we dug and dug, with the case-knives, till most midnight; and then we was dog-tired, and our hands was blistered, and yet you couldn't see we'd done anything, hardly. At last I says:

"This ain't no thirty-seven year job, this is a thirty-eight year job, Tom Sawyer."

He never said nothing. But he sighed, and pretty soon he stopped digging, and then for a good little while I knowed he was thinking. Then he says:

"It ain't no use, Huck, it ain't agoing to work. If we was prisoners would, because then we'd have as many years as we wanted, and no hurry; an we wouldn't get but a few minutes to dig, every day, while they was changin watches, and so our hands wouldn't get blistered, and we could keep it up rig along, year in and year out, and do it right, and the way it ought to be don But *we* can't fool along, we got to rush; we ain't got no time to spare. If we w to put in another night this way, we'd have to knock off for a week to let o hands get well—couldn't touch a case-knife with them sooner."

"Well, then, what we going to do, Tom?"

"I'll tell you. It ain't right, and it ain't moral, and I wouldn't like it to g out—but there ain't only just the one way; we got to dig him out with the pick and *let on* it's case-knives."

"*Now* you're *talking!*" I says; "your head gets leveler and leveler all th time, Tom Sawyer," I says. "Picks is the thing, moral or no moral; and as f me, I don't care shucks for the morality of it, nohow. When I start in to ste a nigger, or a watermelon, or a Sunday-school book, I ain't no ways particul how it's done so it's done. What I want is my nigger; or what I want is m watermelon; or what I want is my Sunday-school book; and if a pick's the han iest thing, that's the thing I'm agoing to dig that nigger or that watermelon that Sunday-school book out with; and I don't give a dead rat what the author ties thinks about it nuther."

"Well," he says, "there's excuse for picks and letting-on in a case like this if it warn't so, I wouldn't approve of it, nor I wouldn't stand by and see the rul broke—because right is right, and wrong is wrong, and a body ain't got no bus ness doing wrong when he ain't ignorant and knows better. It might answer f *you* to dig Jim out with a pick, *without* any letting-on, because you don't kno no better; but it wouldn't for me, because I do know better. Gimme a cas knife."

He had his own by him, but I handed him mine. He flung it down, an says:

"Gimme a *case-knife*."

I didn't know just what to do—but then I thought. I scratched aroun

ongst the old tools, and got a pick-ax and give it to him, and he took it and
nt to work, and never said a word.

He was always just that particular. Full of principle

So then I got a shovel, and then we picked and shoveled, turn about, and

ade the fur fly. We stuck to it
out a half an hour, which was as
ng as we could stand up; but we
d a good deal of a hole to show
r it. When I got up stairs, I
oked out at the window and see
om doing his level best with the
ghtning-rod, but he couldn't come
, his hands was so sore. At last
says:

"It ain't no use, it can't be
one. What you reckon I better
? Can't you think up no way?"

"Yes," I says, "but I reckon
ain't regular. Come up the
airs, and let on it's a lightning-
d."

So he done it.

Next day Tom stole a pewter
oon and a brass candlestick in the

STEALING SPOONS.

use, for to make some pens for Jim out of, and six tallow candles; and I hung
ound the nigger cabins, and laid for a chance, and stole three tin plates. Tom
id it wasn't enough; but I said nobody wouldn't ever see the plates that Jim
rowed out, because they'd fall in the dog-fennel and jimpson weeds under the
indow-hole—then we could tote them back and he could use them over again.
Tom was satisfied. Then he says:

"Now, the thing to study out is, how to get the things to Jim."

"Take them in through the hole," I says, "when we get it done."

He only just looked scornful, and said something about nobody ever heard of such an idiotic idea, and then he went to studying. By-and-by he said he had ciphered out two or three ways, but there warn't no need to decide on any of them yet. Said we'd got to post Jim first.

That night we went down the lightning-rod a little after ten, and took one of the candles along, and listened under the window-hole, and heard Jim snoring, so we pitched it in, and it didn't wake him. Then we whirled in with the pick and shovel, and in about two hours and a half the job was done. We crept in under Jim's bed and into the cabin, and pawed around and found the candle and lit it, and stood over Jim a while, and found him looking hearty and healthy, and then we woke him up gentle and gradual. He was so glad to see us he most cried; and called us honey, and all the pet names he could think of; and was for having us hunt up a cold chisel to cut the chain off of his leg with, right away, and clearing out without losing any time. But Tom he showed him how un regular it would be, and set down and told him all about our plans, and how we could alter them in a minute any time there was an alarm; and not to be the least afraid, because we would see he got away, *sure.* So Jim he said it was all right, and we set there and talked over old times a while, and then Tom asked a lot of questions, and when Jim told him Uncle Silas come in every day or two to pray with him, and Aunt Sally come in to see if he was comfortable and had plenty to eat, and both of them was kind as they could be, Tom says:

"*Now* I know how to fix it. We'll send you some things by them."

I said, "Don't do nothing of the kind; it's one of the most jackass ideas I ever struck;" but he never paid no attention to me; went right on. It was his way when he'd got his plans set.

So he told Jim how we'd have to smuggle in the rope-ladder pie, and other large things, by Nat, the nigger that fed him, and he must be on the lookout, and not be surprised, and not let Nat see him open them; and we would put small things in uncle's coat pockets and he must steal them out; and we would tie things to aunt's apron strings or put them in her apron pocket, if we got a chance; and told him what they would be and what they was for. And told him how to keep a journal on the shirt with his blood, and all that. He told him everything.

m he couldn't see no sense in the most of it, but he all >wed we was white folks
d knowed better than him ; so he was satisfied, and said he would do it all just
Tom said.

Jim had plenty corn-cob pipes and tobacco ; so we had a right down good
ciable time ; then we crawled out through the hole, and so home to bed, with
nds that looked like they'd been chawed. Tom was in high spirits. He said
was the best fun he ever had in his life, and the most intellectural ; and said if
 only could see his way to it we would keep it up all the rest of our lives
d leave Jim to our children to get out ; for he believed Jim would come
 like it better and better the more he got used to it. He said that in that
ay it could be strung out to as much as eighty year, and would be the best
me on record. And he said it would make us all celebrated that had a hand
 it.

In the morning we went out to the wood-pile and chopped up the brass candle-
ick into handy sizes, and Tom put them and the pewter spoon in his pocket.
hen we went to the nigger cabins, and while I got Nat's notice off, Tom shoved
piece of candlestick into the middle of a corn-pone that was in Jim's pan, and
e went along with Nat to see how it would work, and it just worked noble ;
hen Jim bit into it it most mashed all his teeth out ; and there warn't ever any-
1ing could a worked better. Tom said so himself. Jim he never let on but what
 was only just a piece of rock or something like that that's always getting into
read, you know ; but after that he never bit into nothing but what he jabbed his
ork into it in three or four places, first.

And whilst we was a standing there in the dimmish light, here comes a couple
f the hounds bulging in, from under Jim's bed ; and they kept on piling in till
here was eleven of them, and there warn't hardly room in there to get your
reath. By jings, we forgot to fasten that lean-to door. The nigger Nat he
nly just hollered " witches !" once, and keeled over onto the floor amongst the
ogs, and begun to groan like he was dying. Tom jerked the door open and
lung out a slab of Jim's meat, and the dogs went for it, and in two seconds he
vas out himself and back again and shut the door, and I knowed he'd fixed the
ther door too. Then he went to work on the nigger, coaxing him and petting

him, and asking him if he'd been imagining he saw something again.   He rais
up, and blinked his eyes around, and says :

"Mars Sid, you'll say I's a fool, but if I didn't b'lieve I see most a milli
dogs, er devils, er some'n, I wisht I may die right heah in dese tracks. I did, m
sholy. Mars Sid, I *felt* um—I *felt* um, sah ; dey was all over me.   Dad fetch

TOM ADVISES A WITCH PIE.

I jis' wisht I could git my ha
on one er dem witches jis' wur
—on'y jis' wunst—it's all *I*
ast. But mos'ly I wisht dey
lemme 'lone, I does."

Tom says:

"Well, I tell you what
think. What makes them cor
here just at this runaway ni
ger's breakfast-time ? It's b
cause they're hungry; that's tl
reason.   You make them
witch pie ; that's the thing f
you to do."

"But my lan', Mars Si
how's *I* gwyne to make 'm
witch pie ? I doan' know ho
to make it. I hain't ever hea
er sich a thing b'fo.' "

"Well, then, I'll have
make it myself."

"Will you do it, honey ?—will you ? I'll wusshup de groun' und' yo' foot,
will ! "

"All right, I'll do it, seeing it's you, and you've been good to us and showe
us the runaway nigger. But you got to be mighty careful. When we com
around, you turn your back ; and then whatever we've put in the pan, don't yo
let on you see it at all. And don't you look, when Jim unloads the pan—som

ng might happen, I don't know what.　And　above　all, don't you *handle* the
ch-things."

"*Hannel* 'm Mars Sid ?　What *is* you a talkin' 'bout ?　I wouldn' lay de
ght er my finger on um, not f'r ten hund'd thous'n' billion dollars, I
uldn't."

Chapter XXXVII

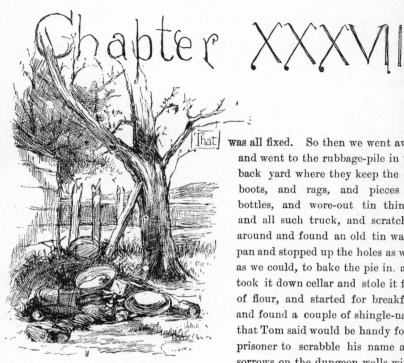

THE RUBBAGE-PILE.

That was all fixed. So then we went away and went to the rubbage-pile in the back yard where they keep the old boots, and rags, and pieces of bottles, and wore-out tin things, and all such truck, and scratched around and found an old tin wash pan and stopped up the holes as well as we could, to bake the pie in. and took it down cellar and stole it full of flour, and started for breakfast and found a couple of shingle-nails that Tom said would be handy for a prisoner to scrabble his name and sorrows on the dungeon walls with, and dropped one of them in Aunt Sally's apron pocket which was hanging on a chair, and t'other we stuck in the band of Uncle Silas's hat, which was on the bureau, because we heard the children say their pa and ma was going to the runaway nigger's house this morning, and then went to breakfast, and Tom dropped the pewter spoon in Uncle Silas's coat pocket, and Aunt Sally wasn't come yet, so we had to wait a little while.

And when she come she was hot, and red, and cross, and couldn't hardly wait for the blessing; and then she went to sluicing out coffee with one hand and

acking the handiest child's head with her thimble with the other, and
s :

"I've hunted high, and I've hunted low, and it does beat all, what *has* be-
me of your other shirt."

My heart fell down amongst my lungs and livers and things, and a hard piece
corn-crust started down my throat after it and got met on the road with a
ugh and was shot across the table and took one of the children in the
e and curled him up like a fishing-worm, and let a cry out of him the size of a
r-whoop, and Tom he turned kinder blue around the gills, and it all
nounted to a considerable state of things for about a quarter of a minute or as
uch as that, and I would a sold out for half price if there was a bidder.   But
ter that we was all right again—it was the sudden surprise of it that knocked
so kind of cold.   Uncle Silas he says :

"It's most uncommon curious, I can't understand it.   I know perfectly well
took it *off*, because——"

"Because you hain't got but one *on*.   Just *listen* at the man !   *I* know you
ok it off, and know it by a better way than your wool-gethering memory, too,
cause it was on the clo'es-line yesterday—I see it there myself.   But it's gone—
at's the long and the short of it, and you'll just have to change to a red flann'l
te till I can get time to make a new one.   And it'll be the third I've made in two
ars ; it just keeps a body on the jump to keep you in shirts ; and whatever you do
anage to *do* with 'm all, is more'n *I* can make out.   A body'd think you *would*
arn to take some sort of care of 'em, at your time of life."

"I know it, Sally, and I do try all I can.   But it oughtn't to be altogether
y fault, because you know I don't see them nor have nothing to do with them
cept when they're on me ; and I don't believe I've ever lost one of them *off*
me."

"Well, it ain't *your* fault if you haven't, Silas—you'd a done it if you could,
reckon.   And the shirt ain't all that's gone, nuther.   Ther's a spoon gone ; and
at ain't all.   There was ten, and now ther's only nine.   The calf got the shirt
reckon, but the calf never took the spoon, *that's* certain."

"Why, what else is gone, Sally ? "

"Ther's six *candles* gone—that's what. The rats could a got the candl
and I reckon they did; I wonder they don't walk off with the whole place, t

"MISSUS, DEY'S A SHEET GONE."

way you're always going to stop their hol
and don't do it; and if they warn't fo
they'd sleep in your hair, Silas—*you'd* ne
find it out; but you can't lay the *spoon*
the rats, and that I *know*."

"Well, Sally, I'm in fault, and I ackno
edge it; I've been remiss; but I won't
to-morrow go by without stopping up th
holes."

"Oh, I wouldn't hurry, next year'll d
Matilda Angelina Araminta *Phelps!*"

Whack comes the thimble, and the ch
snatches her claws out of the sugar-bo
without fooling around any. Just then, t
nigger woman steps onto the passage, a
says:

"Missus, dey's a sheet gone."

"A *sheet* gone! Well, for the lan
sake!"

"I'll stop up them holes *to-day*," sa
Uncles Silas, looking sorrowful.

"Oh, *do* shet up!—spose the rats took the *sheet? Where's* it gone, Lize?
"Clah to goodness I hain't no notion, Miss Sally. She wuz on de clo's-li
yistiddy, but she done gone; she ain' dah no mo,' now."

"I reckon the world *is* coming to an end. I *never* see the beat of it, in a
my born days. A shirt, and a sheet, and a spoon, and six can——"

"Missus," comes a young yaller wench, "dey's a brass cannelstick miss'n."

"Cler out from here, you hussy, er I'll take a skillet to ye!"

Well, she was just a biling. I begun to lay for a chance; I reckoned I wou
sneak out and go for the woods till the weather moderated. She kept a ragi

ht along, running her insurrection all by herself, and everybody else mighty
ek and quiet; and at last Uncle Silas, looking kind of foolish, fishes up that
on out of his pocket. She stopped, with her mouth open and her hands up;
I as for me, I wished I was in Jeruslem or somewheres. But not long; be-
se she says:

"It's *just* as I expected. So you had it in your pocket all the time; and like
not you've got the other things there, too. How'd it get there?"

"I reely don't know, Sally," he says, kind of apologizing, "or you know I
uld tell. I was a-studying over my text in Acts Seventeen, before breakfast,
I I reckon I put it in there, not noticing, meaning to put my Testament in,
I it must be so, because my Testament ain't in, but I'll go and see, and if the
stament is where I had it, I'll know I didn't put it in, and that will show that
uid the Testament down and took up the spoon, and——"

"Oh, for the land's sake! Give a body a rest! Go 'long now, the whole
and biling of ye; and don't come nigh me again till I've got back my peace of
nd."

I'd a heard her, if she'd a said it to herself, let alone speaking it out; and I'd
got up and obeyed her, if I'd a been dead. As we was passing through the
ting-room, the old man he took up his hat, and the shingle-nail fell out on the
or, and he just merely picked it up and laid it on the mantel-shelf, and never
d nothing, and went out. Tom see him do it, and remembered about the
oon, and says:

"Well, it ain't no use to send things by *him* no more, he ain't reliable."
en he says: "But he done us a good turn with the spoon, anyway, without
owing it, and so we'll go and do him one without *him* knowing it—stop up his
-holes."

There was a noble good lot of them, down cellar, and it took us a whole hour,
t we done the job tight and good, and ship-shape. Then we heard steps on
e stairs, and blowed out our light, and hid; and here comes the old man, with
candle in one hand and a bundle of stuff in t'other, looking as absent-minded
year before last. He went a mooning around, first to one rat-hole and then
other, till he'd been to them all. Then he stood about five minutes, picking

tallow-drip off of his candle and thinking. Then he turns off slow and drea▮
towards the stairs, saying :

" Well, for the life of me I can't remember when I done it. I could sh▮
her now that I warn't to blame on account of the rats. But never mind—let
go. I reckon it wouldn't do no good."

And so he went on a mumbling up stairs, and then we left. He was a migl▮
nice old man. And always is.

Tom was a good deal bothered about what to do for a spoon, but he said w▮
got to have it ; so he took a think. When he had ciphered it out, he told me h▮
we was to do ; then we went and waited around the spoon-basket till we ▮
Aunt Sally coming, and then Tom went to counting the spoons and laying th▮
out to one side, and I slid one of them up my sleeve, and Tom says :

" Why, Aunt Sally, there ain't but nine spoons, *yet.*"

She says :

" Go 'long to your play, and don't bother me. I know better, I counted ▮
myself."

" Well, I've counted them twice, Aunty, and *I* can't make but nine."

She looked out of all patience, but of course she come to count—anybo▮
would.

" I declare to gracious ther' *ain't* but nine !" she says. " Why, what in t▮
world—plague *take* the things, I'll count 'm again."

So I slipped back the one I had, and when she got done counting, she says :

" Hang the troublesome rubbage, ther's *ten*, now !" and she looked huffy a▮
bothered both. But Tom says :

" Why, Aunty, *I* don't think there's ten."

" You numskull, didn't you see me *count* 'm ?"

" I know, but——"

" Well, I'll count 'm *again*."

So I smouched one, and they come out nine same as the other time. We
she *was* in a tearing way—just a trembling all over, she was so mad. But s▮
counted and counted, till she got that addled she'd start to count-in the *bask*
for a spoon, sometimes ; and so, three times they come out right, and three tim▮

ey come out wrong. Then she grabbed up the basket and slammed it across the
use and knocked the cat galley-west ; and she said cle'r out and let her have

me peace, and if we come bothering
ound her again betwixt that and
nner, she'd skin us. So we had the
d spoon ; and dropped it in her
ron pocket whilst she was a giving us
r sailing-orders, and Jim got it all
ght, along with her shingle-nail, be-
re noon. We was very well satis-
d with this business, and Tom al-
wed it was worth twice the trouble
took, because he said *now* she
uldn't ever count them spoons twice
ke again to save her life ; and
ouldn't believe she'd counted them
ght, if she *did ;* and said that after
e'd about counted her head off, for
e next three days, he judged she'd
ve it up and offer to kill anybody
at wanted her to ever count them any more.

IN A TEARING WAY.

So we put the sheet back on the line, that night, and stole one out of her
oset ; and kept on putting it back and stealing it again, for a couple of days,
l she didn't know how many sheets she had, any more, and said she didn't
re, and warn't agoing to bullyrag the rest of her soul out about it, and wouldn't
unt them again not to save her life, she druther die first.

So we was all right now, as to the shirt and the sheet and the spoon and the
ndles, by the help of the calf and the rats and the mixed-up counting ; and as
the candlestick, it warn't no consequence, it would blow over by-and-by.

But that pie was a job ; we had no end of trouble with that pie. We fixed it
p away down in the woods, and cooked it there ; and we got it done at last, and
ry satisfactory, too ; but not all in one day ; and we had to use up three wash-

pans full of flour, before we got through, and we got burnt pretty much
over, in places, and eyes put out with the smoke; because, you see, we did
want nothing but a crust, and we couldn't prop it up right, and she wou
always cave in. But of course we thought of the right way at last; which w
to cook the ladder, too, in the pie. So then we laid in with Jim, the second nigl
and tore up the sheet all in little strings, and twisted them together, and lo
before daylight we had a lovely rope, that you could a hung a person wit
We let on it took nine months to make it.

ONE OF HIS ANCESTERS.

And in the forenoon we took it down
the woods, but it wouldn't go in the p
Being made of a whole sheet, that way, the
was rope enough for forty pies, if we'd
wanted them, and plenty left over for sou
or sausage, or anything you choose.
could a had a whole dinner.

But we didn't need it. All we needed w
just enough for the pie, and so we throw
the rest away. We didn't cook none of t
pies in the washpan, afraid the solder wou
melt; but Uncle Silas he had a noble br
warming-pan which he thought considerat
of, because it belonged to one of his ancest
with a long wooden handle that come ov
from England with William the Conquer
in the *Mayflower* or one of them early shi
and was hid away up garret with a lot

other old pots and things that was valuable, not on account of being any accou
because they warn't, but on account of them being relicts, you know, and
snaked her out, private, and took her down there, but she failed on the first pi
because we didn't know how, but she come up smiling on the last one. We to
and lined her with dough, and set her in the coals, and loaded her up with ra
rope, and put on a dough roof, and shut down the lid, and put hot embers

, and stood off five foot, with the long handle, cool and comfortable, and in
een minutes she turned out a pie that was a satisfaction to look at. But the
son that et it would want to fetch a couple of kags of toothpicks along, for
hat rope-ladder wouldn't cramp him down to business, I don't know nothing
at I'm talking about, and lay him in enough stomach-ache to last him till next
e, too.

Nat didn't look, when we put the witch-pie in Jim's pan; and we put the three
plates in the bottom of the pan under the vittles; and so Jim got everything
right, and as soon as he was by himself he busted into the pie and hid the rope-
der inside of his straw tick, and scratched some marks on a tin plate and
owed it out of the window-hole.

Chapter XXXVIII

JIM'S COAT OF ARMS.

Making them pens was a distres[s] tough job, and so was the saw; Jim allowed the inscription going to be the toughest of That's the one which the priso[ner] has to scrabble on the wall. But had to have it; Tom said we'd to; there warn't no case of a st[ate] prisoner not scrabbling his inscr[ip]tion to leave behind, and his coa[t] arms.

"Look at Lady Jane Grey," says; "look at Gilford Dudl[ey] look at old Northumberland! W[ell,] Huck, spose it *is* considerble troub[le] —what you going to do?—how y[ou] going to get around it? Jim's [got] to do his inscription and coat arms. They all do."

Jim says:

"Why, Mars Tom, I hain't got no coat o' arms; I hain't got nuffn but di[s] yer ole shirt, en you knows I got to keep de journal on dat."

"Oh, you don't understand, Jim; a coat of arms is very different."

"Well," I says, "Jim's right, anyway, when he says he hain't got no coat [o'] arms, because he hain't."

' I reckon *I* knowed that," Tom says, " but you bet he'll have one before he
s out of this—because he's going out *right*, and there ain't going to be no
s in his record."

So whilst me and Jim filed away at the pens on a brickbat apiece, Jim a
ting his'n out of the brass and I making mine out of the spoon, Tom set to
k to think out the coat of arms. By-and-by he said he'd struck so many good
s he didn't hardly know which to take, but there was one which he reckoned
l decide on. He says :

"On the scutcheon we'll have a bend *or* in the dexter base, a saltire *murrey*
he fess, with a dog, couchant, for common charge, and under his foot a chain
attled, for slavery, with a chevron *vert* in a chief engrailed, and three
cted lines on a field *azure*, with the nombril points rampant on a dancette
nted ; crest, a runaway nigger, *sable*, with his bundle over his shoulder on a
sinister : and a couple of gules for supporters, which is you and me ;
to, *Maggiore fretta, minore atto.* Got it out of a book—means, the more
e, the less speed."

"Geewhillikins," I says, "but what does the rest of it mean ?"

"We ain't got no time to bother over that," he says, "we got to dig in like
git-out."

"Well, anyway," I says, "what's *some* of it ? What's a fess ?"

"A fess—a fess is—*you* don't need to know what a fess is. I'll show him
to make it when he gets to it."

"Shucks, Tom," I says, " I think you might tell a person. What's a bar
ster ?"

"Oh, *I* don't know. But he's got to have it. All the nobility does."

That was just his way. If it didn't suit him to explain a thing to you, he
ldn't do it. You might pump at him a week, it wouldn't make no
erence.

He'd got all that coat of arms business fixed, so now he started in to finish
the rest of that part of the work, which was to plan out a mournful inscrip-
—said Jim got to have one, like they all done. He made up a lot, and wrote
m out on a paper, and read them off, so :

1. *Here a captive heart busted.*

2. *Here a poor prisoner, forsook by the world and friends, fretted out sorrowful life.*

3. *Here a lonely heart broke, and a worn spirit went to its rest, after thi*
seven years of solitary captivity.

4. *Here, homeless and friendless, after thirty-seven years of bitter captiv*
perished a noble stranger, natural son of Louis XIV.

Tom's voice trembled, whilst he was reading them, and he most broke do
When he got done, he couldn't no way make up his mind which one for Jim
scrabble onto the wall, they was all so good ; but at last he allowed he would
him scrabble them all on.   Jim said it would take him a year to scrabble suc
lot of truck onto the logs with a nail, and he didn't know how to make lett
besides ; but Tom said he would block them out for him, and then he woul
have nothing to do but just follow the lines.   Then pretty soon he says :

"Come to think, the logs ain't agoing to do ; they don't have log walls i
dungeon : we got to dig the inscriptions into a rock.   We'll fetch a rock."

Jim said the rock was worse than the logs ; he said it would take him suc
pison long time to dig them into a rock, he wouldn't ever get out.   But Tom s
he would let me help him do it.   Then he took a look to see how me and .
was getting along with the pens.   It was most pesky tedious hard work and sl
and didn't give my hands no show to get well of the sores, and we didn't seen
make no headway, hardly.   So Tom says :

"I know how to fix it.   We got to have a rock for the coat of arms ı
mournful inscriptions, and we can kill two birds with that same rock.   There
gaudy big grindstone down at the mill, and we'll smouch it, and carve the thi
on it, and file out the pens and the saw on it, too."

It warn't no slouch of an idea ; and it warn't no slouch of a grindst
nuther ; but we allowed we'd tackle it.   It warn't quite midnight, yet, so
cleared out for the mill, leaving Jim at work.   We smouched the grindsto
and set out to roll her home, but it was a most nation tough job.   Sometimes,
what we could, we couldn't keep her from falling over, and she come mig'

· mashing us, every time. Tom said she was going to get one of us, sure,
·re we got through. We got her half way; and then we was plumb played
and most drownded with sweat. We see it warn't no use, we got to go and
h Jim. So he raised up his bed and slid the chain off of the bed-leg, and
pt it round and round his neck, and we crawled out through our hole and
n there, and Jim and me laid into that grindstone and walked her along like

A TOUGH JOB

hing; and Tom superintended. He could out-superintend any boy I ever see.
knowed how to do everything.

Our hole was pretty big, but it warn't big enough to get the grindstone
ough; but Jim he took the pick and soon made it big enough. Then Tom
rked out them things on it with the nail, and set Jim to work on them, with
· nail for a chisel and an iron bolt from the rubbage in the lean-to for a

hammer, and told him to work till the rest of his candle quit on him, and t
he could go to bed, and hide the grindstone under his straw tick and sleep o
Then we helped him fix his chain back on the bed-leg, and was ready for bed
selves.   But Tom thought of something, and says :

"You got any spiders in here, Jim ?"

"No, sah, thanks to goodness I hain't, Mars Tom."

"All right, we'll get you some."

"But bless you, honey, I doan' *want* none.   I's afeard un um.   I jis' 's s
have rattlesnakes aroun'."

Tom thought a minute or two, and says :

"It's a good idea.   And I reckon it's been done.   It *must* a been done
stands to reason.   Yes, it's a prime good idea.   Where could you keep it ?"

"Keep what, Mars Tom ?"

"Why, a rattlesnake."

"De goodness gracious alive, Mars Tom !   Why, if dey was a rattlesnak
come in heah, I'd take en bust right out thoo dat log wall, I would, wid
head."

"Why, Jim, you wouldn't be afraid of it, after a little.   You could tame

"*Tame* it !"

"Yes—easy enough.   Every animal is grateful for kindness and petting,
they wouldn't *think* of hurting a person that pets them.   Any book will
you that.   You try—that's all I ask ; just try for two or three days.   Why,
can get him so, in a little while, that he'll love you ; and sleep with you ;
won't stay away from you a minute ; and will let you wrap him round your n
and put his head in your mouth."

"*Please*, Mars Tom—*doan'* talk so !   I can't *stan'* it !   He'd *let* me shove
head in my mouf—fer a favor, hain't it ?   I lay he'd wait a pow'ful long time
I *ast* him.   En mo' en dat, I doan' *want* him to sleep wid me."

"Jim, don't act so foolish.   A prisoner's *got* to have some kind of a du
pet, and if a rattlesnake hain't ever been tried, why, there's more glory to
gained in your being the first to ever try it than any other way you could e
think of to save your life."

"Why, Mars Tom, I doan' *want* no sich glory. Snake take 'n bite Jim's off, den *whah* is de glory? No, sah, I doan' want no sich doin's."

"Blame it, can't you *try*? I only *want* you to try—you needn't keep it up if on't work."

'But de trouble all *done*, ef de snake bite me while I's a tryin' him. 's Tom, I's willin' to tackle mos' anything 'at ain't onreasonable, but ef you

BUTTONS ON THEIR TAILS.

Huck fetches a rattlesnake in heah for me to tame, I's gwyne to *leave*, dat's e."

"Well, then, let it go, let it go, if you're so bullheaded about it. We can get some garter-snakes and you can tie some buttons on their tails, and let on y're rattlesnakes, and I reckon that'll have to do."

"I k'n stan' *dem*, Mars Tom, but blame' 'f I couldn' get along widout um, ll you dat. I never knowed b'fo', 't was so much bother and trouble to be a soner."

"Well, it *always* is, when it's done right. You got any rats around e?"

"No, sah, I hain't seed none."

"Well, we'll get you some rats."

" Why, Mars Tom, I doan' *want* no rats. Dey's de dad-blamedest creturs
sturb a body, en rustle roun' over 'im, en bite his feet, when he's tryin' to sleep
ever see. No, sah, gimme g'yarter-snakes, 'f I's got to have 'm, but doan' gim
no rats, I ain' got no use f'r um, skasely."

" But Jim, you *got* to have 'em—they all do. So don't make no more f
about it. Prisoners ain't ever without rats. There ain't no instance of
And they train them, and pet them, and learn them tricks, and they get
be as sociable as flies. But you got to play music to them. You got anythi
to play music on ? "

" I ain' got nuffn but a coase comb en a piece o' paper, en a juice-harp;
I reck'n dey wouldn' take no stock in a juice-harp."

" Yes they would. *They* don't care what kind of music 'tis. A jew-shar
plenty good enough for a rat. All animals likes music—in a prison they dote
it. Specially, painful music ; and you can't get no other kind out of a jev
harp. It always interests them ; they come out to see what's the matter with yo
Yes, you're all right ; you're fixed very well. You want to set on your be
nights, before you go to sleep, and early in the mornings, and play your jev
harp ; play The Last Link is Broken—that's the thing that'll scoop a r
quicker'n anything else : and when you've played about two minutes, you'll
all the rats, and the snakes, and spiders, and things begin to feel worr
about you, and come. And they'll just fairly swarm over you, and have a nol
good time."

" Yes, *dey* will, I reck'n, Mars Tom, but what kine er time is *Jim* havir
Blest if I kin see de pint. But I'll do it ef I got to. I reck'n I better keep
animals satisfied, en not have no trouble in de house."

Tom waited to think over, and see if there wasn't nothing else ; and pret
soon he says :

" Oh—there's one thing I forgot. Could you raise a flower here, do y
reckon ? "

" I doan' know but maybe I could, Mars Tom ; but it's tolable dark
heah, en I ain' got no use f'r no flower, nohow, en she'd be a pow'ful sight
trouble."

"Well, you try it, anyway. Some other prisoners has done it."

"One er dem big cat-tail-lookin' mullen-stalks would grow in heah, Mars Tom,
eck'n, but she wouldn' be wuth half de trouble she'd coss."

"Don't you believe it. We'll fetch you a little one, and you plant it in the
rner, over there, and raise it. And don't call it mullen, call it Pitchiola—
t's its right name, when it's in a prison. And you want to water it with your
rs."

"Why, I got plenty spring water, Mars Tom."

"You don't *want* spring water ; you want to water it with your tears. It's
e way they always do."

"Why, Mars Tom, I lay I kin raise one er dem mullen-stalks twyste wid
ing water whiles another man's a *start'n* one wid tears."

"That ain't the idea. You *got* to do it with tears."

"She'll die on my han's, Mars Tom, she sholy will ; kase I doan' skasely ever
r."

So Tom was stumped. But he studied it over, and then said Jim would have

IRRIGATION.

worry along the best he could
th an onion. He promised
would go to the nigger cabins
d drop one, private, in Jim's
ffee-pot, in the morning. Jim
d he would "jis' 's soon have
acker in his coffee ;" and found
much fault with it, and with
e work and bother of raising
e mullen, and jews-harping the
es, and petting and flattering
the snakes and spiders and
ings, on top of all the other
rk he had to do on pens, and
scriptions, and journals, and things, which made it more trouble and worry and
sponsibility to be a prisoner than anything he ever undertook, that Tom most

lost all patience with him ; and said he was just loadened down with m
gaudier chances than a prisoner ever had in the world to make a name for hi
self, and yet he didn't know enough to appreciate them, and they was just abc
wasted on him. So Jim he was sorry, and said he wouldn't behave so no mo
and then me and Tom shoved for bed.

Chapter XXXIX

KEEPING OFF DULL TIMES.

In the morning we went up to the village and bought a wire rat trap and fetched it down, and unstopped the best rat hole, and in about an hour we had fifteen of the bulliest kind of ones; and then we took it and put it in a safe place under Aunt Sally's bed. But while we was gone for spiders, little Thomas Franklin Benjamin Jefferson Elexander Phelps found it there, and opened the door of it to see if the rats would come out, and they did; and Aunt Sally she come in, and when we got back she was a standing on top of the bed raising Cain, and the rats was doing what they could to keep off the dull times for her. So she took and dusted us both with the hickry, and we was as much as two hours catching another fifteen or sixteen, drat that meddlesome cub, and they n't the likeliest, nuther, because the first haul was the pick of the flock. I er see a likelier lot of rats than what that first haul was.

We got a splendid stock of sorted spiders, and bugs, and frogs, and cater-ars, and one thing or another; and we like-to got a hornet's nest, but we n't. The family was at home. We didn't give it right up, but staid with m as long as we could; because we allowed we'd tire them out or they'd got to tire us out, and they done it. Then we got allycumpain and rubbed the places, and was pretty near all right again, but couldn't set down convenies And so we went for the snakes, and grabbed a couple of dozen garters and hous snakes, and put them in a bag, and put it in our room, and by that time it w supper time, and a rattling good honest day's work; and hungry?—oh, no, reckon not! And there warn't a blessed snake up there, when we went back— didn't half tie the sack, and they worked out, somehow, and left. But it did matter much, because they was still on the premises somewheres. So we judg we could get some of them again. No, there warn't no real scarcity of snak about the house for a considerble spell. You'd see them dripping from t rafters and places, every now and then; and they generly landed in your pla or down the back of your neck, and most of the time where you didn't want the Well, they was handsome, and striped, and there warn't no harm in a million them; but that never made no difference to Aunt Sally, she despised snakes, be t breed what they might, and she couldn't stand them no way you could fix it; a every time one of them flopped down on her, it didn't make no difference wh she was doing, she would just lay that work down and light out. I never such a woman. And you could hear her whoop to Jericho. You couldn't g her to take aholt of one of them with the tongs. And if she turned ov and found one in bed, she would scramble out and lift a howl that you wou think the house was afire. She disturbed the old man so, that he said could most wish there hadn't ever been no snakes created. Why, after every l snake had been gone clear out of the house for as much as a week, Aunt Sa warn't over it yet; she warn't near over it; when she was setting thinking abo something, you could touch her on the back of her neck with a feather and s would jump right out of her stockings. It was very curious. But Tom said women was just so. He said they was made that way; for some reason other.

We got a licking every time one of our snakes come in her way; and she lowed these lickings warn't nothing to what she would do if we ever loaded up t place again with them. I didn't mind the lickings, because they didn't amou to nothing; but I minded the trouble we had, to lay in another lot. But we g

m laid in, and all the other things ; and you never see a cabin as blithesome as
n's was when they'd all swarm out for music and go for him.   Jim didn't like
spiders, and the spiders didn't like Jim ; and so they'd lay for him and make
nighty warm for him.   And he said that between the rats, and the snakes, and
grindstone, there warn't no room in bed for him, skasely ; and when there
s, a body couldn't sleep, it was so lively, and it was always lively, he said, be-
se *they* never all slept at one time, but took turn about, so when the snakes
s asleep the rats was on deck, and when the rats turned in the snakes come on
tch, so he always had one gang under him, in his way, and t'other gang hav-
a circus over him, and if he got up to hunt a new place, the spiders would
e a chance at him as he crossed over.   He said if he ever got out, this time, he
uldn't ever be a prisoner again, not for a salary.

Well, by the end of three weeks, everything was in pretty good shape.   The

rt was sent in early, in a pie, and every
ne a rat bit Jim he would get up and
ite a little in his journal whilst the ink
s fresh ; the pens was made, the in-
riptions and so on was all carved on
e grindstone ; the bed-leg was sawed in
o, and we had et up the sawdust, and it
e us a most amazing stomach-ache.
e reckoned we was all going to die, but
ln't.   It was the most undigestible
wdust I ever see ; and Tom said the
ne.   But as I was saying, we'd got all
e work done, now, at last; and we was
    pretty much fagged out, too, but
inly Jim.   The old man had wrote a
uple of times to the plantation below

SAWDUST DIET.

leans to come and get their runaway nigger, but hadn't got no answer, because
ere warn't no such plantation ; so he allowed he would advertise Jim in the St.
uis and New Orleans papers ; and when he mentioned the St. Louis ones, it

give me the cold shivers, and I see we hadn't no time to lose. So Tom sa
now for the nonnamous letters.

"What's them ? " I says.

"Warnings to the people that something is up. Sometimes it's done o
way, sometimes another. But there's always somebody spying around, that gi
notice to the governor of the castle. When Louis XVI. was going to light out
the Tooleries, a servant girl done it. It's a very good way, and so is the no
namous letters. We'll use them both. And it's usual for the prisoner's moth
to change clothes with him, and she stays in, and he slides out in her cloth
We'll do that too."

"But looky here, Tom, what do we want to *warn* anybody for, that son
thing's up ? Let them find it out for themselves—it's their lookout."

"Yes, I know; but you can't depend on them. It's the way they've act
from the very start—left us to do *everything.* They're so confiding and mull
headed they don't take notice of nothing at all. So if we don't *give* them noti
there won't be nobody nor nothing to interfere with us, and so after all o
hard work and trouble this escape 'll go off perfectly flat: won't amount to not
ing—won't be nothing *to* it."

"Well, as for me, Tom, that's the way I'd like."

"Shucks," he says, and looked disgusted. So I says :

"But I ain't going to make no complaint. Anyway that suits you suits n
What you going to do about the servant-girl ? "

"You'll be her. You slide in, in the middle of the night, and hook th
yaller girl's frock."

"Why, Tom, that'll make trouble next morning ; because of course she pro
bly hain't got any but that one."

"I know ; but you don't want it but fifteen minutes, to carry the nonnam
letter and shove it under the front door."

"All right, then, I'll do it ; but I could carry it just as handy in my o
togs."

"You wouldn't look like a servant-girl *then*, would you ?"

"No, but there won't be nobody to see what I look like, *anyway*."

" That ain't got nothing to do with it. The thing for us to do, is just to do duty, and not worry about whether anybody *sees* us do it or not. Hain't you no principle at all ? "

" All right, I ain't saying nothing; I'm the servant-girl. Who's Jim's ther? "

" I'm his mother. I'll k a gown from Aunt ly."

" Well, then, you'll have stay in the cabin when me Jim leaves."

" Not much. I'll stuff 's clothes full of straw lay it on his bed to re-sent his mother in dis-se, and Jim 'll take the ger woman's gown off of and wear it, and we'll all de together. When a pri-er of style escapes, it's led an evasion. It's al-ys called so when a king apes, f'rinstance. And the ne with a king's son ; it 't make no difference ether he's a natural one or an unnatural one."

TROUBLE IS BREWING.

So Tom he wrote the nonnamous letter, and I smouched the yaller wench's ck, that night, and put it on, and shoved it under the front door, the way Tom d me to. It said :

> *Beware. Trouble is brewing. Keep a sharp lookout.* UNKNOWN FRIEND.

Next night we stuck a picture which Tom drawed in blood, of a skull and ssbones, on the front door ; and next night another one of a coffin, on the

back door. I never see a family in such a sweat. They couldn't a been wor
scared if the place had a been full of ghosts laying for them behind everythi
and under the beds and shivering through the air.   If a door banged, Aunt Sa
she jumped, and said " ouch ! " if anything fell, she jumped and said "ouch
if you happened to touch her, when she warn't noticing, she done the same ; sl
couldn't face noway and be satisfied, because she allowed there was somethi
behind her every time—so she was always a whirling around, sudden, and sayi
" ouch," and before she'd get two-thirds around, she'd whirl back again, a
say it again ; and she was afraid to go to bed, but she dasn't set up.   So t
thing was working very well, Tom said ; he said he never see a thing work mo
satisfactory.   He said it showed it was done right.

So he said, now for the grand bulge ! So the very next morning at t
streak of dawn we got another letter ready, and was wondering what we bett
do with it, because we heard them say at supper they was going to have a nigg
on watch at both doors all night.   Tom he went down the lightning-rod to sj
around ; and the nigger at the back door was asleep, and he stuck it in the bac
of his neck and come back.   This letter said :

Don't betray me, I wish to be your friend.   There is a desprate gang of cutthroats from o
in the Ingean Territory going to steal your runaway nigger to-night, and they have been trying
scare you so as you will stay in the house and not bother them.   I am one of the gang, but h
got religgion and wish to quit it and lead a honest life again, and will betray the helish desi
They will sneak down from northards, along the fence, at midnight exact, with a false key, and
in the nigger's cabin to get him.   I am to be off a piece and blow a tin horn if I see any dange
but stead of that, I will BA like a sheep soon as they get in and not blow at all; then whilst they a
getting his chains loose, you slip there and lock them in, and can kill them at your leasure.   Do
do anything but just the way I am telling you, if you do they will suspicion something and ra
whoopjamboreehoo.   I do not wish any reward but to know I have done the right thing.

UNKNOWN FRIEND.

Chapter XL

FISHING.

We was feeling pretty good, after breakfast, and took my canoe and went over the river a fishing, with a lunch, and had a good time, and took a look at the raft and found her all right, and got home late to supper, and found them in such a sweat and worry they didn't know which end they was standing on, and made us go right off to bed the minute we was done supper, and wouldn't tell us what the trouble was, and never let on a word about the new letter, but didn't need to, because we knowed as much about it as anybody did, and as soon as we was

—lf up stairs and her back was turned, we slid for the cellar cubboard and loaded—— a good lunch and took it up to our room and went to bed, and got up —out half-past eleven, and Tom put on Aunt Sally's dress that he stole and —s going to start with the lunch, but says:

"Where's the butter?"

"I laid out a hunk of it," I says, "on a piece of a corn-pone."

"Well, you *left* it laid out, then—it ain't here."

"We can get along without it," I says.

"We can get along *with* it, too," he says; "just you slide down cellar and

fetch it. And then mosey right down the lightning-rod and come along. I'
go and stuff the straw into Jim's clothes to represent his mother in disguise, an
be ready to *ba* like a sheep and shove soon as you get there."

So out he went, and down cellar went I. The hunk of butter, big as
person's fist, was where I had left it, so I took up the slab of corn-pone with
on, and blowed out my light, and started up stairs, very stealthy, and got up t
the main floor all right, but here comes Aunt Sally with a candle, and I clappe
the truck in my hat, and clapped my hat on my head, and the next second sh
see me ; and she says :

" You been down cellar ? "

" Yes'm."

" What you been doing down there ? "

" Noth'n."

" *Noth'n !* "

" No'm."

" Well, then, what possessed you to go down there, this time of night ? "

" I don't know'm."

" You don't *know* ? Don't answer me that way, Tom, I want to know wh
you been *doing* down there ? "

"I hain't been doing a single thing, Aunt Sally, I hope to gracious if
have."

I reckoned she'd let me go, now, and as a generl thing she would ; but
spose there was so many strange things going on she was just in a sweat abo
every little thing that warn't yard-stick straight ; so she says, very decided :

"You just march into that setting-room and stay there till I come. Yo
been up to something you no business to, and I lay I'll find out what it is befo
I'm done with you."

So she went away as I opened the door and walked into the setting-room. My
but there was a crowd there ! Fifteen farmers, and every one of them had a gur
I was most powerful sick, and slunk to a chair and set down. They was settin
around, some of them talking a little, in a low voice, and all of them fidgety an
uneasy, but trying to look like they warn't ; but I knowed they was, because the

as always taking off their hats, and putting them on, and scratching their heads, and changing their seats, and fumbling with their buttons. I warn't easy myself, but I didn't take my hat off, all the same.

I did wish Aunt Sally would come, and get done with me, and lick me, if she wanted to, and let me get away and tell Tom how we'd overdone this thing, and what a thundering hornet's nest we'd got ourselves into, so we could stop

EVERY ONE HAD A GUN.

fooling around, straight off, and clear out with Jim before these rips got out of patience and come for us.

At last she come, and begun to ask me questions, but I *couldn't* answer them straight, I didn't know which end of me was up ; because these men was in such a fidget now, that some was wanting to start right *now* and lay for them desperadoes, and saying it warn't but a few minutes to midnight ; and others was trying to get them to hold on and wait for the sheep-signal ; and here was aunty pegging away at the questions, and me a shaking all over and ready to sink down in my tracks I was that scared ; and the place getting hotter and hotter, and the butter beginning to melt and run down my neck and behind my ears ; and pretty soon, when one of them says, " *I'm* for going and getting in the cabin *first*, an right *now*, and catching them when they come," I most dropped ; and a streak butter come a trickling down my forehead, and Aunt Sally she see it, and turi white as a sheet, and says :

"For the land's sake what *is* the matter with the child !—he's got tl brain fever as shore as you're born, and they're oozing out !"

And everybody runs to see, and she snatches off my hat, and out comes tl bread, and what was left of the butter, and she grabbed me, and hugged me, an says :

"Oh, what a turn you did give me ! and how glad and grateful I am it ain no worse ; for luck's against us, and it never rains but it pours, and when I so that truck I thought we'd lost you, for I knowed by the color and all, it was ju like your brains would be if— Dear, dear, whyd'nt you *tell* me that was wh: you'd been down there for, *I* wouldn't a cared. Now cler out to bed, and don lemme see no more of you till morning ! "

I was up stairs in a second, and down the lightning-rod in another one, an shinning through the dark for the lean-to. I couldn't hardly get my words ou I was so anxious; but I told Tom as quick as I could, we must jump for it, now and not a minute to lose—the house full of men, yonder, with guns !

His eyes just blazed ; and he says:

"No !—is that so ? *Ain't* it bully ! Why, Huck, if it was to do over agai I bet I could fetch two hundred ! If we could put it off till——"

"Hurry ! *hurry !* " I says. " Where's Jim ? "

"Right at your elbow ; if you reach out your arm you can touch him. He dressed, and everything's ready. Now we'll slide out and give the shee signal."

But then we heard the tramp of men, coming to the door, and heard the begin to fumble with the padlock ; and heard a man say :

"I *told* you we'd be too soon ; they haven't come—the door is locked. Her I'll lock some of you into the cabin and you lay for 'em in the dark and kill 'e when they come ; and the rest scatter around a piece, and listen if you can he: 'em coming."

So in they come, but couldn't see us in the dark, and most trod on us whilst
was hustling to get under the bed. But we got under all right, and out
rough the hole, swift but soft—Jim first, me next, and Tom last, which was
cording to Tom's orders. Now we was in the lean-to, and heard trampings
se by outside. So we crept to the door, and Tom stopped us there and put his

e to the crack, but couldn't make out
thing, it was so dark ; and whispered
d said he would listen for the steps to
t further, and when he nudged us Jim
ast glide out first, and him last. So
set his ear to the crack and listened,
d listened, and listened, and the steps
craping around, out there, all the time;
d at last he nudged us, and we slid out,
d stooped down, not breathing, and
t making the least noise, and slipped
ealthy towards the fence, in Injun file,
d got to it, all right, and me and Jim
er it ; but Tom's britches catched
st on a splinter on the top rail, and
en he hear the steps coming, so he
d to pull loose, which snapped the
linter and made a noise ; and as he
opped in our tracks and started,
mebody sings out :

TOM CAUGHT ON A SPLINTER.

" Who's that ? Answer, or I'll shoot ! "

But we didn't answer ; we just unfurled our heels and shoved. Then there
as a rush, and a *bang, bang, bang !* and the bullets fairly whizzed around us !
e heard them sing out :

" Here they are ! They've broke for the river ! after 'em, boys ! And turn
ose the dogs ! "

So here they come, full tilt. We could hear them, because they wore boots,

and yelled, but we didn't wear no boots, and didn't yell. We was in the path t
the mill; and when they got pretty close onto us, we dodged into the bush and l
them go by, and then dropped in behind them. They'd had all the dogs shut u
so they wouldn't scare off the robbers; but by this time somebody had let the
loose, and here they come, making pow-wow enough for a million; but they wa
our dogs; so we stopped in our tracks till they catched up; and when they see
warn't nobody but us, and no excitement to offer them, they only just said howd
and tore right ahead towards the shouting and clattering; and then we up stea
again and whizzed along after them till we was nearly to the mill, and then struc
up through the bush to where my canoe was tied, and hopped in and pulled f
dear life towards the middle of the river, but didn't make no more noise tha
we was obleeged to. Then we struck out, easy and comfortable, for the islan
where my raft was; and we could hear them yelling and barking at each other a
up and down the bank, till we was so far away the sounds got dim and died ou
And when we stepped onto the raft, I says:

"*Now*, old Jim, you're a free man *again*, and I bet you won't ever be a sla
no more."

"En a mighty good job it wuz, too, Huck. It 'uz planned beautiful, en it '
done beautiful; en dey ain't *nobody* kin git up a plan dat's mo' mixed-up e
splendid den what dat one wuz."

We was all as glad as we could be, but Tom was the gladdest of all, becau
he had a bullet in the calf of his leg.

When me and Jim heard that, we didn't feel so brash as what we did befor
It was hurting him considerble, and bleeding; so we laid him in the wigwa
and tore up one of the duke's shirts for to bandage him, but he says:

"Gimme the rags, I can do it myself. Don't stop, now; don't fool aroun
here, and the evasion booming along so handsome; man the sweeps, and set h
loose! Boys, we done it elegant!—'deed we did. I wish *we'd* a had the handlin
of Louis XVI., there wouldn't a been no 'Son of Saint Louis, ascend to heaven
wrote down in *his* biography: no, sir, we'd a whooped him over the *border-*
that's what we'd a done with *him*—and done it just as slick as nothing at all, to
Man the sweeps—man the sweeps!"

But me and Jim was consulting—and thinking. And after we'd thought a
nute, I says :

" Say it, Jim."

So he says :

" Well, den, dis is de way it look to me, Huck.   Ef it wuz *him* dat 'uz
n' sot free, en one er de boys wuz to git shot, would he say, ' Go on
save me, nemmine 'bout a doctor f'r to save dis one ?   Is dat like Mars
m Sawyer ?   Would he say dat ?   You *bet* he wouldn't !   *Well*, den, is *Jim*
yne to say it ?   No, sah—I doan' budge a step out'n dis place, 'dout a *doctor ;*
t if it's forty year ! "

I knowed he was white inside,
d I reckoned he'd say what he did
—so it was all right, now, and I
d Tom I was agoing for a doctor.
e raised considerble row about it,
t me and Jim stuck to it and
uldn't budge ; so he was for crawl-
g out and setting the raft loose
mself ; but we wouldn't let him.
en he give us a piece of his mind
but it didn't do no good.

So when he see me getting the
noe ready, he says :

" Well, then, if you're bound to
, I'll tell you the way to do, when
u get to the village.   Shut the
or, and blindfold the doctor tight
d fast, and make him swear to be
ent as the grave, and put a purse
ll of gold in his hand, and then

JIM ADVISES A DOCTOR.

ke and lead him all around the back alleys and everywheres, in the dark, and
en fetch him here in the canoe, in a roundabout way amongst the islands,

and search him and take his chalk away from him, and don't give it back him till you get him back to the village, or else he will chalk this raft he can find it again. It's the way they all do."

So I said I would, and left, and Jim was to hide in the woods when he s the doctor coming, till he was gone again.

Chapter XLI

THE DOCTOR.

The doctor was an old man ; a very nice, kind-looking old man, when I got him up. I told him me and my brother was over on Spanish Island hunting, yesterday afternoon, and camped on a piece of a raft we found, and about midnight he must a kicked his gun in his dreams, for it went off and shot him in the leg, and we wanted him to go over there and fix it and not say nothing about it, nor let anybody know, because we wanted to come home this evening, and surprise the folks.

"Who is your folks ?" he says.

"The Phelpses, down yonder."

"Oh," he says. And after a minute, he says : "How'd you say he got it ?"

"He had a dream," I says, "and it shot him."

"Singular dream," he says.

So he lit up his lantern, and got his saddle-bags, and we started. But when see the canoe, he didn't like the look of her—said she was big enough for one, didn't look pretty safe for two. I says :

"Oh, you needn't be afeard, sir, she carried the three of us, easy enough."

"What three ?"

" Why, me and Sid, and—and—and *the guns ;* that's what I mean."

" Oh," he says.

But he put his foot on the gunnel, and rocked her ; and shook his head, and said he reckoned he'd look around for a bigger one. But they was all locked and chained, so he took my canoe, and said for me to wait till he come back, or I could hunt around further, or maybe I better go down home and get them ready for the surprise, if I wanted to. But I said I didn't ; so I told him just how to find the raft, and then he started.

I struck an idea, pretty soon. I says to myself, spos'n he can't fix that leg just in three shakes of sheep's tail, as the saying is spos'n it takes him three or four days ? What are we going to do ?—lay around there till he lets the cat out of the bag ? No, sir, I know what I'll do. I'll wait, and when he comes back, if he says he's got to go any more, I'll get down there too, if I swim ; and we'll take and tie him, and keep him, and shove out down the river ; and when Tom's done with him we'll give him what it's worth, or all we got, and then let him get shore.

So then I crept into a lumber-pile to get some sleep ; and next time I waked up the sun was away up over my head ! I shot

Kemble.

UNCLE SILAS IN DANGER.

out and went for the doctor's house, but they told me he'd gone away in the night, some time or other, and warn't back yet. Well, thinks I, that look

werful bad for Tom, and I'll dig out for the island, right off. So away I
oved, and turned the corner, and nearly rammed my head into Uncle Silas's
mach ! He says :

" Why, *Tom !* Where you been, all this time, you rascal ? "

" *I* hain't been nowheres," I says, " only just hunting for the runaway nigger
me and Sid."

" Why, where ever did you go ? " he says. " Your aunt's been mighty un-
sy."

" She needn't," I says, " because we was all right. We followed the men and
e dogs, but they out-run us, and we lost them ; but we thought we heard them
 the water, so we got a canoe and took out after them, and crossed over but
uldn't find nothing of them ; so we cruised along up-shore till we got kind of
ed and beat out ; and tied up the canoe and went to sleep, and never waked
 till about an hour ago, then we paddled over here to hear the news, and
d's at the post-office to see what he can hear, and I'm a branching out to get
mething to eat for us, and then we're going home."

So then we went to the post-office to get " Sid " ; but just as I suspicioned, he
rn't there ; so the old man he got a letter out of the office, and we waited a
ile longer but Sid didn't come ; so the old man said come along, let Sid foot it
 me, or canoe-it, when he got done fooling around—but we would ride. I
uldn't get him to let me stay and wait for Sid ; and he said there warn't no
e in it, and I must come along, and let Aunt Sally see we was all right.

When we got home, Aunt Sally was that glad to see me she laughed and cried
th, and hugged me, and give me one of them lickings of hern that don't amount
 shucks, and said she'd serve Sid the same when he come.

And the place was plumb full of farmers and farmers' wives, to dinner ; and
ch another clack a body never heard. Old Mrs. Hotchkiss was the worst ; her
ngue was agoing all the time. She says :

" Well, Sister Phelps, I've ransacked that-air cabin over an' I b'lieve the
gger was crazy. I says so to Sister Damrell—didn't I, Sister Damrell ?—s'I,
's crazy, s'I—them's the very words I said. You all hearn me : he's crazy, s'I ;
erything shows it, s'I. Look at that-air grindstone, s'I ; want to tell *me*'t any

cretur 'ts in his right mind 's agoin' to scrabble all them crazy things onto
grindstone, s'I?   Here sich 'n' sich a person busted his heart ; 'n' here so 'n' s
pegged along for thirty-seven year, 'n' all that—natcherl son o' Louis somebod
'n' sich everlast'n rubbage. He's plumb crazy, s'I ; it's what I says in th
fust place, it's what I says in the middle, 'n' it's what I says last 'n' all the tin
—the nigger's crazy—crazy 's Nebokoodneezer, s'I."

OLD MRS. HOTCHKISS.

"An' look at that-air ladder ma
out'n rags, Sister Hotchkiss," says o
Mrs. Damrell, "what in the name
goodness *could* he ever want of——"

"The very words I was a-sayin'
longer ago th'n this minute to Sist
Utterback, 'n' she'll tell you so hersel
Sh-she, look at that-air rag ladde
sh-she ; 'n' s'I, yes, *look* at it, s'I—
what *could* he a wanted of it, s
Sh-she, Sister Hotchkiss, sh-she——

"But how in the nation'd th
ever *git* that grindstone *in* there, an

way ɾ 'n' who dug that-air *hole?* 'n' who——"

"My very *words*, Brer Penrod ! I was a-sayin'—pass that-air sasser
m'lasses, won't ye ?—I was a-sayin' to Sister Dunlap, jist this minute, how *d*
they git that grindstone in there, s'I. Without *help*, mind you—'thout *hel*
Thar's wher' 'tis. Don't tell *me*, s'I ; there *wuz* help, s'I ; 'n' ther' wuz a *plen*
help, too, s'I ; ther's ben a *dozen* a-helpin' that nigger, 'n' I lay I'd skin eve
last nigger on this place, but *I'd* find out who done it, s'I ; 'n' moreover, s'I——

"A *dozen* says you !—*forty* couldn't a done everything that's been dor
Look at them case-knife saws and things, how tedious they've been made ; lo
at that bed-leg sawed off with 'm, a week's work for six men ; look at that nigg
made out'n straw on the bed ; and look at——"

"You may *well* say it, Brer Hightower ! It's jist as I was a-sayin' to Br
Phelps, his own self. S'e, what do *you* think of it, Sister Hotchkiss, s'e ? thir

what, Brer Phelps, s'I ? think o' that bed-leg sawed off that a way, s'e ? *think*
it, s'I ? I lay it never sawed *itself* off, s'I—somebody *sawed* it, s'I ; that's my
nion, take it or leave it, it mayn't be no 'count, s'I, but sich as 't is, it's my
nion, s'I, 'n' if anybody k'n start a better one, s'I, let him *do* it, s'I, that's all.
ays to Sister Dunlap, s'I——"

"Why, dog my cats, they must a ben a house-full o' niggers in there every
ht for four weeks, to a done all that work, Sister Phelps. Look at that shirt
very last inch of it kivered over with secret African writ'n done with blood!
st a ben a raft uv 'm at it right along, all the time, amost. Why, I'd give
dollars to have it read to me ; 'n' as for the niggers that wrote it, I 'low I'd
e 'n' lash 'm t'll——"

"People to *help* him, Brother Marples ! Well, I reckon you'd *think* so, if you'd
een in this house for a while back. Why, they've stole everything they could
their hands on—and we a watching, all the time, mind you. They stole that
rt right off o' the line ! and as for that sheet they made the rag ladder out of
r' ain't no telling how many times they *didn't* steal that ; and flour, and
dles, and candlesticks, and spoons, and the old warming-pan, and most a
usand things that I disremember, now, and my new calico dress ; and me, and
as, and my Sid and Tom on the constant watch day *and* night, as I was a tell-
you, and not a one of us could catch hide nor hair, nor sight nor sound of
m ; and here at the last minute, lo and behold you, they slides right in under
noses, and fools us, and not only fools *us* but the Injun Territory robbers too,
l actuly gets *away* with that nigger, safe and sound, and that with sixteen
n and twenty-two dogs right on their very heels at that very time ! I tell you, it
t bangs anything I ever *heard* of. Why, *sperits* couldn't a done better, and
n no smarter. And I reckon they must a *been* sperits—because, *you* know our
gs, and ther' ain't no better ; well, them dogs never even got on the *track* of
once ! You explain *that* to me, if you can !—*any* of you !"

"Well, it does beat——"

"Laws alive, I never——"

"So help me, I wouldn't a be——"

"*House* thieves as well as——"

"Goodnessgracioussakes, I'd a ben afeard to *live* in sich a——"

"'Fraid to *live*!—why, I was that scared I das'nt hardly go to bed, or get up, o lay down, or *set* down, Sister Ridgeway. Why, they'd steal the very—why, good ness sakes, you can guess what kind of a fluster *I* was in by the time midnigh come, last night. I hope to gracious if I warn't afraid they'd steal some o' th family! I was just to that pass, I didn't have no reasoning faculties no more It looks foolish enough, *now*, in the day-time; but I says to myself, there's m two poor boys asleep, 'way up stairs in that lonesome room, and I declare to goo ness I was that uneasy 't I crep' up there and locked 'em in! I *did*. And any body would. Because, you know, when you get scared that way, and it keeps·run ning on, and getting worse and worse, all the time, and your wits gets to addlin and you get to doing all sorts o' wild things, and by-and-by you think to you self, spos'n *I* was a boy, and was away up there, and the door ain't locked, an you——" She stopped, looking kind of wondering, and then she turned he head around slow, and when her eye lit on me—I got up and took a walk.

Says I to myself, I can explain better how we come to not be in that roo this morning, if I go out to one side and study over it a little. So I done it. B I dasn't go fur, or she'd a sent for me. And when it was late in the day, th people all went, and then I come in and told her the noise and shooting wake up me and "Sid," and the door was locked, and we wanted to see the fun, so w went down the lightning-rod, and both of us got hurt a little, and we didn never want to try *that* no more. And then I went on and told her all what told Uncle Silas before; and then she said she'd forgive us, and maybe it was a right enough anyway, and about what a body might expect of boys, for all boys was pretty harum-scarum lot, as fur as she could see; and so, as long as no har hadn't come of it, she judged she better put in her time being grateful we w alive and well and she had us still, stead of fretting over what was past and don So then she kissed me, and patted me on the head, and dropped into a kind of brown study; and pretty soon jumps up, and says:

"Why, lawsamercy, it's most night, and Sid not come yet! What *has* becom of that boy?"

I see my chance; so I skips up and says:

" I'll run right up to town and get him," I says.

" No you won't," she says. " You'll stay right wher' you are ; *one's* enough
e lost at a time. If he ain't here to supper, your uncle 'll go."

Well, he warn't there to supper ; so right after supper uncle went.

He come back about ten, a little bit uneasy ; hadn't run across Tom's track.
t Sally was a good *deal* uneasy ; but Uncle Silas he said there warn't no occa-
to be—boys will be boys, he said, and you'll see this one turn up in the morning,
sound and right. So she had to be
sfied. But she said she'd set up for
a while, anyway, and keep a light
ning, so he could see it.

And then when I went up to bed
come up with me and fetched her
dle, and tucked me in, and
thered me so good I felt mean, and
I couldn't look her in the face ;
she set down on the bed and
ked with me a long time, and said
t a splendid boy Sid was, and didn't
n to want to ever stop talking about
; and kept asking me every now
then, if I reckoned he could a got
, or hurt, or maybe drownded, and
ht be laying at this minute, some-
res, suffering or dead, and she not

AUNT SALLY TALKS TO HUCK.

him to help him, and so the tears would drip down, silent, and I would tell
that Sid was all right, and would be home in the morning, sure ; and she
ld squeeze my hand, or maybe kiss me, and tell me to say it again, and keep
aying it, because it done her good, and she was in so much trouble. And when
was going away, she looked down in my eyes, so steady and gentle, and says :
" The door ain't going to be locked, Tom ; and there's the window and the
; but you'll be good, *won't* you ? And you won't go ? For *my* sake."

Laws knows I *wanted* to go, bad enough, to see about Tom, and was all inten ing to go ; but after that, I wouldn't a went, not for kingdoms.

But she was on my mind, and Tom was on my mind ; so I slept very restle And twice I went down the rod, away in the night, and slipped around fror and see her setting there by her candle in the window with her eyes towards t road and the tears in them ; and I wished I could do something for her, but couldn't, only to swear that I wouldn't never do nothing to grieve her any mor And the third time, I waked up at dawn, and slid down, and she was there ye and her candle was most out, and her old gray head was resting on her hand, an she was asleep.

Chapter XLII

TOM SAWYER WOUNDED.

The old man was up town again, before breakfast, but couldn't get no track of Tom; and both of them set at the table, thinking, and not saying nothing, and looking mournful, and their coffee getting cold, and not eating anything. And by-and-by the old man says:

"Did I give you the letter?"

"What letter?"

"The one I got yesterday out of the post-office."

"No, you didn't give me no letter."

"Well, I must a forgot it."

So he rummaged his pockets, and then went off somewheres where he had it down, and fetched it, and give it to her. She says:

"Why, it's from St. Petersburg—it's from Sis."

allowed another walk would do me good; but I couldn't stir. But before could break it open, she dropped it and run—for she see something. And so . It was Tom Sawyer on a mattress; and that old doctor; and Jim, in *her* dress, with his hands tied behind him; and a lot of people. I hid the behind the first thing that come handy, and rushed. She flung herself at , crying, and says:

" Oh, he's dead, he's dead, I know he's dead ! "

And Tom he turned his head a little, and muttered something or other, whi showed he warn't in his right mind ; then she flung up her hands, and says :

" He's alive, thank God ! And that's enough ! " and she snatched a kiss him, and flew for the house to get the bed ready, and scattering orders right a left at the niggers and everybody else, as fast as her tongue could go, every ju of the way.

I followed the men to see what they was going to do with Jim ; and the doctor and Uncle Silas followed after Tom into the house. The men was v huffy, and some of them wanted to hang Jim, for an example to all the ot niggers around there, so they wouldn't be trying to run away, like Jim done, a making such a raft of trouble, and keeping a whole family scared most to death days and nights. But the others said, don't do it, it wouldn't answer at all, ain't our nigger, and his owner would turn up and make us pay for him, sure. that cooled them down a little, because the people that's always the most anxi for to hang a nigger that hain't done just right, is always the very ones that a the most anxious to pay for him when they've got their satisfaction out of him

They cussed Jim considerble, though, and give him a cuff or two, side head, once in a while, but Jim never said nothing, and he never let on to kn me, and they took him to the same cabin, and put his own clothes on him, a chained him again, and not to no bed-leg, this time, but to a big staple dr into the bottom log, and chained his hands, too, and both legs, and said he wa to have nothing but bread and water to eat, after this, till his owner come or was sold at auction, because he didn't come in a certain length of time. and fil up our hole, and said a couple of farmers with guns must stand watch arou about the cabin every night, and a bull-dog tied to the door in the day-time ; about this time they was through with the job and was tapering off with a k of generl good-bye cussing, and then the old doctor comes and takes a look, says :

" Don't be no rougher on him than you're obleeged to, because he ain't a nigger. When I got to where I found the boy, I see I couldn't cut the bullet without some help, and he warn't in no condition for me to leave, to go and

; and he got a little worse and a little worse, and after a long time he went
of his head, and wouldn't let me come anigh him, any more, and said if I
ked his raft he'd kill me, and no end of wild foolishness like that, and I see
uldn't do anything at all with him ; so I says, I got to have *help*, somehow ;
the minute I says it, out crawls this nigger from somewheres, and says he'll
, and he done it, too, and done it
well. Of course I judged he
t be a runaway nigger, and there
s ! and there I had to stick, right
ght along all the rest of the day,
all night. It was a fix, I tell
! I had a couple of patients with
chills, and of course I'd of liked
in up to town and see them, but
sn't, because the nigger might get
y, and then I'd be to blame ; and
never a skiff come close enough
me to hail. So there I had to
<, plumb till daylight this morn-
; and I never see a nigger that
a better nuss or faithfuller, and
he was resking his freedom to do
nd was all tired out, too, and I
plain enough he'd been worked

THE DOCTOR SPEAKS FOR JIM.

n hard, lately. I liked the nigger for that ; I tell you, gentlemen, a nigger
that is worth a thousand dollars—and kind treatment, too. I had every-
g I needed, and the boy was doing as well there as he would a done at home
etter, maybe, because it was so quiet ; but there I *was*, with both of 'm on my
ds ; and there I had to stick, till about dawn this morning ; then some men
skiff come by, and as good luck would have it, the nigger was setting by the
et with his head propped on his knees, sound asleep ; so I motioned them·in,
·t, and they slipped up on him and grabbed him and tied him before he

knowed what he was about, and we never had no trouble.   And the boy being
a kind of a flighty sleep, too, we muffled the oars and hitched the raft on, a
towed her over very nice and quiet, and the nigger never made the least row
said a word, from the start.   He ain't no bad nigger, gentlemen ; that's wha
think about him."

Somebody says :

" Well, it sounds very good, doctor, I'm obleeged to say."

Then the others softened up a little, too, and I was mighty thankful to t
old doctor for doing Jim that good turn ; and I was glad it was according to
judgment of him, too ; because I thought he had a good heart in him and wa
good man, the first time I see him.   Then they all agreed that Jim had ac
very well, and was deserving to have some notice took of it, and reward.
every one of them promised, right out and hearty, that they wouldn't cuss l
no more.

Then they come out and locked him up.   I hoped they was going to
he could have one or two of the chains took off, because they was rot
heavy, or could have meat and greens with his bread and water, but t
didn't think of it, and I reckoned it warn't best for me to mix in, bu
judged I'd get the doctor's yarn to Aunt Sally, somehow or other, as soon as
got through the breakers that was laying just ahead of me.   Explanations, I me
of how I forgot to mention about Sid being shot, when I was telling how l
and me put in that dratted night paddling around hunting the runaway nigge

But I had plenty time.   Aunt Sally she stuck to the sick-room all day and
night ; and every time I see Uncle Silas mooning around, I dodged him.

Next morning I heard Tom was a good deal better, and they said Aunt S
was gone to get a nap.   So I slips to the sick-room, and if I found him awak
reckoned we could put up a yarn for the family that would wash.   But he
sleeping, and sleeping very peaceful, too ; and pale, not fire-faced the way he
when he come.   So I set down and laid for him to wake.   In about a half
hour, Aunt Sally comes gliding in, and there I was, up a stump again !   She
tioned me to be still, and set down by me, and begun to whisper, and said
could all be joyful now, because all the symptoms was first rate, and he'd l

ping like that for ever so long, and looking better and peacefuller all the
e, and ten to one he'd wake up in his right mind.

So we set there watching, and by-and-by he stirs a bit, and opened his eyes
natural, and takes a look, and says :

"Hello, why I'm at *home!* How's that? Where's the raft?"

"It's all right," I says.

"And *Jim?*"

"The same," I says, but couldn't say it pretty brash. But he never noticed,
says :

"Good! Splendid! *Now* we're all right and safe! Did you tell Aunty?"

I was going to say yes ; but she chipped in and says :

"About what, Sid?"

"Why, about the way the whole thing was done."

"What whole thing?"

"Why, *the* whole thing. There ain't but one ; how we set the runaway nig-
free—me and Tom."

"Good land! Set the run— What *is* the child talking about! Dear, dear,
of his head again!"

"*No*, I ain't out of my HEAD ; I know all what I'm talking about. We *did*
him free—me and Tom. We laid out to do it, and we *done* it. And we done
legant, too." He'd got a start, and she never checked him up, just set and
ed and stared, and let him clip along, and I see it warn't no use for *me* to put

"Why, Aunty, it cost us a power of work—weeks of it—hours and hours,
ry night, whilst you was all asleep. And we had to steal candles, and the
et, and the shirt, and your dress, and spoons, and tin plates, and case-knives,
the warming-pan, and the grindstone, and flour, and just no end of things, and
can't think what work it was to make the saws, and pens, and inscriptions,
one thing or another, and you can't think *half* the fun it was. And we had
nake up the pictures of coffins and things, and nonnamous letters from the
bers, and get up and down the lightning-rod, and dig the hole into the cabin,
make the rope-ladder and send it in cooked up in a pie, and send in spoons
things to work with, in your apron pocket "——

" Mercy sakes ! "

——" and load up the cabin with rats and snakes and so on, for company f
Jim ; and then you kept Tom here so long with the butter in his hat that you co
near spiling the whole business, because the men come before we was out of t
cabin, and we had to rush, and they heard us and let drive at us, and I got n
share, and we dodged out of the path and let them go by, and when the do
come they warn't interested in us, but went for the most noise, and we got o
canoe, and made for the raft, and was all safe, and Jim was a free man, and
done it all by ourselves, and *wasn't* it bully, Aunty ! "

" Well, I never heard the likes of it in all my born days ! So it was *you*, y
little rapscallions, that's been making all this trouble, and turned everybody's w
clean inside out and scared us all most to death. I've as good a notion as ever
had in my life, to take it out o' you this very minute. To think, here I've bee
night after night, a—*you* just get well once, you young scamp, and I lay I
tan the Old Harry out o' both o' ye ! "

But Tom, he *was* so proud and joyful, he just *couldn't* hold in, and his tong
just *went* it—she a-chipping in, and spitting fire all along, and both of them g
ing it at once, like a cat-convention ; and she says :

" *Well*, you get all the enjoyment you can out of it *now*, for mind I tell y
if I catch you meddling with him again—— "

" Meddling with *who* ? " Tom says, dropping his smile and looking surpris

" With *who* ? Why, the runaway nigger, of course. Who'd you reckon

Tom looks at me very grave, and says :

" Tom, didn't you just tell me he was all right ? Hasn't he got away ? "

" *Him* ? " says Aunt Sally ; " the runaway nigger ? 'Deed he hasn't. They
got him back, safe and sound, and he's in that cabin again, on bread and wat
and loaded down with chains, till he's claimed or sold ! "

Tom rose square up in bed, with his eye hot, and his nostrils opening a
shutting like gills, and sings out to me :

" They hain't no *right* to shut him up ! *Shove !*—and don't you lose a minu
Turn him loose ! he ain't no slave ; he's as free as any cretur that walks this earth

" What *does* the child mean ? "

"I mean every word I *say*, Aunt Sally, and if somebody don't go, *I*'ll go. I've knowed him all his life, and so has Tom, there. Old Miss Watson died two months ago, and she was ashamed she ever was going to sell him down the river, and *said* so; and she set him free in her will."

"Then what on earth did *you* want to set him free for, seeing he was already free?"

"Well, that *is* a question, I must say; and *just* like women! Why, I wanted the *adventure* of it; and I'd a waded neck-deep in blood to—goodness alive, AUNT POLLY!"

If she warn't standing right there, just inside the door, looking as sweet and contented as an angel half-full of pie, I wish I may never!

Aunt Sally jumped for her, and

TOM ROSE SQUARE UP IN BED.

just hugged the head off of her, and cried over her, and I found a good enough place for me under the bed, for it was getting pretty sultry for *us*, seemed to me. And I peeped out, and in a little while Tom's Aunt Polly shook herself loose and stood there looking across at Tom over her spectacles—kind of grinding him into the earth, you know. And then she says:

"Yes, you *better* turn y'r head away—I would if I was you, Tom."

"Oh, deary me!" says Aunt Sally; "*is* he changed so? Why, that ain't *Tom*, it's Sid; Tom's—Tom's—why, where is Tom? He was here a minute ago."

"You mean where's Huck *Finn*—that's what you mean! I reckon I hain't raised such a scamp as my Tom all these years, not to know him when I *see* him. That *would* be a pretty howdy-do. Come out from under that bed, Huck Finn."

So I done it. But not feeling brash.

Aunt Sally she was one of the mixed-upest looking persons I ever see; except one, and that was Uncle Silas, when he come in, and they told it all to him. kind of made him drunk, as you may say, and he didn't know nothing at all t rest of the day, and preached a prayer-meeting sermon that night that give a rattling ruputation, because the oldest man in the world couldn't a understo it. So Tom's Aunt Polly, she told all about who I was, and what ; and I had up and tell how I was in such a tight place that when Mrs. Phelps took me i Tom Sawyer—she chipped in and says, " Oh, go on and call me Aunt Sally, I used to it, now, and 'tain't no need to change "—that when Aunt Sally took i for Tom Sawyer, I had to stand it—there warn't no other way, and I knowed wouldn't mind, because it would be nuts for him, being a mystery, and h make an adventure out of it and be perfectly satisfied. And so it turned o and he let on to be Sid, and made things as soft as he could for me.

And his Aunt Polly she said Tom was right about old Miss Watson setti Jim free in her will ; and so, sure enough, Tom Sawyer had gone and took that trouble and bother to set a free nigger free ! and I couldn't ever understand, before, until that minute and that talk, how he *could* help a body set a nigger free, with his bringing-up.

"HAND OUT THEM LETTERS.

Well, Aunt Polly she said that when Aunt Sally wrote to her that Tom and *Sid* had come, all right and safe, she says to herself :

" Look at that, now ! I might have expected it, letting him go off that way without anybody to watch him. So now I got to go and trapse all the way down the river, eleven hundred mile, and find out what that creetur's up to, *this* time ; as long as I couldn't seem to get any answer out of you about it."

" Why, I never heard nothing from you," says Aunt Sally.

"Well, I wonder ! Why, I wrote to you twice, to ask you what you cou mean by Sid being here."

"Well, I never got 'em, Sis."

Aunt Polly, she turns around slow and severe, and says :

"You, Tom !"

"Well—*what ?* " he says, kind of pettish.

"Don't you what *me*, you impudent thing—hand out them letters."

"What letters ?"

"*Them* letters. I be bound, if I have to take aholt of you I'll——"

"They're in the trunk. There, now. And they're just the same as they s when I got them out of the office. I hain't looked into them, I hain't uched them. But I knowed they'd make trouble, and I thought if you warn't no hurry, I'd—— "

"Well, you *do* need skinning, there ain't no mistake about it. And I wrote other one to tell you I was coming ; and I spose he—— "

"No, it come yesterday ; I hain't read it yet, but *it's* all right, I've got at one."

I wanted to offer to bet two dollars she hadn't, but I reckoned maybe it was st as safe to not to. So I never said nothing.

Chapter the Last

OUT OF BONDAGE.

The first time I catched Tom, pr
vate, I asked him what was h
idea, time of the evasion ?—what
was he'd planned to do if the eva
sion worked all right and he man
aged to set a nigger free that wa
already free before ? And he said
what he had planned in his head
from the start, if we got Jim out a
safe, was for us to run him down th
river, on the raft, and have advent
ures plumb to the mouth of th
river, and then tell him about hi
being free, and take him back u
home on a steamboat, in style, an
pay him for his lost time, and writ
word ahead and get out all the nig
gers around, and have them walt
him into town with a torchligh
procession and a brass band, and then he would be a hero, and so would we
But I reckened it was about as well the way it was.

We had Jim out of the chains in no time, and when Aunt Polly and Uncl
Silas and Aunt Sally found out how good he helped the doctor nurse Tom, the
made a heap of fuss over him, and fixed him up prime, and give him all h
wanted to eat, and a good time, and nothing to do. And we had him up to th

k-room ; and had a high talk ; and Tom give Jim forty dollars for being
isoner for us so patient, and doing it up so good, and Jim was pleased most to
ath, and busted out, and says :

" *Dah*, now, Huck, what I tell you ?—what I
l you up dah on Jackson islan' ?   I *tole* you I
t a hairy breas', en what's de sign un it ; en I
'e you I ben rich wunst, en gwineter to be rich
in ; en it's come true ; en heah she *is ! Dah,*
w ! doan' talk to *me*—signs is *signs,* mine
tell you ; en I knowed jis' 's well 'at I 'uz
'ineter be rich agin as I's a stannin' heah dis
nute ! "

TOM'S LIBERALITY.

And then Tom he talked along, and talked
ong, and says, le's all three slide out of here,
e of these nights, and get an outfit, and go for
wling adventures amongst the Injuns, over in
e Territory, for a couple of weeks or two ; and
says, all right, that suits me, but I aint got no
oney for to buy the outfit, and I reckon I couldn't get none from home, because
s likely pap's been back before now, and got it all away from Judge Thatcher
d drunk it up.

" No he hain't," Tom says ; " it's all there, yet—six thousand dollars and
ore ; and your pap hain't ever been back since.   Hadn't when I come away,
yhow."

Jim says, kind of solemn :

" He ain't a comin' back no mo', Huck."

I says :

" Why, Jim ? "

" Nemmine why, Huck — but he ain't comin' back no mo'."

But I kept at him ; so at last he says :

" Doan' you 'member de house dat was float'n down de river, en dey wuz **a**
an in dah, kivered up, en I went in en unkivered him **and** didn' let **you**

come in ?   Well, den, you k'n git yo' money when you wants it ; kase dat w
him."

Tom's most well, now, and got his bullet around his neck on a watch-gua
for a watch, and is always seeing what time it is, and so there ain't nothing mo
to write about, and I am rotten glad of it, because if I'd a knowed what a troul
it was to make a book I wouldn't a tackled it and aint't agoing to no more.   B
I reckon I got to light out for the Territory ahead of the rest, because Aunt Sal
she's going to adopt me and sivilize me and I can't stand it.   I been there befo

THE END.   YOURS TRULY, HUCK FINN.

Biographical Sources

IN *Huckleberry Finn,* as in many other works of his, Mark Twain dre[w] upon memories of boyhood days in Hannibal, Missouri, for characters an[d] incidents. The following passages show what some of these memories mu[st] have been. The passages vary greatly: One is part of a letter written by th[e] humorist to the *Alta California,* for which Twain was a traveling featu[re] writer, in 1867 when he paid a visit to the town of his youth. Two are fro[m] Twain's *Autobiography,* dictated by the author during his later years an[d] published in 1924. Two are from Dixon Wecter's *Sam Clemens of Hanniba[l]* an exhaustive account of the author's boyhood based upon a study of th[e] Mark Twain papers and a great variety of other sources. One is drawn fro[m] depositions taken by the author's father, John Marshall Clemens, justice [of] the peace, concerning a murder in Hannibal. All may be compared wit[h] passages in the novel which treat similar matters (see pp. 530-531 of th[e] book for suggestions).

The passages concerning Tom Blankenship and the Blankenship fami[ly] contrast interestingly with the picturing in the novel of Huck and Pap Fin[n.]

"Jimmy Finn's Reformation" provides the factual basis for the accou[nt] of Pap Finn's adventures in the final four paragraphs of Chapter V.

Mark Twain's memories of the Quarles Farm furnished details for th[e] description of the Grangerford mansion (Chapter XVII) and that of th[e] Phelps Plantation (Chapter XXXII). The slave, Uncle Dan'l, as Twain say[s] is the prototype of Huck's companion, Jim.

Details set forth in Wecter's account of John Marshall Clemens ma[y] profitably be compared and contrasted with those included by Huck in h[is] picturing of two characters—Colonel Grangerford in Chapters XVII an[d] XVIII and Colonel Sherburn in Chapters XXI and XXII.

The factual account of the murder of Smarr by Owsley furnishes an i[l]luminating comparison with the murder of Boggs by Sherburn in Chapte[r] XXI. Sam Clemens, age nine, was a witness to the killing in Hannibal, an[d] he testifies in his *Autobiography* that the memory of the scene haunted hi[m] for many years.

[TOM BLANKENSHIP]*

Mark Twain

HUCKLEBERRY FINN" was Tom Blankenship. . . . Tom's father was at one me Town Drunkard, an exceedingly well-defined and unofficial office of nose days. He succeeded General—(I forget the General's name)[1] and for a me he was sole and only incumbent of the office; but afterward Jimmy inn proved competency and disputed the place with him, so we had two wn drunkards at one time—and it made as much trouble in that village as hristendom experienced in the fourteenth century, when there were two 'opes at the same time.

In *Huckleberry Finn* I have drawn Tom Blankenship exactly as he was. Ie was ignorant, unwashed, insufficiently fed; but he had as good a heart as ver any boy had. His liberties were totally unrestricted. He was the only ally independent person—boy or man—in the community, and by conse-uence he was tranquilly and continuously happy, and was envied by all the est of us. We liked him; we enjoyed his society. And as his society was orbidden us by our parents, the prohibition trebled and quadrupled its value, nd there-[174/175]fore we sought and got more of his society than of any ther boy's. I heard, four years ago, that he was justice of the peace in a remote illage in Montana, and was a good citizen and greatly respected.

---

* From *Mark Twain's Autobiography,* ed. Albert Bigelow Paine (New York: Harper & Brothers, 1924), II, 174-175.
[1] Gaines.

[THE BLANKENSHIPS]*

Dixon Wecter

ONE SUCH family, whose invincible cheerfulness seemed no less a community scandal than its indolence, is thus sketched in Mark's reminiscent notes "Blankenships. The parents paupers and drunkards; the girls charged with prostitution—not proven. Tom, a kindly young heathen. Bence, a fisherman. These children were never sent to school or church. Played out and disappeared." They lived in a ramshackle old barn of a house on Hill Street—distance quickly covered by Sam when summoned with stealthy cat-calls from Tom. The site is now cherished by the Chamber of Commerce as that of "Huck Finn's home," although the house no longer stands, following several generations of habitation by Negro families whose petty thefts, cutting scrapes, and the didos of a one-time denizen called Cocaine Nell Smith left it a repute still more dubious than it enjoyed in the Blankenships' day.

Head of the family was Woodson Blankenship, a ne'er-do-well from South Carolina, who fitfully worked at the old sawmill but drank whenever possessed of cash to jingle in his jeans. In 1845 he appears on the roll of tax delinquents as owing twenty-nine cents. His eldest boy Benson, called Bence, did odd jobs but preferred to angle for catfish and tease the play mates of Sam Clemens by knotting their clothes when they went swimming, or clodding them when they came ashore. But he had a kind streak too—probably furnishing the original for Tom and Huck's friend Muff Potter, who loafed and drank, but shared his catch if they [147/148] were hungry and mended their kites. In the summer of 1847 Bence befriended secretly a runaway Negro whom he found hiding among the swampy thickets of Sny Island, a part of Illinois's Pike County that hugged the opposite bank of the river from Hannibal. Ignoring the reward posted for the black man, Bence carried food to him week after week and kept mum about his hiding place—thus inspiring that rare tribute to loyalty in *Huckleberry Finn,* in which the homeless river rat rejects all temptations of gain and even elects to "go to Hell" rather than betray his friend Nigger Jim.

* From Dixon Wecter, *Sam Clemens of Hannibal* (Boston: Houghton Mifflin Company, 1952), pp. 147-148.

[JIMMY FINN'S REFORMATION]*

Mark Twain

ANNIBAL has had a hard time of it ever since I can recollect, and I was
aised" there. First, it had me for a citizen, but I was too young then to
ally hurt the place. Next, Jimmy Finn, the town drunkard, reformed, and
at broke up the only saloon in the village. But the temperance people
ked it; they were willing enough to sacrifice public prosperity to public
orality. And so they made much of Jimmy Finn—dressed him up in new
othes, and had him out to breakfast and to dinner, and so forth, and
owed him off as a great living curiosity—a shining example of the power
temperance doctrines when earnestly and eloquently set forth. Which was
l very well, you know, and sounded well, and looked well in print, but
mmy Finn couldn't stand it. He got remorseful about the loss of his
perty; and then he got melancholy from thinking about it so much; and
ter that, he got drunk. He got awfully drunk in the chief citizen's house,
d the next morning that house was as if the swine had tarried in it. That
traged the temperance people and delighted the opposite faction. The
rmer rallied and reformed Jim once more, but in an evil hour temptation
me upon him, and he sold his body to a doctor for a quart of whiskey,
d that ended all his earthly troubles. He drank it all at one sitting, and his
ul went to its long account and his body went to Dr. Grant. This was an-
her blow to Hannibal. Jimmy Finn had always kept the town in a sweat
out something or other, and now it nearly died from utter inanition.

---

* From Mark Twain's Letter to the *Alta California,* dated April 16, 1867, and
ublished May 26, 1867, p. 1.

[THE QUARLES FARM]*

Mark Twain

MY UNCLE, John A. Quarles, was a farmer, and his place was in the count
four miles from Florida. He had eight children and fifteen or twenty negroe
and was also fortunate in other ways, particularly in his character. I have n
come across a better man than he was. I was his guest for two or three mont
every year, from the fourth year after we removed to Hannibal till I w
eleven or twelve years old. I have never consciously used him or his wife
a book, but his farm has come very handy to me in literature once or twic
In *Huck Finn* and in *Tom Sawyer, Detective* I moved it down to Arkansa
It was all of six hundred miles, but it was no trouble; it was not a very lar
farm—five hundred acres, perhaps—but I could have done it if it had bee
twice as large. And as for the morality of it, I cared nothing for that;
would move a state if the exigencies of literature required it.

It was a heavenly place for a boy, that farm of my uncle John's. Th
house was a double log one, with a spacious floor (roofed in) connecting
with [96/97] the kitchen. In the summer the table was set in the middle
that shady and breezy floor, and the sumptuous meals—well, it makes me c
to think of them. . . . [97/98] . . .

The farmhouse stood in the middle of a very large yard, and the yard w
fenced on three sides with rails and on the rear side with high palings; again
these stood the smoke-house; beyond the palings was the orchard; beyond th
orchard were the negro quarters and the tobacco fields. The front yard w
entered over a stile made of sawed-off logs of graduated heights; I do n
remember any [98/99] gate. In a corner of the front yard were a dozen lof
hickory trees and a dozen black walnuts, and in the nutting season riches we
to be gathered there.

Down a piece, abreast the house, stood a little log cabin against the ra
fence; and there the woody hill fell sharply away, past the barns, the cor
crib, the stables, and the tobacco-curing house, to a limpid brook which sa

---

* From *Mark Twain's Autobiography*, ed. Albert Bigelow Paine (New Yor
Harper & Brothers, 1924), I, 96-103.

ong over its gravelly bed and curved and frisked in and out and here and
ere and yonder in the deep shade of overhanging foliage and vines—a
vine place for wading, and it had swimming pools, too, which were for-
dden to us and therefore much frequented by us. For we were little Chris-
n children and had early been taught the value of forbidden fruit.

In the little log cabin lived a bedridden white-headed slave woman whom
e visited daily and looked upon with awe, for we believed she was upward
a thousand years old and had talked with Moses. The younger negroes
dited these statistics and had furnished them to us in good faith. We ac-
mmodated all the details which came to us about her; and so we believed
at she had lost her health in the long desert trip coming out of Egypt, and
d never been able to get it back again. She had a round bald place on the
own of her head, and we used to creep around and gaze as it in reverent
ence, and reflect that it was caused by fright through seeing Pharaoh
owned. We called her "Aunt" Hannah, Southern fashion. She was super-
tious, like the other [99/100] negroes; also like them, she was deeply
ligious. Like them, she had great faith in prayer and employed it in all
dinary exigencies, but not in cases where a dead certainty of result was
gent. Whenever witches were around she tied up the remnant of her wool
little tufts, with white thread, and this promptly made the witches impotent.

All the negroes were friends of ours, and with those of our own age we
ere in effect comrades. I say in effect, using the phrase as a modification. We
ere comrades, and yet not comrades; color and condition interposed a subtle
ne which both parties were conscious of and which rendered complete fusion
mpossible. We had a faithful and affectionate good friend, ally, and adviser
"Uncle Dan'l," a middle-aged slave whose head was the best one in the
egro quarter, whose sympathies were wide and warm, and whose heart was
onest and simple and knew no guile. He has served me well these many,
any years. I have not seen him for more than half a century, and yet spiritu-
ly I have had his welcome company a good part of that time, and have
aged him in books under his own name and as "Jim," and carted him all
ound—to Hannibal, down the Mississippi on a raft, and even across the
esert of Sahara in a balloon—and he has endured it all with the patience
d friendliness and loyalty which were his birthright. It was on the farm that
got my strong liking for his race and my appreciation of certain of its fine
alities. This feeling and this estimate have stood [100/101] the test of
xty years and more, and have suffered no impairment. The black face is
welcome to me now as it was then.

In my schoolboy days I had no aversion to slavery. I was not aware th
there was anything wrong about it. No one arraigned it in my hearing; th
local papers said nothing against it; the local pulpit taught us that God ap
proved it, that it was a holy thing, and that the doubter need only look in th
Bible if he wished to settle his mind—and then the texts were read aloud t
us to make the matter sure; if the slaves themselves had an aversion to slaver
they were wise and said nothing. In Hannibal we seldom saw a slave misused
on the farm, never.... [101/102] ...

I can see the farm yet, with perfect clearness. I can see all its belonging
all its details; the family room of the house, with a "trundle" bed in on
corner and a spinning-wheel in another—a wheel whose rising and fallin
wail, heard from a distance, [102/103] was the mournfulest of all sounds t
me, and made me homesick and low spirited, and filled my atmosphere wit
the wandering spirits of the dead; the vast fireplace, piled high, on wint
nights, with flaming hickory logs from whose ends a sugary sap bubbled ou
but did not go to waste, for we scraped it off and ate it; the lazy cat spread ou
on the rough hearthstones; the drowsy dogs braced against the jambs an
blinking; my aunt in one chimney corner, knitting; my uncle in the othe
smoking his corn-cob pipe; the slick and carpetless oak floor faintly mirrorin
the dancing flame tongues and freckled with black indentations where fir
coals had popped out and died a leisurely death; half a dozen children romp
ing in the background twilight; "split"-bottomed chairs here and there, som
with rockers; a cradle—out of service, but waiting, with confidence; in th
early cold mornings a snuggle of children, in shirts and chemises, occupyin
the hearthstone and procrastinating—they could not bear to leave that con
fortable place and go out on the wind-swept floor space between the hou
and kitchen where the general tin basin stood, and wash.... [end 103]

[JOHN MARSHALL CLEMENS]*

Dixon Wecter

. . His tall spare frame, piercing gray eyes, hair brushed vigorously back,
ad mouth that rarely smiled and never laughed, belonged to a stern, proud,
ugal disposition whose bent determined his life. Almost fanatic in his
ruples touching honesty, Marshall Clemens was long remembered as "sternly
ad irreproachably moral." Despite a high-strung, irritable temper—the result
f "shattered nerves," his family believed, in blaming it all upon those early
ears of night labor and exhaustion—he almost never swore, and then only at
hite heat. The product of inherited Virginia pride and straitened circum-
ances, of a stepchildhood and precocious responsibilities, Marshall Clemens
as [14/15] also a true scion of pioneer Kentucky. He belonged to that
lf-dosing generation of chills and fevers and perennial stomach complaint,
hose chronic sickliness went apace with the gaunt physique and wiry con-
itution, as in Old Hickory himself, whom he is alleged to have resembled.
ut as befitted his Federalist name, John Marshall Clemens in politics fol-
wed "Young Harry of the West" as a firm Henry Clay Whig. In religion
e kept aloof from churches and creeds, being regarded in later days as a
reethinker or agnostic, yet confounding the godly with his stern Puritan
orality. . . .   [end 15]

    In a novel begun in middle life but unfinished and never published,
Mark Twain sketches the likeness of a small-town dignitary called Judge
Griswold, a gentleman of Virginia stock raised among the buckskin gentry of
arly Kentucky. He was "very tall, very spare, with a long, thin, smooth-
aaven intellectual face, and long black hair that lay close to his head, was
ept to the rear by his ears as one keeps curtains back by brackets, and fell
raight to his coat collar without a single tolerant kink or relenting curve.
Ie had an eagle's beak and an eagle's eye. Judge Griswold's manner and
arriage were of the courtly old-fashioned sort; he had never worked; he was
gentleman." Punctiliously upright, he was not in religious matters a believer,

---

    * From Dixon Wecter, *Sam Clemens of Hannibal* (Boston: Houghton Mifflin Com-
any, 1952), pp. 14-15, 66-67.

although from decorum he gave some support to the church. An implacab
hater, he could be equally strong in devotion—his favorite being his on
daughter, aged sixteen—but of emotion he made no demonstration. Tl
image of this parochial Jehovah, the upright judge, the austere lawgiver, tl
father who dealt sternly with his sons but softly with his daughter, return
insistently in the pages of Mark Twain. And it is significant that Pame
Clemens, deeply devoted to [66/67] her father, never agreed with h
brothers about his glacial temperament.

At the age of thirty-four, doing potboilers for the *Galaxy,* Mark recall
his father as "a stern, unsmiling man" who read poetry aloud "with the san
inflectionless judicial frigidity" used in the courtroom. He detested the pe
precocity of his son Sam, in the rare intervals when Sam stepped out of h
early character as "a backward, cautious, unadventurous boy." "My father ar
I were always on the most distant terms when I was a boy—a sort of arme
neutrality, so to speak." A quarter-century later, in *Following the Equato*
Mark harked back to that "sternly just and upright man" who "laid his har
upon me in punishment only twice in his life, and then not heavily; once f
telling him a lie—which surprised me, and showed me how unsuspicious I
was, for that was not my maiden effort. He punished me those two times onl
and never any other member of the family at all." In the "Villagers of 1840-3
Mark jotted: "Stern, unsmiling, never demonstrated affection for wife
child. . . . Silent, austere, of perfect probity and high principle; ungentle
manner toward his children, but always a gentleman in his phrasing—ar
never punished them—a look was enough, and more than enough." . .

[end 67

[OWSLEY MURDERS SMARR]*

RLY in January, 1845, "Uncle Sam" Smarr traveled from his farm to
arby Hannibal for one of his occasional sprees. Shortly, as was his custom
en turbulent with drink, he began cussing out wealthy merchant Owsley
the audience of townfolk. "When on my way home, when opposite to
dge Clemens' office, I heard Mr. Smarr five times call out at different points
the street 'O yes! O yes, here is Bill Owsley, has got a big stack of goods
re, and stole two thousand dollars from Thompson in Palmyra.' . . . I
urned and went to Mr. Selms' store—Mr. Davis and Mr. Smarr were in
ere—Davis then went out and I heard the report of a pistol—Mr. Davis
d Jimmy Finn then both came in, Jim remarked, 'that would have made a
le in a man's belly. . . .' "

In his store, Owsley, a haughty dandified migrant from Kentucky, heard
e shouting and shooting. "He had a kind of twitching," a customer testified,
nd said it was insufferable." But the merchant did nothing that night, and
arr returned home.

Some days later, Smarr was again in Hannibal, on the corner of Hill and
ain (just a few yards from the Clemens house). Smarr was with a friend
med Brown, who later testified that Owsley came up behind them and called
t, " 'You Sam Smar'—Mr. Smar turned around, seeing Mr. Owsley in the
of drawing a pistol from his pocket, said Mr. Owsley don't fire, or some-
ng to that effect. Mr. Owsley was within about four paces of Mr. Smar
en he drew the pistol and fired twice in succession, after the second fire,
r. Smarr fell, when Mr. Owsley turned on his heel and walked off. After
r. Smarr fell he raised his head and called, 'Brown come take me up I am
ot and will soon be a dead man.' Dr. Grant then came up and invited us
take him to his store. We did so. The while he was begging us to lay
m on his back. He then begged me not to leave him saying he must soon
e. In about half an hour from the time he was shot he expired."

---

* Based upon depositions taken in longhand by John Marshall Clemens, Mark
vain's father, in 1845.

QUESTIONS

1. (A) How do Huck and Jim resemble and differ from their originals, To[m]
Blankenship and Uncle Dan'l? (B) Suggest the values of these change[s]
the reduction of Huck's family to one—Pap; the representation of Hu[ck]
as a person not "tranquilly and continually happy."
2. (A) What characteristics of John Marshall Clemens are similar to th[ose]
of Colonel Grangerford and Colonel Sherburn? (B) What are the diff[er]
ences? (C) Relate the changes—particularly the enlargement of Sherbur[n's]
background—to Twain's representation of the human race in the novel.
3. Comparing Jimmy Finn's reformation with Pap's, discuss the ways [in]
which (A) Pap's backsliding differs from Jimmy's; (B) the characteristi[cs]
of the reformers differ; and (C) the attitudes of the narrators differ. R[e]
late the differences to the characterization of Pap and of Huck.
4. (A) Contrast the descriptions of the Quarles farm with Huck's descri[p]
tion of the Grangerfords' (Chapter XVII) and the Phelps' (Chap[ter]
XXXIV), noting particularly the language, the selection of details, a[nd]
the tone of each. (B) Relate the differences to the fictional point of vie[w]
of the novel and the development of a theme.
5. What details invented by Twain, that is, not to be found in the accou[nt]
of the murder of Smarr by Owsley (A) make Boggs more sympathet[ic]
than Smarr, (B) make Sherburn more sympathetic than Owsley? (C) R[e]
late the changes to Twain's picturing of Bricksville and other riversi[de]
communities.
6. Generalize about Mark Twain's use of biographical elements in *A[d]
ventures of Huckleberry Finn,* and justify your generalizations by citi[ng]
specific instances.

Literary Sources

THE FOLLOWING passages are all possible literary sources for portions
Huckleberry Finn. Evidence for Mark Twain's acquaintance with each follow

Samuel Clemens and William Wright (pseudonym, Dan De Quille
were fellow reporters on the Virginia City *Territorial Enterprise* betwee
1862 and 1864, and for a time they were roommates. After Clemens settled
the East, they corresponded. When in 1875 Clemens heard that Wrig
planned to write a book on the Virginia City Comstock Lode, he urged h
friend to come to Hartford so he could give assistance: "we will grind liter
ture all day in the same room . . . get up a book that children will cry for
For several weeks, using clippings and notes which Wright had brought alon
the pair worked on the book. Clemens arranged for his publisher to issu
History of the Big Bonanza and prefaced it with an introduction dated Ma
1876, testifying to its author's competence. In sentences preceding the passag
about Pike, companions on a prospecting trip notice that Pike is nervo
about an Indian attack. Chapters in *Huck* which may have been influence
I, VIII, and XV.

Charles Dickens had been popular since Clemens's boyhood, and Cleme
read him from 1855 on. Eventually *A Tale of Two Cities* (1859) became
favorite book, read frequently. The precise date is not known but a chapt
in *Tom Sawyer* (1875) seems to echo one in Dickens's novel. Albert Bigelo
Paine in his *Mark Twain: A Biography* (II, 644), tells of his rereading th
book in Paris in 1879; and one of Mark Twain's notebook entries in 188
indicates acquaintance with Jeremy Cruncher. The passages from *A Tale* ma
be compared with Chapters II, III, XXXV, and XL.

Thomas Carlyle, *The French Revolution: A History* (1837), so Cleme
remembered, he first read in 1871. Thereafter he reread it every year or tw
for decades (*Mark Twain's Letters,* II, 489-90). On August 6, 1877, he spok
of it as "one of the greatest creations that ever flowed from a pen" (*Mar
Twain to Mrs. Fairbanks,* ed. Dixon Wecter [San Marino, 1949], p. 207
Chapters which may have been influenced: VI, XIV, XXI.

Mrs. Julia A. Moore, *The Sentimental Song Book* (1876) is mentione
by Mark Twain in *Following the Equator* (1897), Chapter XXXVI: "I fir
in [the poems] the same grace and melody that attracted me when they we
first published, twenty years ago, and have held me in happy bonds ever sinc
The Sentimental Song Book has long been out of print, and has been fo
gotten by the world in general, but not by me. I carry it with me always.
Mark Twain praises the poet for having "the touch that makes an intentional

morous episode pathetic and an intentionally pathetic one funny." He then
otes one of the poems. Mrs. Moore's preface and some of her songs may
ell have suggested details in the picturing of Emmeline Grangerford as well
the composition by her which Huck quotes in Chapter XVII.

In 1879, Clemens conceived the idea of compiling an anthology of
merican and British humor. After he had done a great deal of work on the
ok—eventually a collection of American humorous passages only—and after
hers had given a fair amount of assistance, he published it as *Mark Twain's
brary of Humor* in 1888. Letters show that he made selections which by
arch, 1882, totaled 93,000 words, and that he probably compiled additional
lections during the following summer. Among the humorists Mark Twain
ed were several who influenced *Huck*. He wrote two notes about one of the
ost infamous characters in backwoods humor, Captain Simon Suggs, whose
otto was "It is good to be shifty in a new country." On one occasion in
80, Mark Twain simply jotted down the name "Simon Suggs," but on
other, he wrote, "The man who 'went in on nary a pair' (at camp meet-
g)." The latter reference, to a specific story in Johnson J. Hooper's *Some
dventures of Captain Simon Suggs . . .*, one called "The Captain Attends a
amp-Meeting," shows Mark Twain's knowledge of an episode he adapted in
hapter XX.

In working note A-6 (1879-1880) Mark Twain suggested that he have
uck visit a circus and show astonishment "when the drunkard invades the
ng, scuffles with clown & ringmaster, then rides & strips." The incident had
en developed often in earlier humorous writings, notably by William
appan Thompson as "The Great Attraction," published in a book of 1843,
845, and subsequent years. The story by Thompson, whom Clemens had
nitated in 1857 and whose name he mentioned twice in lists of humorists
r his book, included details resembling those of the note. In 1881, Richard
alcolm Johnston published a version of the story in *Scribner's Monthly,* in
883 in his book, *Dukesborough Tales.* Thompson is represented in *Mark
wain's Library of Humor* but not by his circus story; Johnston is represented
y his "The Expensive Treat of Col. Moses Grice," with an acknowledgment
the publisher of Johnston's book. While the working note may have been
fluenced by Thompson, the version of Chapter XXII of *Huck* is closer to
at of Johnston.

In the summer, 1874, W. E. H. Lecky, *History of European Morals from
ugustus to Charlemagne,* first issued in two volumes in 1869, came to Clem-
s' attention. That summer and later Clemens and his brother-in-law

Theodore Crane often discussed it at the humorist's summer haven, Quar Farm, near Elmira, N. Y. As marginal comments and underlinings in tw copies (one the 1874 edition) attest, it became a great favorite. Lecky echoed in some passages in *Tom Sawyer* (1876). Though Clemens agreed wi some ideas expressed in the study, he was of two minds about the opposir groups described by Lecky: Lecky favored the intuitionists; Clemens admir Lecky's stand and in one marginal note called the book "noble" and "beaut ful." And he pictured the innately good Huck and Jim arriving at right dec sions intuitively, guided by what he once called "sound hearts." But Clemens Calvinistic rearing, an overactive conscience which magnified his misdeeds ar made him wish he were not responsible, disillusionment, and logic all drov him toward the belief that man was not innately and intuitively good—th man's heredity (his "make") and his environment, plus selfish urges, shape his decisions and actions. His notations (see "Mark Twain's Religious Belie as Indicated by Notations in His Books," ed. Chester L. Davis, *The Twainia* May-December, 1956) constantly argued against Lecky. In February, 188 the humorist read a paper opposing Lecky's attitude and soon after *Huck* w. published, so he indicated, he became a determinist. Relevant passages occ in Chapters II, VIII, XII, XV, XVI, XXII, XXIII, XXXI of *Huckleber Finn*.

HISTORY OF THE BIG BONANZA*

Dan De Quille (William Wright)

---

* (Hartford: American Publishing Company, 1876; San Francisco: A. L. Bancroft Co., 1876), pp. 272-273, 366-369, 551-555.

CHAPTER XXXVIII.

SKETCHES OF INDIAN LIFE.

SHORTLY after the so-called Indian war I took a pro-specting trip into the wilderness lying to the eastward of the sinks or lakes of the Carson and Humboldt Rivers. I had with me two white men, and we roamed through the Indian country for nearly a month. During the greater part of this time we had with us a Piute guide known as Captain or " Capitan " Juan.

When Fremont passed through the country and took Captain Trucker into his service as a guide, Juan and nine other adventurous Piute youths accompanied him. When they reached California, these young Piutes liked the country so well, that the majority of them remained there several years. Juan lived there ten years. He worked upon a ranche and could plow and plant, reap and thresh grain as well as any white man. Then he learned the Spanish language, which he spoke quite as well as the Mexicans generally speak it. He also speaks pretty fair English, but mixed in a good deal of Spanish, when a little excited. He proved a trusty and excellent guide, and we retained him as long as we remained in his country. Captain Juan had seen his ups and downs in the world as well as the rest of us.

One evening when we were all seated about our camp-fire, after a hearty supper, being in a talkative mood, he said: " I was pretty well off once, over in California—I had *fifty dollars.*" He named the amount with an emphasis which showed that he considered the announcement one of considerable importance.

404 THE ART OF HUCKLEBERRY FINN

"Indeed!—Had you so much money?" said I.

"O, yes; I was well off—*many ricos!*"

"And what became of all this wealth?"

"Me burst all to smash!"

"Well, that was bad. In kind of speculation?"

"Me not understand spectoolation. What you call um spectoolation?"

"Well, it's when you put your money into something that you expect to make plenty more money out off—like you plant wheat. You plant your money in some speculation to get more money."

"Yes; well, me make one bad plant."

"One bad speculation, eh?"

"Yes; *muy malo*—one *mucho* bad spectoolashe. She was one Spanish spectoolashe. Me marry one Spanish woman. She purty soon got all me money. She say, Juan you got-a some money?' Me say, 'No; no, got-a money?' She say, 'Juan, you no ketch-a money you vamose—you git!' Me no like *los senoritas.* Spanish spectoolashe no good for Piute man—you think?"

"No; very bad speculation. But I suppose you went to work and earned more money for your Spanish wife?"

"No; me stop work—heap mad. Me no want no more money—no more senorita. Too much all time want new dress. One night me vamose. Me come over mountains to my people, ketch me one Piute wife. She no all time want money, money.'"

"Then you have a good Piute wife?"

"O, yes; *muy bueno*—muy bonita! Me keep-a her *mucho* well dress,—give her many shirt. She got heap-a shirt. Not many Piute woman get so much shirt!"

Why, John, you surprise me. How many shirts has she got—twenty? Juan looked astounded and abashed at this extravagant guessing. He scratched his head, looked at me, then at the fire, and seemed to have some notion of not telling me the exact "quantity" of shirt in which his wife rejoiced. At length he slowly said:

"Well, she got two shirt—two shirt, but all fix up nice— plenty braid, *mucho* ribbon, O, very nice! Twenty shirt no

Curious characters are frequently encountered in towns of the silver-mines—queer customers from all parts of the world. A few drinks generally bring out the peculiarities of these men. One day an odd-looking, wiry old chap, evidently from some ranch in the Sierra Nevada Mountains, and apparently a man rich in flocks and herds, made his way to the bar of one of the first-class two-bit saloons of Virginia City. His "keg" was evidently "full" to overflowing, yet he was still athirst. Cocking one eye upon the bar-keeper and the other on the array of bottles before him, he thrust his right hand deep into his breeches' pocket and there stirred up a stunning jingle of coin. Turning to a gentleman standing near, the little old man said : " Stranger, excuse me, but will yer jine in a drink ? "

" Please excuse me, sir," said the gentleman addressed, " I've just drank."

" Stand another, can't yer ? "

" No ; I'm much obliged. I don't wish to drink."

Turning to another gentleman, the old fellow said : " Take a drink, sir—with me ? "

" No, sir ; I thank you, I've just been to dinner," and this man turned and walked away.

The little old man of the mountains looked annoyed and irritated, and turning from the bar, he walked across the saloon to where three or four gentlemen were conversing together : " Gentlemen," said he, " you must excuse me, I'm a stranger here, but I never like to drink alone. Now, will you oblige me by all comin' up and takin' a drink at my expense ? I'm one of your sociable kind, and never like to go in a drove by myself."

Thinking the old fellow had drank about as much as was good for him, all declined the proffered treat. This exasperated the old chap. Jerking his cap off his head and slapping it against his thigh, he broke loose with : " Well, now, this beats my time ! Not a man in this room that will drink with me ! Damme ! I'll go forth into the street and bring in the rabble ! I'll be like that old rancher down in the Valley of Galilee, that the Bible tells of. He was one of my kind. When he had a frolic he wanted to see things whiz ! "

"Which of the old patriarchs was that?" asked a gentleman present, who thought it might be worth while to draw the old fellow out.

"I'm not much of a biblist," said the old man, "but I mean that jolly old cock that lived somewhere down in Galilee or Nazareth. The old gentleman, you know, that gave the big blow-out when his oldest gal got married. You recollect he killed a lot of oxen, and sheep, and calves, and goats, and had a tearin' barbacue, invitin' all the neighbors for miles round. But devil a one came near the house. All too durned high-toned! Then what does that old chap do but git up on his ear and swear the thing shall be a success. So he sends his hired man out to gather up all of the old bummers and dead-beats, the lame, halt, and blind, sayin: 'Bring 'em all in, and we'll have a regular tear—the big blow-out of the season!'

"Then the hungry and thirsty old bummers and gutter-snipes all came charging in from the back alleys, and tumblin' up from the lumber-yards, and they piled in and they made it hot for that lunch, and whiskey, and lager-beer, and they fiddled and danced till they all got blind drunk and broke up in a row. But the gal had a stavin' lively weddin' after all!

"Now that's the kind of man I am. Ef you *gentlemen* won't drink with me, damme, I'll go out and bring in the rabble and we'll eat up all the free-lunch, drink ourselves disorderly, and have a reg'lar weddin' feast right hyar!"

This little oration had the desired effect. All in the room shook hands with the old chap and took a drink with him, when he exultantly exclaimed, bringing his fist down upon the counter, as he emptied his glass: "Damme, you don't know Old Sol Winters down hyar; but he's a pretty big Injun when he's at home, up in Orion Valley!"

Another curious old 'coon was "Old Taggart." Old Taggart is dead. We planted him under the sod in 1874. Where the soul of Old Taggart has gone to, nobody knows. Old Taggart was a good sort of man, but had his "ways." Old Taggart didn't fear death. As he lay on his death-bed, he was conscious, calm, and serene to the last. Said he toward the close:

THE ART OF HUCKLEBERRY FINN **407**

"During these many years I have thought it all over, and I am ready to take the chances."

Being what is called a "pious" woman, Old Taggart's wife was a good deal disturbed by the thought of seeing her husband die without having "experienced religion." She worried the old man a good deal toward the last on this account.

Old Taggart said: "Wife, I'm as sorry for all the bad things I have done during my life, and as much ashamed of all the mean things, as any man could be."

Still the old lady wanted to see him "experience a change of heart." So she sent for Deacon Dudley to come and talk to the old man. The deacon came, and, seating himself by the bedside, turned to the sick man and told him about the wonders and the glories of heaven. He told him all about the New Jerusalem, where the streets are paved with gold, and where angels "touch the soft lyre and tune the vocal lay." He then asked Old Taggart if he didn't think he'd like to go up there.

"No;" said Old Taggart, "I don't think I should feel at home in the kind of place you tell about."

"But, my dear friend," said the Deacon, "you are at the point of death—you should not talk in this way about heaven!"

"Well, Deacon, I'll jist die and trust to the Almighty. I'll jist settle down wherever he puts me. I don't know nothin' about the lay of the land in 'tother world myself, but I'll chance Him."

"I'm surprised, my good friend, to hear that you don't want to be one of that heavenly band that sit before the throne, playing on golden harps, and singing praises forever and forever!"

"Me play on a harp, Deacon?" said Old Taggart, smiling faintly.

"Yes; upon the wondrous golden harp!" briskly replied the Deacon.

"There," said Old Taggart, doggedly, "I don't want to go to that part of heaven. The Lord will give me a place out in some of the back settlements, like. He'll find a place for me, I'll be bound!"

"It's wicked to talk as you are doing," said the Deacon.

"You have the worst ideas about heaven of any man I ever saw!"

"Can't help it, Deacon," said Old Taggart, "its all nonsense to talk about me playin' a harp. I tell you plainly, Deacon, that I don t want to go among the musicians up there. It wouldn't suit me!"

"This is absolutely sinful!" said the Deacon.

"Can't help it," said the old man, "can't help it! It's no use of talkin'; I'll die my own way, and trust to the Almighty. I've a notion that when Old Taggart comes to Him, He will make him comfortable somewheres up there in the kingdom."

Here Old Taggart gave a gasp or two, and was dead. He has probably found a place "up there."

Then there was Old Daniels, a queer old fellow who lived at Gold Hill. Old Daniels would sometimes get so drunk that he didn't know whether he was dead or alive. Very late one night some wags found Old Daniels lying in an alley so much intoxicated that they at first thought he was dead. They got a hand-barrow and carried him out to the graveyard. They there found the grave of a Chinaman that had been opened in order that the bones of the defunct might be sent back to China. The old shattered coffin of the Chinaman still lay beside the open grave, and alongside of the coffin they laid Old Daniels.

The wags then secreted themselves near the spot in order to see how the old fellow would act when he came to his senses, for he was sleeping like a log. They were obliged to wait a long time—till very weary of it—but about daylight, when the air began to grow cold, Old Daniels began to toss and tumble uneasily, and presently was fully awake. He arose to a sitting posture and began a deliberate survey of his surroundings—the empty coffin by his side, the open grave, the tombstones all round.

"The day of resurrection!" said he solemnly, then took another survey of the graveyard. "Yes;" said he, "the day of resurrection, and I'm the first son of a gun out of the ground!"

In the early days, a Frenchman brought to Nevada half a dozen camels, which he placed on his ranche, on the Carson

21

off Hank, who was trying to make him lie still, so that he could get to sleep. There was a high hill on the east side of the cañon, covered on the side next to us with shelly slate rock, and whenever a fox, coyote, or even a rat ran over this it caused a great clatter, the scales of slate ringing like pieces of pottery. This was a place fruitful of alarms and caused Pike to be upon his knees about every five minutes, but about midnight he could keep his eyes open no longer. Hank made the signal agreed upon, by holding up his hat, when two of the boys crept cautiously out of the camp with six-shooters in their hands. By following up a little ravine they were able to gain the summit of the slaty hill without making the slightest noise, as there was no loose rock except on the slope. Presently they started down the slope through the loose rock, leaping and making as much noise as though old Winnemucca and half the Piute tribe were coming down the mountain. At the same time they began yelling and firing their revolvers. At the first racket made on the hill Pike was on his feet and came running toward us, who were returning the fire of the supposed Indians, and yelling as we fired, making altogether enough noise for half a dozen small battles. When Pike reached us two or three of our men fell, crying out that they were killed, and at the same time Hank fell and caught him about the legs, crying: " I'm wounded. Carry me off and hide me in the bushes!"

"Let go of me, Hank, there's five hundred of 'em comin'!"

"I'll never let go of you," said Hank. "Carry me off!"

Pike then lifted Hank who was groaning at a terrible rate, and carrying him about two rods, pitched him, neck and heels, into a clump of thorny bushes. This done Pike rushed down the cañon at the speed of an antelope. Tom rolled on the ground and laughed until he almost smothered himself. "I'm even with Pike on the prickly-pear business!" cried he, as soon as he was able to speak, "he shall never hear the last of this Injun fight!" For my part, now that the fun was all over, I began to feel quite miserable over the whole affair. I feared that in his great fright Pike might dash his brains out against a tree or break his neck among the rocks. I firmly resolved never to take part in another affair of the kind, calling to mind several sham fights and other deviltry in California that had been attended by fatal results to the victims.

In the morning we were ready for a start at sunrise. The first thing I saw was Pike's hat, lying near the place where he had spread his blankets the night before. The sight gave me quite a shock, as it seemed to be the hat of a dead man. I soon found that the others were beginning to feel much as I did about the matter, for, as Pike's blankets were being rolled up to be packed on Tom's horse, one of the boys said: "I hope nothing has happened to Pike." Another said: "O, he's all right!" but at the same time it was easy to see that the speaker feared that he was not "all right."

As we passed down the cañon, I could not help thinking that we should presently find Pike lying wounded or already dead in some rocky pit or pile of boulders near the trail, and most of our party looked quite solemn. The man who carried Pike's hat looked as though he were in a funeral procession, carrying a portion of the corpse. At length we were through the cañon, and having reached the level plain without finding Pike's remains, we all felt quite jolly again and immediately set to work and planned another surprise for him, when we should find him. Instead of fording the river, as we had done in going out, we went some two miles further down and crossed at a ferry. We inquired of the colored man in charge if anyone had crossed during the night. He assured us that no one had crossed, as he found the boat tied up on the west bank, as he had left it the evening before.

We now knew that Pike must have crossed at the ford and again began to feel uneasy, fearing that reaching the river in a state of exhaustion, he had plunged in and had been swept under by the current. One of two things was certain: he was either safe across, or was drowned, as the Mississippi itself would not have stayed his flight. On turning into the main street of Chinatown we came suddenly upon a group of men with minie muskets in their hands and in their midst stood Pike, with a handkerchief tied about his head. He had a musket in his hand and was the centre of attraction. We could see that he was telling those about him of the dreadful affair of the previous night. All those surrounding him were listening so intently that we approached without being observed. Pike was just saying: "Yes; Hank may be alive. I carried him about two miles on my back, with the red cusses yellin' at my heels, then laid him down and kivered him up with brush. But all the rest—" Here Pike turned and saw our party. His jaw dropped, and his eyes almost started from their sockets.

"Well, what of the rest?" said one of his auditors.

"Why, my God! they are all here!" said Pike. "There they all stand!"

The crowd now turned to us, and began to ask: "Who was killed?" "Were there many Indians?" and many other like questions. Not a word of this, however, could we be made to understand. We had seen no Indians; we had never dreamed of any danger from Indians. The whole crowd at once turned to Pike for an explanation. Some of the men hinted that unless he gave a pretty satisfactory explanation of his strange stories he would get into trouble. Pike was thunderstruck and gazed at us with a look of utter helplessness. At last he stammered: "Tom, wasn't you killed?"

"If I was killed I wouldn't be here, would I?"

"I thought I saw you fall," and Pike's face wore the most puzzled look imaginable. His fingers sought the yellowish tuft of hair on his chin and gazing at one and another of us he sighed: "I don't understand it all."

"We none of us understand it," said one of the crowd, sneeringly.

"All here—all here!" said Pike, his countenance wearing the look of an insane person.

"Pike," said I, "you must have dreamt all this about Indians."

Pike's face brightened for a moment, but soon resumed its old look of despair. "No, no," said he, "no dream. I saw them all killed."

"But, Pike, look at us; we are all here—all alive and well!"

Pike looked vacantly about him at the boys, and said: "Yes, I know, but I don't understand it at all."

"Well," said I, "all there is about it is that you were

dreaming and suddenly rose up shouting 'Injuns! Injuns! and before we could stop you, you ran away down the cañon."

"Yes," said Pike, "it must have been a dream. You are all here—it must have been a dream. But it don't seem that way at all."

"Don't seem what way?"

"Why, the way you tell it."

"Well, how does it seem. Let us hear you tell it. Let us have your dream."

"Give us the dream!" Let's have yer dream!" cried the crowd.

"Well, you see I was a layin' thar in my blankets—But I'll be dogoned ef I believe I did dream it!" cried Pike. "I can almost hear the guns crack now!"

"Of course you dreamt it. Ain't we all here?"

"Yes; I know. But how did I act—what did I do?"

"Why, I've just told you all you did. You know that after you went to bed you was bouncing up on your knees every five minutes, and at last you bounced up and took to your heels."

"Yes; I know I was a little oneasy like. I kept a-hearin' somethin' rattle up on that hill, so I kinder kept on my guard like."

"Well, let us have the dream," all again cried.

"Well," began Pike, "at first I was a-dreamin' along kinder nice and easy like, when all at once I heard the rocks clatter —I mean I thonght I heard 'em clatter. Then bang, bang! pop, pop! went the guns, and O! sich yells—sich yells! I thought my hair riz straight on end, and I seed more'n five hundred Injuns, all a-hoppin' down the hill like turkeys. All this time I thought that you fellers was a blazin' away at about two hundred of 'em that was all round you, and about five hundred on the hill. Then I thought I grabbed up a pick and went right inter the thick of the cusses and fit and fit till I'd wore out the pick, and then fit a long time with the handle. By this time I thought you fellers was all killed and I thought I'd git up and dust. But jist then I thought that Hank got holt round my legs and said he was wounded, and wouldn't let go of me 'thout I'd carry him off. I thought I tuck him on my back and carried him 'bout four miles, and hid him in some brush. Then I thought I run on and waded across the river—"

"No, no! you didn't dream that! You did actually wade across the river."

"Well, then what part of it did I dream? Can anybody tell me that?" and poor Pike looked more puzzled than ever.

"You must have waded the river, you know, or you would not be here."

"Well, yes; I s'pose I did, but that don't seem a bit plainer, nor hardly half as plain as the shootin' and yellin' part. That was the dogonest plainest dream I ever did hev!"

"Yet, as we are all here, alive and well; it must have been a dream?"

"Oh, yes, it was a dream, sartain and sure, but what gits me was its bein' so astonishin' plain—jist the same as bein' wide awake!"

Pike continued to tell his dream for some years, constantly adding new matter, till at last it was a wonderful yarn. He enlarged greatly on the part he took in the fight, and after wearing out the pick on the skulls of the Indians, wound up by thrusting the handle down the throat of a brave, as his last act before beating a retreat. Tom more than once told him the truth about the whole affair, bringing in half a dozen of the "boys" to corroborate what he said, but not a word of it would Pike believe.

"Do you think," he would say, "that I was fool enough to believe that sich things actually happened? No, it was all a dream from fust to last, and the biggest and plainest dream I ever had!"

The account I have given of our prospecting trip is a fair sample of all such expeditions—though this trip "panned out" rather more than the usual amount of deviltry. Parties of men frequently travel two or three hundred miles to prospect a certain region, and when they reach it, merely scratch about on the surface for a day or two and if nothing is then found they curse the place and strike out for some other section, when the same surface scratching is repeated. With prospectors the "big thing" is always just ahead, never in

31

A TALE OF TWO CITIES*

Charles Dickens

* (London, 1866), pp. 52-55, 152-157.

THE ART OF HUCKLEBERRY FINN **417**

the invention of a popular game, by a lady who had bestowed her name upon it.)

Mr. Cruncher's apartments were not in a savoury neighbourhood, and were but two in number, even if a closet with a single pane of glass in it might be counted as one. But, they were very decently kept. Early as it was, on the windy March morning, the room in which he lay a-bed was already scrubbed throughout; and between the cups and saucers arranged for breakfast, and the lumbering deal table, a very clean white cloth was spread.

Mr. Cruncher reposed under a patchwork counterpane, like a Harlequin at home. At first, he slept heavily, but, by degrees, began to roll and surge in bed, until he rose above the surface, with his spiky hair looking as if it must tear the sheets to ribbons. At which juncture, he exclaimed, in a voice of dire exasperation:

" Bust me, if she ain't at it agin !"

A woman of orderly and industrious appearance rose from her knees in a corner, with sufficient haste and trepidation to show that she was the person referred to.

" What !" said Mr. Cruncher, looking out of bed for a boot. " You're at it agin, are you ?"

After hailing the morn with this second salutation, he threw a boot at the woman as a third. It was a very muddy boot, and may introduce the odd circumstance connected with Mr. Cruncher's domestic economy, that, whereas he often came home after banking hours with clean boots, he often got up next morning to find the same boots covered with clay.

" What," said Mr. Cruncher, varying his apostrophe after missing his mark—" what are you up to, Aggerawayter ?"

" I was only saying my prayers."

" Saying your prayers. You're a nice woman ! What do you mean by flopping yourself down and praying agin me ?"

" I was not praying against you ; I was praying for you."

" You weren't. And if you were, I won't be took the liberty with. Here ! your mother's a nice woman, young Jerry, going a praying agin your father's prosperity. You've got a dutiful mother, you have, my son. You've got a religious mother, you have, my boy: going and flopping herself down, and praying that the bread-and-butter may be snatched out of the mouth of her only child!"

Master Cruncher (who was in his shirt) took this very ill, and, turning to his mother, strongly deprecated any praying away of his personal board.

"And what do you suppose, you conceited female," said Mr. Cruncher, with unconscious inconsistency, "that the worth of *your* prayers may be? Name the price that you put *your* prayers at!"

"They only come from the heart, Jerry. They are worth no more than that."

"Worth no more than that," repeated Mr. Cruncher. "They ain't worth much, then. Whether or no, I won't be prayed agin, I tell you. I can't afford it. I'm not a going to be made unlucky by *your* sneaking. If you must go flopping yourself down, flop in favour of your husband and child, and not in opposition to 'em. If I had had any but a unnat'ral wife, and this poor boy had had any but a un at'ral mother, I might have made some money last week, instead of being counterprayed and countermined and religiously circumvented into the worst of luck. Bu-u-ust me!" said Mr. Cruncher, who all this time had been putting on his clothes, "if I ain't, what with piety and one blowed thing and another, been choused this last week into as bad luck as ever a poor devil of a honest tradesman met with! Young Jerry, dress yourself, my boy, and while I clean my boots keep a eye upon your mother now and then, and if you see any signs of more flopping, give me a call. For, I tell you," here he addressed his wife once more, "I won't be gone agin, in this manner. I am as rickety as a hackney-coach, I'm as sleepy as laudanum, my lines is strained to that degree that I shouldn't know, if it wasn't for the pain in 'em, which was me and which somebody else, yet I'm none the better for it in pocket; and it's my suspicion that you've been at it from morning to night to prevent me from being the better for it in pocket, and I won't put up with it, Aggerawayter, and what do you say now!"

Growling, in addition, such phrases as "Ah! yes! You're religious, too. You wouldn't put yourself in opposition to the interests of your husband and child, would you? Not you!" and throwing off other sarcastic sparks from the whirling grindstone of his indignation, Mr. Cruncher betook himself to his boot-cleaning and his general preparations for business. In the mean time, his son, whose head was garnished with tenderer spikes, and whose young eyes stood close by one another, as his father's did, kept the required watch upon his mother. He greatly disturbed that poor woman at intervals, by darting out of his sleeping closet, where he made his toilet, with a suppressed cry of "You are going to flop, mother.—Halloa, father!" and, after raising this fictitious alarm, darting in again with an undutiful grin.

Mr. Cruncher's temper was not at all improved when he came to his breakfast. He resented Mrs. Cruncher's saying Grace with particular animosity.

"Now, Aggerawayter! What are you up to? At it agin?"

His wife explained that she had merely "asked a blessing."

"Don't do it!" said Mr. Cruncher, looking about, as if he rather expected to see the loaf disappear under the efficacy of his wife's petitions. "I ain't a going to be blest out of house and home. I won't have my wittles blest off my table. Keep still!"

Exceedingly red-eyed and grim, as if he had been up all night at a party which had taken anything but a convivial turn, Jerry Cruncher worried his breakfast rather than ate it, growling over it like any four-footed inmate of a menagerie. Towards nine o'clock he smoothed his ruffled aspect, and, presenting as respectable and business-like an exterior as he could overlay his natural self with, issued forth to the occupation of the day.

It could scarcely be called a trade, in spite of his favourite description of himself as "a honest tradesman." His stock consisted of a wooden stool, made out of a broken-backed chair cut down, which stool young Jerry, walking at his father's side, carried every morning to beneath the banking-house window that was nearest Temple Bar: where, with the addition of the first handful of straw that could be gleaned from any passing vehicle to keep the cold and wet from the odd-job-man's feet, it formed the encampment for the day. On this post of his, Mr. Cruncher was as well known to Fleet-street and the Temple, as the Bar itself— and was almost as ill-looking.

Encamped at a quarter before nine, in good time to touch his three-cornered hat to the oldest of men as they passed in to Tellson's, Jerry took up his station on this windy March morning, with Young Jerry standing by him, when not engaged in making forays through the Bar, to inflict bodily and mental injuries of an acute description on passing boys who were small enough for his amiable purpose. Father and son, extremely like each other, looking silently on at the morning traffic in Fleet-street, with their two heads as near to one another as the two eyes of each were, bore a considerable resemblance to a pair of monkeys. The resemblance was not lessened by the accidental circumstance, that the mature Jerry bit and spat out straw, while the twinkling eyes of the youthful Jerry were as restlessly watchful of him as of everything else in Fleet-street.

The head of one of the regular in-door messengers attached to Tellson's establishment was put through the door, and the word was given :

" Porter wanted !"

" Hooray, father ! Here's an early job to begin with !"

Having thus given his parent God speed, Young Jerry seated himself on the stool, entered on his reversionary interest in the straw his father had been chewing, and cogitated.

" Al-ways rusty ! His fingers is al-ways rusty !" muttered Young Jerry. " Where does my father get all that iron rust from ? He don't get no iron rust here !"

CHAPTER XIV.

THE HONEST TRADESMAN.

To the eyes of Mr. Jeremiah Cruncher, sitting on his stool in Fleet-street with his grisly urchin beside him, a vast number and variety of objects in movement were every day presented. Who could sit upon anything in Fleet-street during the busy hours of the day, and not be dazed and deafened by two immense processions, one ever tending westward with the sun, the other ever tending eastward from the sun, both ever tending to the plains beyond the range of red and purple where the sun goes down!

With his straw in his mouth, Mr. Cruncher sat watching the two streams, like the heathen rustic who has for several centuries been on duty watching one stream—saving that Jerry had no expectation of their ever running dry. Nor would it have been an expectation of a hopeful kind, since a small part of his income was derived from the pilotage of timid women (mostly of a full habit and past the middle term of life) from Tellson's side of the tides to the opposite shore. Brief as such companionship was in every separate instance, Mr. Cruncher never failed to become so interested in the lady as to express a strong desire to have the honour of drinking her very good health. And it was from the gifts bestowed upon him towards the execution of this benevolent purpose, that he recruited his finances, as just now observed.

Time was, when a poet sat upon a stool in a public place, and mused in the sight of men. Mr. Cruncher, sitting on a stool in a public place, but not being a poet, mused as little as possible, and looked about him.

It fell out that he was thus engaged in a season when crowds were few, and belated women few, and when his affairs in general were so unprosperous as to awaken a strong suspicion in his breast that Mrs. Cruncher must have been "flopping" in some pointed manner, when an unusual concourse pouring down Fleet-street westward, attracted his attention. Looking that way, Mr. Cruncher made out that some kind of funeral was coming along, and that there was popular objection to this funeral, which engendered uproar.

"Young Jerry," said Mr. Cruncher, turning to his offspring, "it's a buryin'."

"Hooroar, father!" cried Young Jerry.

The young gentleman uttered this exultant sound with mysterious significance. The elder gentleman took the cry so ill, that he watched his opportunity, and smote the young gentleman on the ear.

"What d'ye mean? What are you hooroaring at? What do you want to convey to your own father, you young Rip? This boy is getting too many for *me!*" said Mr. Cruncher, surveying him. "Him and his hooroars! Don't let me hear no more of you, or you shall feel some more of me. D'ye hear?"

"I warn't doing no harm," Young Jerry protested, rubbing his cheek.

"Drop it then," said Mr. Cruncher; "I won't have none of *your* no harms. Get a top of that there seat, and look at the crowd."

His son obeyed, and the crowd approached; they were bawling and hissing round a dingy hearse and dingy mourning coach, in which mourning coach there was only one mourner, dressed in the dingy trappings that were considered essential to the dignity of the position. The position appeared by no means to please him, however, with an increasing rabble surrounding the coach, deriding him, making grimaces at him, and incessantly groaning and calling out: "Yah! Spies! Tst! Yaha! Spies!" with many compliments too numerous and forcible to repeat.

Funerals had at all times a remarkable attraction for Mr. Cruncher; he always pricked up his senses, and became excited, when a funeral passed Tellson's. Naturally, therefore, a funeral with this uncommon attendance excited him greatly, and he asked of the first man who ran against him:

"What is it, brother? What's it about?"

"*I* don't know," said the man. "Spies! Yaha! Tst! Spies!"

He asked another man. " Who is it ?"

" *I* don't know," returned the man: clapping his hands to his mouth nevertheless, and vociferating in a surprising heat and with the greatest ardour, " Spies! Yaha! Tst, tst! Spi-ies!"

At length, a person better informed on the merits of the case, tumbled against him, and from this person he learned that the funeral was the funeral of one Roger Cly.

" Was He a spy ?" asked Mr. Cruncher.

" Old Bailey spy," returned his informant. " Yaha! Tst! Yah! Old Bailey Spi-i-ies!"

" Why, to be sure!" exclaimed Jerry, recalling the Trial at which he had assisted. " I've seen him. Dead, is he ?"

" Dead as mutton," returned the other, " and can't be too dead. Have 'em out, there! Spies! Pull 'em out, there! Spies!"

The idea was so acceptable in the prevalent absence of any idea, that the crowd caught it up with eagerness, and loudly repeating the suggestion to have 'em out, and to pull 'em out, mobbed the two vehicles so closely that they came to a stop. On the crowd's opening the coach doors, the one mourner scuffled out of himself and was in their hands for a moment; but he was so alert, and made such good use of his time, that in another moment he was scouring away up a by-street, after shedding his cloak, hat, long hatband, white pocket-handkerchief, and other symbolical tears.

These, the people tore to pieces, and scattered far and wide with great enjoyment, while the tradesmen hurriedly shut up their shops; for a crowd in those times stopped at nothing, and was a monster much dreaded. They had already got the length of opening the hearse to take the coffin out, when some brighter genius proposed instead, its being escorted to its destination amidst general rejoicing. Practical sugges-tions being much needed, this suggestion, too, was received with acclamation, and the coach was immediately filled with eight inside and a dozen out, while as many people got on the roof of the hearse as could by any exercise of ingenuity stick upon it. Among the first of these volunteers was Jerry Cruncher himself, who modestly concealed his spiky head from the observation of Tellson's, in the further corner of the mourning coach.

The officiating undertakers made some protest against these changes in the ceremonies; but, the river being alarmingly near, and several voices remarking on the efficacy of cold immersion in bringing refractory members of the profession to reason, the protest was faint and brief. The remodelled procession started, with a chimney-sweep driving the hearse—advised by the regular driver, who was perched beside him, under close inspection, for the purpose—and with a pieman, also attended by his cabinet minister, driving the mourning coach. A bear-leader, a popular street character of the time, was impressed as an additional ornament, before the cavalcade had gone far down the Strand; and his bear, who was black and very mangy, gave quite an Undertaking air to that part of the procession in which he walked.

Thus, with beer-drinking, pipe-smoking, song-roaring, and infinite caricaturing of woe, the disorderly procession went its way, recruiting at every step, and all the shops shutting up before it. Its destination was the old church of Saint Pancras, far off in the fields. It got there in course of time; insisted on pouring into the burial-ground; finally, accomplished the interment of the deceased Roger Cly in its own way, and highly to its own satisfaction.

The dead man disposed of, and the crowd being under the necessity of providing some other entertainment for itself, another brighter genius (or perhaps the same) conceived the humour of impeaching casual passers-by, as Old Bailey spies, and wreaking vengeance on them. Chase was given to some scores of inoffensive persons who had never been near the Old Bailey in their lives, in the realisation of this fancy, and they were roughly hustled and maltreated. The transition to the sport of window-breaking, and thence to the plundering of public-houses, was easy and natural. At last, after several hours, when sundry summer-houses had been pulled down, and some area railings had been torn up, to arm the more belligerent spirits, a rumour got about that the Guards were coming. Before this rumour, the crowd gradually melted away, and perhaps the Guards came, and perhaps they never came, and this was the usual progress of a mob.

Mr. Cruncher did not assist at the closing sports, but had remained behind in the churchyard, to confer and condole with the undertakers. The place had a soothing influence on him. He procured a pipe from a neighbouring public-house, and smoked it, looking in at the railings and maturely considering the spot.

"Jerry," said Mr. Cruncher, apostrophising himself in his usual way, "you see that there Cly that day, and you see with your own eyes that he was a young 'un and a straight made 'un."

Having smoked his pipe out, and ruminated a little longer, he turned himself about, that he might appear, before the hour of closing, on his station at Tellson's. Whether his meditations on mortality had touched his liver, or whether his general health had been previously at all amiss, or whether he desired to show a little attention to an eminent man, is not so much to the purpose, as that he made a short call upon his medical adviser—a distinguished surgeon—on his way back.

Young Jerry relieved his father with dutiful interest, and reported No job in his absence. The bank closed, the ancient clerks came out, the usual watch was set, and Mr. Cruncher and his son went home to tea.

"Now, I tell you where it is!" said Mr. Cruncher to his wife, on entering. "If, as a honest tradesman, my wenturs goes wrong to-night, I shall make sure that you've been praying again me, and I shall work you for it just the same as if I seen you do it."

The dejected Mrs. Cruncher shook her head.

"Why, you're at it afore my face!" said Mr. Cruncher, with signs of angry apprehension.

"I am saying nothing."

"Well, then; don't meditate nothing. You might as well flop as meditate. You may as well go again me one way as another. Drop it altogether."

"Yes, Jerry."

"Yes, Jerry," repeated Mr. Cruncher, sitting down to

tea. "Ah! It *is* yes, Jerry. That's about it. You may say yes, Jerry."

Mr. Cruncher had no particular meaning in these sulky corroborations, but made use of them, as people not unfrequently do, to express general ironical dissatisfaction.

"You and your yes, Jerry," said Mr. Cruncher, taking a bite out of his bread-and-butter, and seeming to help it down with a large invisible oyster out of his saucer. "Ah! I think so. I believe you."

"You are going out to-night?" asked his decent wife, when he took another bite.

"Yes, I am."

"May I go with you, father?" asked his son, briskly.

"No, you mayn't. I'm a going—as your mother knows—a fishing. That's where I'm going to. Going a fishing."

"Your fishing-rod gets rayther rusty; don't it, father?"

"Never you mind."

"Shall you bring any fish home, father?"

"If I don't, you'll have short commons to-morrow," returned that gentleman, shaking his head; "that's questions enough for you; I ain't a going out, till you've been long a-bed."

He devoted himself during the remainder of the evening to keeping a most vigilant watch on Mrs. Cruncher, and sullenly holding her in conversation that she might be prevented from meditating any petitions to his disadvantage. With this view, he urged his son to hold her in conversation also, and led the unfortunate woman a hard life by dwelling on any causes of complaint he could bring against her, rather than he would leave her for a moment to her own reflections. The devoutest person could have rendered no greater homage to the efficacy of an honest prayer than he did in this distrust of his wife. It was as if a professed unbeliever in ghosts should be frightened by a ghost story.

"And mind you!" said Mr. Cruncher. "No games to-morrow! If I, as a honest tradesman, succeed in providing a jinte of meat or two, none of your not touching of it, and sticking to bread. If I, as a honest tradesman, am able to provide a little beer, none of your declaring on water.

THE FRENCH REVOLUTION*

Thomas Carlyle

---

* (London, 1837), II, 100-102 and III, 353-360 and 394-396.

CHAPTER II.

ARREARS AND ARISTOCRATS.

INDEED, as to the general outlook of things, Bouillé himself augurs not well of it. The French Army, ever since those old Bastille days, and earlier, has been universally in the questionablest state, and growing daily worse. Discipline, which is at all times a kind of miracle, and works by faith, broke down then; one sees not with what near prospect of recovering itself. The Gardes Françaises played a deadly game; but how they won it, and wear the prizes of it, all men know. In that general overturn, we saw the Hired Fighters refuse to fight. The very Swiss of Château-Vieux, which indeed is a kind of French Swiss, from Geneva and the Pays de Vaud, are understood to have declined. Deserters glided over; Royal-Allemand itself looked disconsolate, though stanch of purpose. In a word, we there saw *Military Rule*, in the shape of poor Besenval with that convulsive unmanageable Camp of his, pass two martyr days on the Champ-de-Mars; and then, veiling itself, so to speak, 'under cloud of night,' depart 'down the left bank of the Seine,' to seek refuge elsewhere; *this* ground having clearly become too hot for it.

But what new ground to seek, what remedy to try?

Quarters that were 'uninfected:' this doubtless, with judicious strictness of drilling, were the plan. Alas, in all quarters and places, from Paris onward to the remotest hamlet, is infection, is seditious contagion: inhaled, propagated by contact and converse, till the dullest soldier catch it! There is speech of men in uniform with men not in uniform; men in uniform read journals, and even write in them.* There are public petitions or remonstrances, private emissaries and associations; there is discontent, jealousy, uncertainty, sullen suspicious humour. The whole French Army, fermenting in dark heat, glooms ominous, boding good to no one.

So that, in the general social dissolution and revolt, we are to have this deepest and dismallest kind of it, a revolting soldiery? Barren, desolate to look upon is this same business of revolt under all its aspects; but how infinitely more so, when it takes the aspect of military mutiny! The very implement of rule and restraint, whereby all the rest was managed and held in order, has become precisely the frightfullest immeasurable implement of misrule; like the element of Fire, our indispensable all-ministering servant, when it gets the *mastery*, and becomes conflagration. Discipline we called a kind of miracle: in fact, is it not miraculous how one man moves hundreds of thousands; each unit of whom it may be loves him not, and singly fears him not, yet has to obey him, to go hither or go thither, to march and halt, to give death, and even to receive it, as if a Fate had spoken; and the word-of-command becomes, almost in the literal sense, a magic-word?

* *See* Newspapers of July 1789 (in Hist. Parl. ii. 35), &c.

Which magic-word, again, if it be once *forgotten;*
the spell of it once broken!   The legions of assiduous
ministering spirits rise on you now as menacing fiends;
your free orderly arena becomes a tumult-place of the
Nether Pit, and the hapless magician is rent limb from
limb.   Military mobs are mobs with muskets in their
hands; and also with death hanging over their heads,
for death is the penalty of disobedience and they have
disobeyed.   And now if all mobs are properly frenzies,
and work frenetically with mad fits of hot and of cold,
fierce rage alternating so incoherently with panic terror,
consider what your military mob will be, with such a
conflict of duties and penalties, whirled between remorse and fury, and, for the hot fit, loaded fire-arms in
its hand!   To the soldier himself, revolt is frightful,
and oftenest perhaps pitiable; and yet so dangerous, it
can only be hated, cannot be pitied.   An anomalous
class of mortals these poor Hired Killers!   With a
frankness, which to the Moralist in these times seems
surprising, they have sworn to become machines; and
nevertheless they are still partly men.   Let no prudent
person in authority remind them of this latter fact; but
always let force, let injustice above all, stop short
clearly on *this* side of the rebounding-point!   Soldiers,
as we often say, do revolt: were it not so, several
things which are transient in this world might be
perennial.

Over and above the general quarrel which all sons
of Adam maintain with their lot here below, the griev-
ances of the French soldiery reduce themselves to two.
First that their Officers are Aristocrats; secondly that

CHAPTER II.

DANTON, NO WEAKNESS.

DANTON, meanwhile, has been pressingly sent for from Arcis: he must return instantly, cried Camille, cried Phélippeaux and Friends, who scented danger in the wind. Danger enough! A Danton, a Robespierre, chief-products of a victorious Revolution, are now arrived in immediate front of one another; must ascertain how they will live together, rule together. One conceives easily the deep mutual incompatibility that divided these two: with what terror of feminine hatred the poor seagreen Formula looked at the monstrous colossal Reality, and grew greener to behold him;—the Reality, again, struggling to think no ill of a chief-product of the Revolution; yet feeling at bottom that such chief-product was little other than a chief wind-bag, blown large by Popular air; not a man with the heart of a man, but a poor spasmodic incorruptible pedant, with a logic-formula instead of heart; of Jesuit or Methodist-Parson nature; full of sincere-cant, incorruptibility, of virulence, poltroonery; barren as the east-wind! Two such chief-products are too much for one Revolution.

Friends, trembling at the results of a quarrel on their part, brought them to meet. " It is right," said

Danton, swallowing much indignation, " to repress the
Royalists: but we should not strike except where it is
useful to the Republic; we should not confound the
innocent and the guilty."—" And who told you," replied Robespierre with a poisonous look, " that one
innocent person had perished?"—" *Quoi*," said Danton,
turning round to Friend Pâris self-named Fabricius,
Juryman in the Revolutionary Tribunal: " *Quoi*, not
one innocent? What sayest thou of it, Fabricius!"*—
Friends, Westermann, this Pâris and others urged him
to shew himself, to ascend the Tribune and act. The
man Danton was not prone to shew himself; to act, or
uproar for his own safety. A man of careless, large,
hoping nature; a large nature that could rest: he
would sit whole hours, they say, hearing Camille
talk, and liked nothing so well. Friends urged him
to fly; his Wife urged him: " Whither fly?" answered
he: " If freed France cast me out, there are only dun-
geons for me elsewhere. One carries not his country
with him at the sole of his shoe!" The man Danton
sat still. Not even the arrestment of Friend Hérault,
a member of *Salut*, yet arrested by *Salut*, can rouse
Danton.—On the night of the 30th of March, Juryman
Pâris came rushing in; haste looking through his eyes:
A clerk of the *Salut* Committee had told him Danton's
warrant was made out, he is to be arrested this very
night! Entreaties there are and trepidation, of poor
Wife, of Pâris and Friends: Danton sat silent for a
while; then answered, " *Ils n'oseraient*, They dare not;"
and would take no measures. Murmuring " They dare
not," he goes to sleep as usual.

* Biographie des Ministres, § Danton.

And yet, on the morrow morning, strange rumour spreads over Paris City: Danton, Camille, Phélippeaux, Lacroix have been arrested over night! It is verily so: the corridors of the Luxembourg were all crowded, Prisoners crowding forth to see this giant of the Revolution enter among them. " Messieurs," said Danton politely, " I hoped soon to have got you all out of this: but here I am myself; and one sees not where it will end."—Rumour may spread over Paris: the Convention clusters itself into groups; wide-eyed, whispering, " Danton arrested!" Who then is safe? Legendre, mounting the Tribune, utters, at his own peril, a feeble word for him; moving that he be heard at that Bar before indictment; but Robespierre frowns him down: " Did you hear Chabot, or Bazire? Would you have two weights and measures?" Legendre cowers low; Danton, like the others, must take his doom.

Danton's Prison-thoughts were curious to have; but are not given in any quantity: indeed few such remarkable men have been left so obscure to us as this Titan of the Revolution. He was heard to ejaculate: " This time twelvemonth, I was moving the creation of that same Revolutionary Tribunal. I crave pardon for it of God and man. They are all Brothers Cain: Brissot would have had me guillotined as Robespierre now will. I leave the whole business in a frightful welter (*gâchis épouvantable*): not one of them understands anything of government. Robespierre will follow me; I drag down Robespierre. O, it were better to be a poor fisherman than to meddle with governing of men." —Camille's young beautiful Wife, who had made him rich not in money alone, hovers round the Luxembourg, like a disembodied spirit, day and night. Camille's stolen letters to her still exist; stained with the mark of his tears.* " I carry my head like a Saint-Sacrament?" so Saint-Just was heard to mutter: " Perhaps he will carry his like a Saint-Dennis."

Unhappy Danton, thou still unhappier light Camille, once light *Procureur de la Lanterne*, ye also have arrived, then, at the Bourne of Creation, where, like Ulysses Polytlas at the limit and utmost Gades of his voyage, gazing into that dim Waste beyond Creation, a man does see *the Shade of his Mother*, pale, ineffectual;— and days when his Mother nursed and wrapped him are all-too sternly contrasted with this day! Danton, Camille, Hérault, Westermann, and the others, very strangely massed up with Bazires, Swindler Chabots, Fabre d'Eglantines, Banker Freys, a most motley Batch, ' *Fournée*' as such things will be called, stand ranked at the Bar of Tinville. It is the 2d of April 1794. Danton has had but three days to lie in Prison; for the time presses.

What is your name? place of abode? and the like, Fouquier asks; according to formality. " My name is Danton," answers he; " a name tolerably known in the Revolution: my abode will soon be Annihilation (*dans le Néant*); but I shall live in the Pantheon of History." A man will endeavour to say something forcible, be it by nature or not! Hérault mentions epigrammatically that he " sat in this Hall, and was detested of Parlementeers." Camille makes

* Aperçus sur Camille Desmoulins (in Vieux Cordelier, Paris, 1825), p. 1-29.

answer, " My age is that of the *bon Sansculotte Jésus;* an age fatal to Revolutionists." O Camille, Camille! And yet in that Divine Transaction, let us say, there did lie, among other things, the fatallest Reproof ever uttered here below to Worldly Right-honourableness; ' the highest Fact,' so devout Novalis calls it, ' in the ' Rights of Man.' Camille's real age, it would seem, is thirty-four. Danton is one year older.

Some five months ago, the Trial of the Twenty-two Girondins was the greatest that Fouquier had then done. But here is a still greater to do; a thing which tasks the whole faculty of Fouquier; which makes the very heart of him waver. For it is the voice of Danton that reverberates now from these domes; in passionate words, piercing with their wild sincerity, winged with wrath. Your best Witnesses he shivers into ruin at one stroke. He demands that the Committee-men themselves come as Witnesses, as Accusers; he " will cover them with ignominy." He raises his huge stature, he shakes his huge black head, fire flashes from the eyes of him, — piercing to all Republican hearts: so that the very Galleries, though we filled them by ticket, murmur sympathy; and are like to burst down, and raise the People, and deliver him! He complains loudly that he is classed with Chabots, with swindling Stockjobbers; that his Indictment is a list of platitudes and horrors. " Danton hidden on the Tenth of August?" reverberates he, with the roar of a lion in the toils: " Where are the men that had to press Danton to shew himself, that day? Where are these high-gifted souls of whom he borrowed energy? Let them appear, these Accusers of mine:

I have all the clearness of my self-possession when I demand them. I will unmask the three shallow scoundrels," *les trois plats coquins*, Saint-Just, Couthon, Lebas, " who fawn on Robespierre, and lead him towards his destruction. Let them produce themselves here; I will plunge them into Nothingness, out of which they ought never to have risen." The agitated President agitates his bell; enjoins calmness, in a vehement manner: " What is it to thee how I defend myself?" cries the other: " the right of dooming me is thine always. The voice of a man speaking for his honour and his life may well drown the jingling of thy bell!" Thus Danton, higher and higher; till the lion voice of him ' dies away in his throat:' speech will not utter what is in that man. The Galleries murmur ominously; the first day's Session is over.

O Tinville, President Herman, what will ye do? They have two days more of it, by strictest Revolutionary Law. The Galleries already murmur. If this Danton were to burst your meshwork!—Very curious indeed to consider. It turns on a hair: and what a Hoitytoity were *there*, Justice and Culprit changing places; and the whole History of France running changed! For in France there is this Danton only that could still try to govern France. He only, the wild amorphous Titan;—and perhaps that other olive-complexioned individual, the Artillery Officer at Toulon, whom we left pushing his fortune in the South?

On the evening of the second day, matters looking not better but worse and worse, Fouquier and Herman, distraction in their aspect, rush over to *Salut Public*. What is to be done? *Salut Public* rapidly concocts a new Decree; whereby if men ' insult Justice,' they may be ' thrown out of the Debates.' For indeed, withal, is there not ' a Plot in the Luxembourg Prison?' *Ci-devant* General Dillon, and others of the Suspect, plotting with Camille's Wife to distribute *assignats*; to force the Prisons, overset the Republic? Citizen Laflotte, himself Suspect but desiring enfranchisement, has reported said Plot for us:—a report that may bear fruit! Enough, on the morrow morning, an obedient Convention passes this Decree. *Salut* rushes off with it to the aid of Tinville, reduced now almost to extremities. And so, *Hors des Débats*, Out of the Debates, ye insolents! Policemen do your duty! In such manner, with a deadlift effort, *Salut*, Tinville Herman, Leroi *Dix-Août*, and all stanch jurymen setting heart and shoulder to it, the Jury becomes ' sufficiently instructed;' Sentence is passed, is sent by an Official, and torn and trampled on: *Death this day*. It is the 5th of April, 1794. Camille's poor Wife may cease hovering about this Prison. Nay let her kiss her poor children; and prepare to enter it, and to follow!—

Danton carried a high look in the Death-cart. Not so Camille: it is but one week, and all is so topsy-turvied; angel Wife left weeping; love, riches, Revolutionary fame, left all at the Prison-gate; carnivorous Rabble now howling round. Palpable, and yet incredible; like a madman's dream! Camille struggles and writhes; his shoulders shuffle the loose coat off them, which hangs knotted, the hands tied: " Calm, my friend," said Danton; " heed not that vile canaille (*laissez là cette vile canaille*)." At the foot of the

Scaffold, Danton was heard to ejaculate : " O my Wife, my well-beloved, I shall never see thee more then !"— but, interrupting himself : " Danton, no weakness !" He said to Hérault-Séchelles stepping forward to embrace him : " Our heads will meet *there*," in the Headsman's sack. His last words were to Samson the Headsman himself : " Thou wilt shew my head to the people ; it is worth shewing."

So passes, like a gigantic mass, of valour, ostentation, fury, affection and wild revolutionary manhood, this Danton, to his unknown home. He was of Arcis-sur-Aube ; born of ' good farmer-people' there. He had many sins ; but one worst sin he had not, that of Cant. No hollow Formalist, deceptive and self-deceptive, *ghastly* to the natural sense, was this ; but a very Man : with all his dross he was a Man ; fiery-real, from the great fire-bosom of Nature herself. He saved France from Brunswick ; he walked straight his own wild road, whither it led him. He may live for some generations in the memory of men.

Stumbling in again, the wretched drunk-sobered Henriot announces: " All is lost !"　" *Misérable* ! it is thou that hast lost it," cry they; and fling him, or else he flings himself, out of window: far enough down; into masonwork and horror of cesspool; not into death but worse. Augustin Robespierre follows him; with the like fate. Saint-Just called on Lebas to kill him; who would not. Couthon crept under a table; attempting to kill himself; not doing it.—On entering that Sanhedrim of Insurrection, we find all as good as extinct; undone, ready for seizure. Robespierre was sitting on a chair, with pistol-shot blown through, not his head, but his under jaw; the suicidal hand had failed.* With prompt zeal, not without trouble, we gather these wrecked Conspirators; fish up even Henriot and Augustin, bleeding and foul; pack them all, rudely enough, into carts; and shall, before sunrise, have them safe under lock and key. Amid shoutings and embracings.

Robespierre lay in an anteroom of the Convention Hall, while his Prison-escort was getting ready; the mangled jaw bound up rudely with bloody linen: a spectacle to men. He lies stretched on a table, a deal-box his pillow; the sheath of the pistol is still clenched convulsively in his hand. Men bully him, insult him: his eyes still indicate intelligence; he speaks no word. ' He had on the sky-blue coat he

---

* Méda, p. 384. (Méda asserts that it was he who, with infinite courage, though in a lefthanded manner, shot Robespierre. Méda got promoted for his services of this night; and died General and Baron. Few credited Méda, in what was otherwise incredible.)

' had got made for the Feast of the *Etre Suprême'*—
O reader, can thy hard heart hold out against that?
His trousers were nankeen; the stockings had fallen
down over the ancles. He spake no word more in
this world.

And so, at six in the morning, a victorious Convention adjourns. Report flies over Paris as on golden
wings; penetrates the Prisons; irradiates the faces of
those that were ready to perish: turnkeys and *moutons*,
fallen from their high estate, look mute and blue.
It is the 28th day of July, called 10th of Thermidor,
year 1794.

Fouquier had but to identify; his Prisoners being
already Out of Law. At four in the afternoon, never
before were the streets of Paris seen so crowded.
From the Palais de Justice to the Place de la Révolution, for *thither* again go the Tumbrils this time, it is
one dense stirring mass; all windows crammed; the
very roofs and ridge-tiles budding forth human
Curiosity, in strange gladness. The Death-tumbrils,
with their motley Batch of Outlaws, some Twenty-
three or so, from Maximilien to Mayor Fleuriot and
Simon the Cordwainer, roll on. All eyes are on
Robespierre's Tumbril, where he, his jaw bound in
dirty linen, with his half-dead Brother, and half-dead
Henriot, lie shattered; their ' seventeen hours' of
agony about to end. The Gendarmes point their
swords at him, to shew the people which is he. A
woman springs on the Tumbril; clutching the side of
it with one hand; waving the other Sibyl-like; and
exclaims: " The death of thee gladdens my very heart,
m'enivre de joie;" Robespierre opened his eyes;

" *Scélérat,* go down to Hell, with the curses of all wives and mothers !"—At the foot of the scaffold, they stretched him on the ground till his turn came. Lifted aloft, his eyes again opened; caught the bloody axe. Samson wrenched the coat off him; wrenched the dirty linen from his jaw : the jaw fell powerless, there burst from him a cry ;—hideous to hear and see. Samson, thou canst not be too quick !

Samson's work done, there bursts forth shout on shout of applause. Shout, which prolongs itself not only over Paris, but over France, but over Europe, and down to this Generation. Deservedly, and also undeservedly. O unhappiest Advocate of Arras, wert thou worse than other Advocates ? Stricter man, according to his Formula, to his Credo and his Cant, of probities, benevolences, pleasures-of-virtue, and such like, lived not in that age. A man fitted, in some luckier settled age, to have become one of those incorruptible barren Pattern-Figures, and have had marble-tablets and funeral-sermons ! His poor landlord, the Cabinet-maker in the Rue Saint-Honoré, loved him; his Brother died for him. May God be merciful to him, and to us !

This is the end of the Reign of Terror; new glorious *Revolution* named *of Thermidor ;* of Thermidor 9th, year 2; which being interpreted into old slave-style means 27th of July, 1794. Terror is ended ; and death in the Place de la Révolution, were the ' *Tail* ' of Robespierre' once executed; which service Fouquier in large Batches is swiftly managing.

THE SENTIMENTAL SONG BOOK*

Julia A. Moore

* (Grand Rapids, Mich.: C. M. Loomis, 1876), pp. 20-21, 28-29, 44-45.

LITTLE HENRY.

AIR—" *Minnie Lee.*"

OH! come listen to my story
   Of a little infant child—
His spirit is up in heaven—
   It has left us for a while.
Death has robbed us of our Henry,
   He is with our Savior now,
Where there is no pain or sorrow
   Comes to cloud his little brow.

CHORUS: God has taken their little treasure,
         And his name I'll tell you now,
      He has gone from earth forever,
         Their little Charles Henry House.

His cheeks were red as roses,
   And his eyes were black as coals,
His lips were red as rubies,
   And his little hair it curled.
And they called him little Charlie,
   He was full of joyful mirth—
Now his little form is lying
   'Neath the cold and silent earth.

It was the eleventh of December,
   On a cold and windy day,
Just at the close of evening,
   When the sunlight fades away;
Little Henry he was dying,
   In his little crib he lay,
With the soft winds round him sighing
   From early morn till close of day.

Parents, brothers, sisters weeping,
　For their cup of sorrow's full,
And his little playthings keeping,
　That he thought so beautiful—
Tears from parents' eyes were starting
　For their little loving one.
Oh! how painful was the parting
　From their little infant son.

Oh! how often have they kissed him,
　And caressed his little brow—
To his little voice have listened,
　But his place is vacant now.
And they called him little Charley,
　And his loving name they called,
But they could not keep their darling
　From the loving Savior's call.

But they must now cease their mourning,
　For his little soul is at rest,
Where there can no storms of trouble
　Roll across his peaceful breast.
For his little form is sleeping
　In the cold and silent tomb,
And his friends are left a weeping,
　In his dear and loving home.

It was the eleventh of December,
　Eighteen seventy was the year,
Kind friends will all remember—
　Silently let fall a tear.
But we must not trouble borrow,
　For the God of heaven is just;
No one knows a parent's sorrow,
　Till a little one they have lost.

HATTIE HOUSE.

Air—"*Lilly Dale.*"

COME all kind friends, wherever you may be,
　Come listen to what I say,
It's of a little girl that was pleasant to see,
　And she died while out doors at play.

Chorus:
　Oh! Hattie, dear Hattie,
　　Sweet little Hattie House—
　May the flowers ever bloom o'er the little tomb
　　Of our loved one, Hattie House.

Hattie had blue eyes and light flaxen hair,
　Her little heart was light and gay,
And she said to her mother, that morning fair,
　"Mother can I go out and play?"

Her mother tied her little bonnot on,
　Not thinking it would be the last
She would ever see her dear little one,
　In this world, little Hattie House.

She left the house, this merry little girl,
　That bright and pleasant day—
She went out to play with two little girls
　That were near about her age.

She was not gone but a little while
   When they heard her playmates call—
Her friends hastened there to save the child,
   But, alas, she was dead and gone.

Those little girls will not forget
   The day little Hattie died,
For she was with them when she fell in a fit,
   While playing by their side.

She was her parents' only child,
   And her age was near six years,
And she has left them for a while—
   Left all her friends in tears.

Left this world of grief and woe,
   Dear friends, she has left behind—
She is waiting on the other shore,
   To meet them bye and bye.

One fine morning, the fifth of July,
   The summer flowers were in bloom.
Eighteen and seventy-one, little Hattie died,
   And is sleeping in her tomb.

Roll on Time, Roll on.

AIR—"*Roll on, Silver Moon.*"

ROLL on time, roll on, as it always has done,
  Since the time that this world first begun;
It can never change my love that I gave a dear one,
  Faithful friend, that I gave my heart and hand.

CHORUS: Roll on time, roll on, it can never turn back
      To the time of my happy maiden days—
    To the time of my youth it can never turn back
      When I wandered with my love, bright and gay.

Oh, I was happy then as a girl could ever be,
  And live on this earth here below—
I was happy as a lark and as busy as a bee,
  For in fashion or in style I did not go.

My parents were poor and they could not dress me so,
  For they had not got the money to spare,
And it may be better so, for I do not think fine clothes
  Make a person any better than they are.

Some people are getting so they think a poor girl,
  Though she be bright and intelligent and gay,
She must have nice clothes, or she is nothing in this
    world,
  If she is not dressed in style every day.

Remember never to judge people by their clothes,
  For our brave, noble Washington said,
" Honorable are rags, if a true heart they inclose,"
  And I find it was the truth when I married.

LITTLE SUSAN.

AIR—" *The Pride of Caldair.*"

ONCE there was a little girl
  And her friends loved her dear—
Her parents loved their little girl,
  And she did their hearts cheer.
Ah! they loved their little darling,
  As with them she did roam,
And they called her little Susan,
  The pride of their home.

Little Susan had light blue eyes
  And light flaxen hair,
And she was a pleasant child,
  So beautiful and fair.
With her parents she will never more
  On earth with them roam—
Oh! they loved their little Susan,
  The pride of their home.

Her parents had more children,
  There were nine of them all—
There are now eight living,
  For God but one called.
It was the flower of their family
  God called to his home,
It was their little Susan,
  The pride of their home.

Her friends will not forget her,
  Though she died years ago—
It was John H. Moore's daughter,
  And her age was four years old.
She is waiting in heaven,
  Waiting for her friends to come
And be with their little Susan,
  The pride of their home.

SIMON SUGGS' ADVENTURES*

Johnston Jones Hooper

* *Simon Suggs' Adventures, Late of the Tallapoosa Volunteers* (Philadelphia: T. B. Peterson and Brothers, 1881), pp. 130-145.

CHAPTER THE TENTH.

THE CAPTAIN ATTENDS A CAMP-MEETING.

CAPTAIN SUGGS found himself as poor at the conclusion of the Creek war, as he had been at its commencement. Although no "arbitrary," "despotic," "corrupt," and "unprincipled" judge had fined him a thousand dollars for his proclamation of martial law at Fort Suggs, or the enforcement of its rules in the case of Mrs. Haycock; yet somehow—the thing is alike inexplicable to him and to us—the money which he had contrived, by various shifts to obtain, melted away and was gone for ever. To a man like the Captain, of intense domestic affections, this state of destitution was most distressing. "He could stand it himself—didn't care a d—n for it, no way," he observed, "but the old woman and the children; *that* bothered him!"

As he sat one day, ruminating upon the unpleasant condition of his "financial concerns," Mrs. Suggs informed him that "the sugar and coffee was nigh about out," and that there were not "a dozen j'ints and middlins, *all put together*, in the smoke-house." Suggs bounced up on the instant, exclaiming, "D—n it! *somebody* must suffer!" But whether this remark was intended to convey the idea that he and his family were about to experience the want of the necessaries of life; or that some other, and as yet unknown individual should "suffer" to prevent that prospective exigency, must be left to the commentators, if perchance any of that ingenious class of persons should hereafter see proper to write notes for this history. It is enough for us that we give all the facts in this connection, so that ignorance of the subsequent conduct of Captain Suggs may not lead to an erroneous judgment in respect to his words.

Having uttered the exclamation we have repeated —and perhaps, hurriedly walked once or twice across the room—Captain Suggs drew on his famous old green-blanket overcoat, and ordered his horse, and within five minutes was on his way to a camp-meeting, then in full blast on Sandy creek, twenty miles distant, where he hoped to find amusement, at least. When he arrived there, he found the hollow square of the encampment filled with people, listening to the mid-day sermon and its dozen accompanying " exhortations." A half-dozen preachers were dispensing the word; the one in the pulpit, a meek-faced old man, of great simplicity and benevolence. His voice was weak and cracked, notwithstanding which, however, he contrived to make himself heard occasionally, above the din of the exhorting, the singing, and the shouting which were going on around him. The rest were walking to and fro, (engaged in the other exercises we have indicated,) among the " mourners"—a host of whom occupied the seat set apart for their especial use—or made personal appeals to the mere spectators. The excitement was intense. Men and women rolled about on the ground, or lay sobbing or shouting in promiscuous heaps. More than all, the negroes sang and screamed and prayed. Se-

8

veral, under the influence of what is technically called "the jerks," were plunging and pitching about with convulsive energy. The great object of all seemed to be, to see who could make the greatest noise—

> "And each—for madness ruled the hour—
> Would try his own expressive power."

"Bless my poor old soul!" screamed the preacher in the pulpit; "ef yonder aint a squad in that corner that we aint got one outen yet! It'll never do"— raising his voice—"you must come outen that! Brother Fant, fetch up that youngster in the blue coat! I see the Lord's a-workin' upon him! Fetch him along—glory—yes!—hold to him!"

"Keep the thing warm!" roared a sensual seem-ing man, of stout mould and florid countenance, who was exhorting among a bevy of young women, upon whom he was lavishing caresses. "Keep the thing warm, breethring!—come to the Lord, honey!" he added, as he vigorously hugged one of the damsels he sought to save.

"Oh, I've got him!" said another in exulting tones, as he led up a gawky youth among the mourn-ers—"I've got him—he tried to git off, but—ha! Lord!"—shaking his head as much as to say, it took a smart fellow to escape him—"ha! Lord!"—and he wiped the perspiration from his face with one hand, and with the other, patted his neophyte on the shoulder—"he couldn't do it! No! Then he tried to argy wi' me—but bless the Lord!—he couldn't do that nother! Ha! Lord! I tuk him, fust in the Old Testament—bless the Lord!—and I argyed him all

thro' Kings—then I throwed him into Proverbs.—
and from that, here we had it up and down, kleer
down to the New Testament, and then I begun to see
it work him!—then we got into Matthy, and from
Matthy right straight along to Acts; and *thar* I
throwed him! Y–e–s L–o–r–d!"—assuming the
nasal twang and high pitch which are, in some parts,
considered the perfection of rhetorical art—" Y–e–s
L–o–r–d! and h–e–r–e he is! Now g–i–t down
thar," addressing the subject, "and s–e–e ef the
L–o–r–d won't do somethin' f–o–r you!" Having
thus deposited his charge among the mourners, he
started out, summarily to convert another soul!

" Gl–o–*ree!*" yelled a huge, greasy negro woman,
as in a fit of the jerks, she threw herself convulsively
from her feet, and fell " like a thousand of brick,"
across a diminutive old man in a little round hat,
who was squeaking consolation to one of the
mourners.

" Good Lord, have mercy!" ejaculated the little
man earnestly and unaffectedly, as he strove to crawl
from under the sable mass which was crushing him.

In another part of the square a dozen old women
were singing. They were in a state of absolute ex-
tasy, as their shrill pipes gave forth,

> "I rode on the sky,
> Quite ondestified I,
> And the moon it was under my feet!"

Near these last, stood a delicate woman in that
hysterical condition in which the nerves are incon-
trollable, and which is vulgarly—and almost blas-

phemously—termed the "holy laugh." A hideous grin distorted her mouth, and was accompanied with a maniac's chuckle; while every muscle and nerve of her face twitched and jerked in horrible spasms.*

Amid all this confusion and excitement Suggs stood unmoved. He viewed the whole affair as a grand deception—a sort of "opposition line" running against his own, and looked on with a sort of professional jealousy. Sometimes he would mutter running comments upon what passed before him.

"Well now," said he, as he observed the full-faced brother who was "officiating" among the women, "that ere feller takes *my* eye!—thar he's een this half-hour, a-figurin amongst them galls, and's never said the fust word to nobody else. Wonder what's the reason these here preachers never hugs up the old, ugly women? Never seed one do it in my life—the sperrit never moves 'em that way! It's nater tho'; and the women, *they* never flocks round one o' the old dried-up breethring—bet two to one old splinter-legs thar,"—nodding at one of the ministers—"won't git a chance to say turkey to a good-

---

* The reader is requested to bear in mind, that the scenes described in this chapter are not *now* to be witnessed. Eight or ten years ago, all classes of population of the Creek country were very different from what they now are. Of course, no disrespect is intended to any denomination of Christians. We believe that camp-meetings are not peculiar to any church, though most usual in the Methodist—a denomination whose respectability in Alabama is attested by the fact, that *very many* of its worthy clergymen and lay members, hold honourable and profitable offices in the gift of the state legislature; of which, indeed, almost a controlling portion are themselves Methodists.

lookin gall to-day! Well! who blames 'em? Nater will be nater, all the world over; and I judge ef I was a preacher, I should save the purtiest souls fust, myself!"

While the Captain was in the middle of this con versation with himself, he caught the attention of the preacher in the pulpit, who inferring from an indescribable something about his appearance that he was a person of some consequence, immediately determined to add him at once to the church if it could be done; and to that end began a vigorous, direct personal attack.

"Breethring," he exclaimed, "I see yonder a man that's a sinner; I *know* he's a sinner! Thar he stands," pointing at Simon, " a missubble old crittur, with his head a-blossomin for the grave! A few more short years, and d–o–w–n he'll go to perdition, lessen the Lord have mer–cy on him! Come up here, you old hoary-headed sinner, a–n–d git down upon your knees, a–n–d put up your cry for the Lord to snatch you from the bottomless pit! You're ripe for the devil—you're b–o–u–n–d for hell, and the Lord only knows what'll become on you!"

" D—n it," thought Suggs, " *ef* I only had you down in the krick swamp for a minit or so, *I'd* show you who's *old! I'd* alter your tune *mighty* sudden, you sassy, 'saitful old rascal!" But he judiciously held his tongue and gave no utterance to the thought.

The attention of many having been directed to the Captain by the preacher's remarks, he was soon surrounded by numerous well-meaning, and doubtless very pious persons, each one of whom seemed bent on the application of his own particular recipe for the salvation of souls. For a long time the Captain stood silent, or answered the incessant stream of exhortation only with a sneer; but at length, his countenance began to give token of inward emotion. First his eye-lids twitched—then his upper lip quivered—next a transparent drop formed on one of his eye-lashes, and a similar one on the tip of his nose—and, at last, a sudden bursting of air from nose and mouth, told that Captain Suggs was overpowered by his emotions. At the moment of the explosion, he made a feint as if to rush from the crowd, but he was in experienced hands, who well knew that the battle was more than half won.

" Hold to him !" said one—" it's a-workin in him as strong as a Dick horse !"

" Pour it into him," said another, " it'll all come right directly !"

" That's the way I love to see 'em do," observed a third ; when you begin to draw the water from their eyes, taint gwine to be long afore you'll have 'em on their knees !"

And so they clung to the Captain manfully, and half dragged, half led him to the mourner's bench ; by which he threw himself down, altogether unmanned, and bathed in tears. Great was the rejoicing of the brethren, as they sang, shouted, and prayed around him—for by this time it had come to be generally known that the " convicted" old man was Captain Simon Suggs, the very " chief of sinners" in all that region.

The Captain remained grovelling in the dust dur

ing the usual time, and gave vent to even more than
the requisite number of sobs, and groans, and heart-
piercing cries.   At length, when the proper time had
arrived, he bounced up, and with a face radiant with
joy, commenced a series of vaultings and tumblings,
which "laid in the shade" all previous performances
of the sort at that camp-meeting.   The brethren were
in extasies at this demonstrative evidence of completion of the work; and whenever Suggs shouted
"Gloree!" at the top of his lungs, every one of them
shouted it back, until the woods rang with echoes.

The effervescence having partially subsided, Suggs
was put upon his pins to relate his experience, which
he did somewhat in this style—first brushing the
tear-drops from his eyes, and giving the end of his
nose a preparatory wring with his fingers, to free it
of the superabundant moisture:

"Friends," he said, "it don't take long to curry
a short horse, accordin' to the old sayin', and I'll give
you the perticklers of the way I was 'brought to a
knowledge' "—here the Captain wiped his eyes,
brushed the tip of his nose and snuffled a little—"in
less'n no time."

"Praise the Lord!" ejaculated a bystander.

"You see I come here full o' romancin' and devilment, and jist to make game of all the purceedins.
Well, sure enough, I done so for some time, and was
a-thinkin how I should play some trick—"

"Dear soul alive! *don't* he talk sweet!" cried an
old lady in black silk—"Whar's John Dobbs? You
Sukey!" screaming at a negro woman on the other
side of the square—"ef you don't hunt up your mass

John in a minute, and have him here to listen to his 'sperience, I'll tuck you up when I git home and give you a hundred and fifty lashes, madam!—see ef I don't! Blessed Lord!"—referring again to the Captain's relation—" aint it a *precious* 'scource!"

" I was jist a-thinkin' how I should play some trick to turn it all into redecule, when they began to come round me and talk. Long at fust I didn't mind it, but arter a little that brother"—pointing to the reverend gentlemen who had so successfully carried the unbeliever through the Old and New Testaments, and who Simon was convinced was the " big dog of the tanyard"—" that brother spoke a word that struck me kleen to the heart, and run all over me, like fire in dry grass—"

" *I–I–I* can bring 'em!" cried the preacher alluded to, in a tone of exultation—" Lord thou knows ef thy servant can't stir 'em up, nobody else needn't try— but the glory aint mine! I'm a poor worrum of the dust" he added, with ill-managed affectation.

" And so from that I felt somethin' a-pullin' me inside—"

" Grace! grace! nothin' but grace!" exclaimed one ; meaning that " grace" had been operating in the Captain's gastric region.

" And then," continued Suggs, " I wanted to git off, but they hilt me, and bimeby I felt so missuble, I had to go yonder"—pointing to the mourners' seat —" and when I lay down thar it got wuss and wuss, and 'peared like somethin' was a-mashin' down on my back—"

" 'That was his load o' sin," said one of the brethren—" never mind, it'll tumble off presently, see ef it don't!" and he shook his head professionally and knowingly.

" And it kept a-gittin heavier and heavier, ontwell it looked like it might be a four year old steer, or a big pine log, or somethin' of that sort—"

" Glory to my soul," shouted Mrs. Dobbs, " it's the sweetest talk I *ever* hearn! You Sukey! aint you got John yit? never mind, my lady, *I'll* settle wi' you!" Sukey quailed before the finger which her mistress shook at her.

" And arter awhile," Suggs went on, " 'peared like I fell into a trance, like, and I seed—"

" Now we'll git the good on it!" cried one of the sanctified."

" And I seed the biggest, longest, rip-roarenest, blackest, scaliest—" Captain Suggs paused, wiped his brow, and ejaculated " Ah, L–o–r–d!" so as to give full time for curiosity to become impatience to know what he saw.

" *Sarpent!* warn't it?" asked one of the preachers.

" No, not a sarpent," replied Suggs, blowing his nose.

" Do tell us *what* it war, soul alive!—whar *is* John?" said Mrs. Dobbs.

" Alligator!" said the Captain.

" Alligator!" repeated every woman present, and screamed for very life.

Mrs. Dobb's nerves were so shaken by the announcement, that after repeating the horrible word, she screamed to Sukey, " you Sukey, I say, you Su–u–ke–e–y! ef you let John come a-nigh this way,

whar the dreadful alliga—shaw! what am I thinkin'
'bout? 'Twarn't nothin' but a vishin!''

"Well," said the Captain in continuation, "the
allegator kept a-comin' and a-comin' to'ards me, with
his great long jaws a-gapin' open like a ten-foot pair
o' tailors' shears—"

"Oh! oh! oh! Lord! gracious above!" cried the
women.

"SATAN!" was the laconic ejaculation of the oldest preacher present, who thus informed the congregation that it was the devil which had attacked Suggs
in the shape of an alligator.

"And then I concluded the jig was up, 'thout I
could block his game some way; for I seed his idee
was to snap off my head—"

The women screamed again.

"So I fixed myself jist like I was purfectly willin'
for him to take my head, and rather he'd do it as
not"—here the women shuddered perceptibly—"and
so I hilt my head straight out"—the Captain illustrated by elongating his neck—"and when he come
up and was a gwine to *shet down* on it, I jist pitched
in a big rock which choked him to death, and that
minit I felt the weight slide off, and I had the best
feelins—sorter like you'll have from *good* sperrits—
any body ever had!"

"Didn't I *tell* you so? Didn't I *tell* you so?"
asked the brother who had predicted the off-tumbling
of the load of sin. "Ha, Lord! fool *who!* I've been
all along thar!—yes, *all along thar!* and I know
every inch of the way jist as good as I do the road
home!"—and then he turned round and round, and

464 THE ART OF HUCKLEBERRY FINN

looked at all, to receive a silent tribute to his supe
rior penetration.

Captain Suggs was now the "lion of the day."
Nobody could pray so well, or exhort so movingly,
as "brother Suggs." Nor did his natural modesty
prevent the proper performance of appropriate exercises. With the reverend Bela Bugg (him to whom,
under providence, he ascribed his conversion,) he
was a most especial favourite. They walked, sang,
and prayed together for hours.

"Come, come up ; thar's room for all!" cried brother Bugg, in his evening exhortation. "Come to
the ' seat,' and ef you won't pray yourselves, let *me*
pray for you!"

"Yes!" said Simon, by way of assisting his
friend ; "it's a game that all can win at! Ante up!
ante up, boys—friends I mean—don't back out!"

"Thar aint a sinner here," said Bugg, "no matter
ef his soul's black as a nigger, but what thar's room
for him!"

"No matter what sort of a hand you've got,"
added Simon in the fulness of his benevolence ;
"take stock! Here am *I*, the wickedest and blind-
est of sinners—has spent my whole life in the sarvice
of the devil—has now come in on *narry pair* and
won a *pile!*" and the Captain's face beamed with
holy pleasure.

"D–o–n–'t be afeard!" cried the preacher; "come
along! the meanest won't be turned away! humble
yourselves and come!"

"No!" said Simon, still indulging in his favourite
style of metaphor; "the bluff game aint played here!

No runnin' of a body off! Every body holds four aces, and when you bet, you win!"

And thus the Captain continued, until the services were concluded, to assist in adding to the number at the mourners' seat; and up to the hour of retiring, he exhibited such enthusiasm in the cause, that he was unanimously voted to be the most efficient addition the church had made during that meeting.

The next morning, when the preacher of the day first entered the pulpit, he announced that "brother Simon Suggs," mourning over his past iniquities, and desirous of going to work in the cause as speedily as possible, would take up a collection to found a church in his own neighbourhood, at which he hoped to make himself useful as soon as he could prepare himself for the ministry, which the preacher didn't doubt, would be in a very few weeks, as brother Suggs was "a man of mighty good judgement, and of *a great discorse.*" The funds were to be collected by "brother Suggs," and held in trust by brother Bela Bugg, who was the financial officer of the circuit, until some arrangement could be made to build a suitable house.

"Yes, breethring," said the Captain, rising to his feet; "I want to start a little 'sociation close to me, and I want you all to help. I'm mighty poor myself, as poor as any of you—don't leave breethring"—observing that several of the well-to-do were about to go off—"don't leave; ef you aint able to afford any thing, jist give us your blessin' and it'll be all the same!"

This insinuation did the business, and the sensitive individuals re-seated themselves.

"It's mighty little of this world's goods I've got," resumed Suggs, pulling off his hat and holding it before him; "but I'll bury *that* in the cause any how," and he deposited his last five-dollar bill in the hat.

There was a murmur of approbation at the Captain's liberality throughout the assembly.

Suggs now commenced collecting, and very prudently attacked first the gentlemen who had shown a disposition to escape. These, to exculpate themselves from any thing like poverty, contributed handsomely.

"Look here, breethring," said the Captain, displaying the bank-notes thus received, "brothei Snooks has drapt a five wi' me, and brother Snodgrass a ten! In course 'taint expected that you *that aint as well off as them*, will give *as much;* let every, one give *accordin'* to ther means."

This was another chain-shot that raked as it went! "Who so low" as not to be able to contribute as much as Snooks and Snodgrass?

"Here's all the *small* money I've got about me," said a burly old fellow, ostentatiously handing to Suggs, over the heads of a half dozen, a ten dollar bill.

"That's what I call maganimus!" exciaimed the Captain; "that's the way *every* rich man ought to do!"

These examples were followed, more or less closely, by almost all present, for Simon had excited the pride of purse of the congregation, and a very handsome sum was collected in a very short time.

The reverend Mr. Bugg, as soon as he observed that our hero had obtained all that was to be had at that time, went to him and inquired what amount had been collected. The Captain replied that it was still uncounted, but that it couldn't be much under a hundred.

" Well, brother Suggs, you'd better count it and turn it over to me now. I'm goin' to leave presently."

" No!" said Suggs—" can't do it!"

" Why?—what's the matter?" inquired Bugg.

" It's got to be *prayed over*, fust!" said Simon, a heavenly smile illuminating his whole face.

" Well," replied Bugg, " less go one side and do it!"

" No!" said Simon, solemnly.

Mr. Bugg gave a look of inquiry.

" You see that krick swamp?" asked Suggs— " I'm gwine down in *thar*, and I'd gwine to lay this money down *so*"—showing how he would place it on the ground—" and I'm gwine to git on these here knees"—slapping the right one—" and I'm *n-e-v-e-r* gwine to quit the grit ontwell I feel it's got the blessin'! And nobody aint got to be thar but me!"

Mr. Bugg greatly admired the Captain's fervent piety, and bidding him God-speed, turned off.

Captain Suggs " struck for" the swamp sure enough, where his horse was already hitched. " Ff them fellers aint done to a cracklin," he muttered to himself as he mounted, " *I*'ll never bet on two pair agin! They're peart at the snap game, theyselves; but they're badly lewed this hitch! Well! Live and let live is a good old motter, and it's my sentiments adzactly!" And giving the spur to his horse, off he cantered.

THE EXPENSIVE TREAT OF COLONEL
MOSES GRICE*

Richard Malcolm Johnston

ьSIDES an incipient ventriloquist who had included it in a limited provincial
ır which he was making in some hope of larger development of his artistic
wers, the only show that had visited Dukesborough thus far was the wax
ures. The recollection of that had ever remained unsatisfactory. I can
st remember that one of the figures was William Pitt, and another the
eeping Beauty; that the former was the saddest and the yellowest great
atesman that I had had opportunity, thus far, to look upon, and the latter—
ell, it is not pleasant, even now, to recall how dead, how long time dead,
e appeared. When Aggy, my nurse, seeing me appalled at the sight, re-
atedly asseverated, "De lady is jes' a-tired and a-takin' of a nap," I cried the
ıder, and plucked so at Aggy that she had to take me away. Though not
ıs demonstrative, yet even elderly country people acknowledged to disap-
intment, and there was a general complaint that if what had been was the
st that could be done by Dukesborough in the way of public entertainment,
might as well take itself away from the great highway of human travel,
spend its school, sell out its two stores at cost, abolish its tavern and post-
ice, tear down its blacksmith's and shoe shops, and, leaving only its
eeting-house, resolve itself into the elements from which it had been ag-
egated. Not that these were the very words; but surely their full equivalents
ere employed when William Pitt, the Sleeping Beauty, and their pale asso-
ıtes had silently left the town.

As for a circus, such an institution was not known, except by hearsay,
en to Colonel Moses Grice, of the Fourteenth Regiment Georgia Militia,
ough he was a man thirty-five years old, over six feet high, of proportional
eight, owned a good plantation and at least twenty negroes, and had seen
e theatre as many as three times in the city of Augusta. The ideas the Colonel
d received there were such, he said, as would last him to the end of his
ys—a period believed to be remote, barring, of course, all contingencies of

* *Scribner's Monthly,* XXI (January, 1881), pp. 370-376.

future wars. To this theatrical experience he had been desirous, for some ti
to add that of the circus, assured in his mind that, from what he had hea
it was a good thing. It happened once, while on a visit to Augusta, whith
he had accompanied a wagon-load of his cotton, partly on that business,
mainly to see the great world there, that he met, at Collier's tavern, where
sojourned, a circus forerunner, who was going the rounds with his advert
ments. Getting soon upon terms of intimacy with one who seemed to him
most agreeable, entertaining, and intelligent gentleman that he had ever m
Colonel Grice imparted to him such information about Dukesborough th
although that village was not upon the list of appointments,—Dukesborou
in point of fact (to his shame the agent confessed it), not having been ev
heard of,—yet a day was set for its visitation, and when visited, another v
set for the appearance there of the Great World-Renowned Circus, whi
claimed for its native homes London, Paris, and New York.

It would be entertaining to a survivor of that period to make even sm
boys, from families of most limited means in this generation, comprehend t
interest excited by those advertisements, in huge black and red letters, th
were tacked upon the wall of Spouter's tavern. From across Beaver Da
Rocky Creek, the Ogeechee, from even the head-waters of streams leading
the Oconee, they came to read over and spell over the mighty words. Colo
Grice, who had been found, upon his own frank admission, to be the ma
mover, was forced to answer all inquiries concerning its magnitude, its pos
ble influences upon the future of Dukesborough, and kindred subjects. The
would have been a slight drawback to the general eager expectation,
grounds moral and religious; but the World-Renowned had anticipated a
provided against that, as will hereafter appear. Then Colonel Grice had s
nified his intention of meeting the impending institution on the occasion of
least two of its exhibitions before its arrival and should take it upon himself
warn it of the kind of people it was coming among.

The Colonel resided five miles south of the village. He had a wife, b
no child (a point on which he was perhaps a little sore), was not in del
was hospitable, an encourager, especially in words, of public and private ente
prises, and enthusiastically devoted, though without experience in wars, to t
military profession, which—if he might use the expression—he would call h
[370/371] second wife. Off the muster-field he habitually practiced that aff
bility which is so pleasant because so rare to see in the warrior class. Wh
in full uniform and at the head of the regiment, with girt sword and pisto
holster, he did indeed look like a man not to be fooled with, and the sou

his voice in utterance of military orders was such as to show that he in-
ded those orders to be heard and obeyed. When the regiment was dis-
ded, the sternness would depart from his mien, and, though yet unstripped
weapons and regalia, he would smile blandly, as if to re-assure spectators
t, for the present, the danger was over, and friends might approach with-
apprehension.

The Colonel met the circus even further away than he at first had in-
ded. He had determined to study it, he said, and he traveled some seventy
es on horseback, attending daily and nightly exhibitions. Several times
ing this travel and afterward, on the forenoon of the great day in Dukes-
ough, he was heard to say that, if he were limited to one word with which
describe what he had seen, that word would be—*grandeur*. "As for what
t of people them circus people are," he said, "in a moral and in a religious
se, now—ahem! you know, gentlemen and ladies, especially ladies—ah,
—I'm not a member, but I'm as great a respecter of religion as can be
nd in the whole State of Georgia. Bein' raised to that, I pride myself on
t. Now, these circus people, they aint what I should call a highly moral,
t is, a strictly religious people. You see, gentlemen, that aint, so to speak,
ir business. They aint goin' about preachin', and havin' camp-meetin'
ivals, and givin' singin'-school lessons. They are—I wish I could explain
self about these circus people. These circus people are a-tryin'—you know,
tlemen, different people makes their livin' in different ways; and these
us people are jest a-tryin' to do exactly the same thing in jest exactly the
le way. Well, gentlemen, *grandeur* is the word I should say about their
formances. I should not confine myself to the word *religion*. Strictly
akin', that word do not embrace all the warious warieties, so to speak, of
ircus. *My* word would be GRANDEUR; and I think that's the word you all
ll use when that tent is up, that door is opened, and you are rushin' into
—its—I don't know whether to use the word *jaws* or *departments*. But, for
sake of decency, I'll say—*departments*. As for moral and religious, gentle-
n,—*and* 'specially ladies,—I tell you, it aint neither a camp-meetin', a
ciation, a quarterly meetin', nor a singin'-school. I'm not a member, but I'm
respecter; and as to all that, and all them, Dukesborough may go farther
d fare worse. That's all I got to say."

On the day before, Colonel Grice, by this time grown intimate with the
nager, and as fond of him as if he had been his own brother (some said
en fonder), in the fullness of his heart had invited the whole force to
akfast with him on the way to Dukesborough, and the invitation had been

accepted. What was consumed was enormous; but he could afford it, and
wife, especially with distinguished visitors, was as hospitable and open-hear
as himself.

Other persons besides boys believed in their hearts that they might
have been able to endure another day's delay of the show. For a brief per
the anxiety of school children amounted to anguish when the master expres
doubts as to a holiday; for holidays then were infrequent, and school-mast
had to be over-persuaded. But the present incumbent yielded early, w
becoming reluctance, to what seemed to be the general desire. The eage
expected morning came at last. Many who knew that the circus was linger
at Colonel Grice's went forth to meet it, some on foot, some on horseba
Some started even in gigs and other carriages, but being warned by old p
ple, turned, unhooked their horses, and hitched them to swinging limbs in
very farthest part of the grave-yard grove, and then set out on foot. The gr
show had put foremost its best wagon, but nobody had any sort of idea wh
things those were which the military gentlemen who rode in it carried in th
hands. One person, known generally to carry a cool head, said that one
these things looked to him like a drum, though of a size comparatively en
mous, but the idea was generally scorned.

"Where you goin' there, Poll Ann?" said Mrs. Watts to her lit
daughter, who was opening the gate. "Stay behind there, you, Jack, and yo
Susan! You want to git eat up by them camels and varmints? I never see si
children for cur'osity. They've got as much cur'osity as—as——"

"As we have," said Mrs. Thompson, laughing, as she attempted in va
to drive back her own little brood.

The effect of the music in the long, covered wagon, drawn by six gr
horses [371/372] slowly before the long procession, no words can describ
It put all, the aged and the young, into a tremor. Old Mr. Leadbetter, one
the deacons, who had been very "jubous," as he said, about the whole thin
was trying to read a chapter somewhere in Romans, when, at the very fi
blast, his spectacles jumped off his nose, and he told a few of the brethr
afterward, confidentially, that he never could recollect, afterward, where
had left off. As for Mrs. Bland, she actually danced in her piazza, for, pro
ably, as many as a dozen bars, and, when "had up" about it, pleaded that sh
couldn't help it. It might have gone hard with the defendant had not son
of her triers been known to march in time to the band, and, besides, they ha
staid after the close of the animal show, contrary to the special inhibitic
against the circus. For the World-Renowned had provided against the scrupl

the straightest sects by attaching to itself a small menagerie of animals,
ose exhibition had been appointed for the opening. There were a camel,
on, a zebra, a hyena, two leopards, a porcupine, six monkeys, a bald eagle,
some parrots. By some means, never fully known, the most scrupulous of
spectators had gotten (late during this first act) to the very loftiest and
otest seats in the amphitheater, and when the animals were shut from the
w, these persons, though anxious, were unable to retire without stepping
r the shoulders of those beneath—a thing that no decent person could be
ected to do. So Mrs. Bland got off with a mild rebuke.

As the cavalcade proceeded, it was a sight to see those who came in late
vehicles hastily turning in, apprehensive of the effect upon their horses of
music and the smell of the wild animals. For the first and only time in the
tory of Dukesborough, there was momentary danger of a blockade of wheels
its one street.

"A leetle more," said old Tony to the other negroes at home that night—
was the driver of the Booker carriage—"a leetle more, and I'd 'a' driv'
ht into the camel's mouth."

For some reason, possibly its vast size and the peculiar dip of its under-
in the pictures, the camel seemed to be regarded as the most carnivorous of
wild beasts, and especially fond of human flesh.

The place selected for the tent was the area west of Sweep's shoe-shop,
the foot of the hill on which the Basil mansion stood. When the door was
ened at last, the crowd surged in. Colonel Grice waited long, in order to
that no one of any condition was excluded for want of the entrance fee.
r at last this was regarded by him rather as a treat of his own to his neigh-
rs, and he wanted it to be complete. Then he walked in with the deliberate-
ss of an owner of the establishment, and contemplated everything with be-
gnant complaisance. Those ladies and gentlemen who were within the sound
his voice, as he went the rounds of the boxes containing the animals, were
rtunate.

"Be keerful there, boys—be keerful," he said kindly but seriously to some
tle fellows who were leaning against the rope and studying the porcupine.
e keerful. That's the cilibrated pockapine. You see them sharp things on
n? Well, them's his quills, and which, when he's mad, he shoots 'em like a
w-'narrow, and they goes clean through people."

The boys backed, although the little creature looked as if his quiver had
en well-nigh exhausted in previous wars.

"That's the hyner," said the Colonel, moving on, "and they say he's the

most rhinocerous varmint of 'em all. Of all victuals he loves folks the b
though he some rather that somebody or something else would kill 'em,
then him come on about a week or sich a matter afterward. They scratches
grave-yards, and in the countries where they raise, people has to bury their k
folks in stone coffins.''

''Oh, goodness gracious, Colonel! Let's go on!''

This exclamation was made by Miss Angeline Spouter, the thinnest of
party, who was locked arm in arm with Miss Georgiana Pea, the thickest.

''No danger, Miss Angeline—no danger at all,'' answered the Colon
briskly raising his arm aloft that all might see what was between them and
beast, at which he looked as if it were his own pet hyena and would not th
of leaving its lair without his order. ''No danger whatsomever. Even if
could git out, he'd have to ride over me, and, besides, it's mostly corpses th
he'd be arfter, and—ah—I don't think, anyway, that *you'd* be in the slight
danger.''

As he said this, the Colonel looked rather argumentatively, and at M
Pea more than Miss Spouter.

''Oh,'' said Miss Pea, gayly, ''if the creetur could git out, and then took
[372/373] notion for live folks, I'd be the one he'd make for, certain sur

Just as the party was about to pass on, the wretched beast, stopping fo
moment, his snout pressed to the roof, uttered several short, loud, hoarse, terri
howls. Miss Spouter screamed, Miss Pea laughed hysterically, and Colon
Grice, before he knew it, was on the outside of his knot of followers. Recov
ing himself,—for he was without his sword and pistol-holster,—he stepp
quickly back to the front, looked threateningly, and afterward disdainfully,
the hyena, who had resumed his walks, and said:

''You rhinoceros varmint, you! Thinkin' of them grave-yards you'
robbed, and hungry for some more of 'em, ah! These is live folks, my boy; a
they aint quite ready for you yit, nor wont be for some time, I hope.'' Then
led on to the monkeys.

''Hello, Bill! I knowed you'd be here; got your boys with you, too, I see

The person addressed by Colonel Grice was a tall, stout young farme
Over his other clothes he wore a loosely fitting round jacket, of thick, hom
made stuff, with capacious pockets. In each of these were one foot and a co
siderable portion of a leg of a child about two years old. Their other feet reste
easily in the man's hands, which were tucked up for that purpose, while o
arm of each was around his neck. The children were exactly alike, except

ide's difference in the color of their eyes. This was Mr. William Williams,
io, three years before, had been married to Miss Caroline Thigpen. At this
uble birth, Mr. Williams was proud and even exultant. Out of the many
nes suggested for the twins, he early selected those of the renowned offspring
Mars and Rhea Sylvia. Modifying them, however, somewhat for his own
sons, he called and so wrote them in his Bible, "Romerlus" and "Remerlus."

"*Remus,* Mr. Williams," urged the friend who had suggested the names.
emus, not Remulus: Romulus and Remus are the names."

"No, Philip," he answered; "it's Romerlus and Remerlus. One's jest as
l as t'other, or nigh and about; and he's as big, and he's as good-lookin', and
brother's name sha'n't be no bigger'n his'n."

As soon as they were able to stand without harm, he accustomed them to
s mode of travel, and he was never so contented as when he and they went
t thus together.

"I knowed you'd be here, Bill, and your boys."

"Yes, Kurnel, I thought comin' to see the beastesses and varmints might
rt o' be a start to 'em in jography. You, Rom—you, Reme, you needn't
ueeze me so tight. They aint no danger in *them* things."

The children, plucky for their age, and with considerable experience in
vel, had gone easily enough thus far; but when they looked upon these
atures, so like yet so unlike mankind, they shrank from the view, and clung
sely to their father. Colonel Grice, recovered from the embarrassment oc-
sioned by the hyena, was pleased at the apprehension of the twins.

"Natchel, Bill, perfec'ly natchel. You know some folks says monkeys is
n to us, and the boys, mebbe, don't like the looks of their relations."

"They aint no kin o' mine, Kurnel, nor theirn," answered Mr. Bill. "Ef
u think they're humans, supposin' you—as you haint no children of your
vn—supposin' you adopt one of 'em."

Mr. Bill suspected that the Colonel might be alluding to the fabled she-
olf. The Colonel, however, had never heard of the distinguished originals of
oman story. His remark was a mere *jeu d'esprit,* springing naturally from the
merous sources of satisfaction of the occasion.

The wild beasts were finally hidden from view, and all repaired to their
ats. Colonel Grice sat high, and near the entrance of the rear tent from which
e circus performers were to emerge. Mr. Williams sat on the lowest tier, near
e main entrance. He had taken his boys out of his pockets and held them on
s knees. The Colonel, when he could get an opportunity, quietly, and in a

very pleasant way, called the ring-master's attention to him, who smiled a
nodded. Then the curtain was pushed aside from the rear tent, the band stru
up, and the piebald horses came marching in with their silent riders, who,
first, looked as if they had just come from the bath and had had time for or
a limited toilet. Old Miss Sally Cash, cousin and close neighbor of Color
Grice, exclaimed:

"Lor'-a-mercy, Mose! Them aint folks, is they? Them's wax figgers, a
they?"

"I assure you, Cousin Sally, that they're folks," answered the Colonel, wi
marked [373/374] candor. He had great respect for his cousin Sally, and sor
awe.

"I thought they was wax figgers, sot on springs. They aint like no fol
that I've ever saw, and I've saw a good many people in my time, both here a
in Agusty." It was one of Miss Cash's boasts, which few countrywomen of th
generation could make, that she had once been to that famous city. After a sho
interval, she added: "I b'lieve yit they're wax figgers."

At that moment the clown, all spotted and streaked, bringing up the rea
shouted:

"Here we all are, my masters."

"My Lord-a'mighty!" exclaimed Miss Cash and some three hundred oth
females. Only Colonel Grice, and a very few others who had been at yesterday
exhibition, could preserve any amount of coolness. The rest abandoned then
selves to unlimited wonder.

"I'm sixty-nine year old," said old Mr. Pate, "and I never see sich as th
before, and I never 'spected to see sich as that."

As they made their involutions and evolutions, destined, apparently, to l
endless in number and variety, the old man looked on as if in his age he wa
vouchsafed the witness of the very last and highest achievement of huma
endeavor.

"Do you think that's decent, Mose?" asked Miss Cash. The performe
were then in the act of the "ground and lofty tumbling," turning somersaul
forward, backward, over one another, lying on their backs, throwing up the
legs, and springing to their feet, etc., until they were panting and blue in th
face. Miss Cash was not disposed that her Cousin Mose should know how muc
she was interested in this performance.

"I shouldn't say it was *on*decent, Cousin Sally."

"I don't say it is," said Miss Cash.

"You know," said the Colonel, winking slyly to his wife, and other friend

both sexes, "nobody is obleeged to stay and see the show. Anybody can go
t wants to. They aint no law agin goin', if anybody's desires is to git away."

"No," answered Miss Cash, downright. "I've paid my half a dollar, and
y sha'n't cheat me out of it, nor nary part of it."

The next scene was one which Colonel Grice had eagerly anticipated. A
d rushed into the ring. He was as wild, apparently, as Mazeppa's, and the
wn, when the ring-master inquired for the rider, answered, in a pitiful tone,
t he was sick, and none other of the *troupe* would dare to take his place.
en followed the usual fun of the master ordering the clown to ride the horse,
l the clown, after vain remonstrance, trying to catch the horse, and the horse
using to be caught; and, finally, the giving up the chase, and the master
hing the recusant beast around the ring, and wishing in vain for a rider to
him off properly. In the midst of this, an extremely drunken young man,
nely clad, came through the main entrance, after a dispute and a scuffle with
door-keeper, and, staggering to where Mr. Bill Williams sat, looked down
on him.

"Two babies. One *(hic)* yours, s'pose."

"Yes," said Mr. Bill.

"And *(hic)* t'other——"

"My wife's; but that aint nobody's business but ourn. You pass on."

The stranger declined, and fixing his muddled attention on what was going
in the ring, said:

"I can *(hic)* ride that horse——"

The words were no sooner uttered than the man stumbled upon the track,
t after the horse had dashed past. The whole audience, except Colonel Grice
l the select few, rose and cried out in horror.

"Take him out, Bill! Take him out!" cried Colonel Grice. Indeed, Mr.
l had already slid his babies into his wife's lap, and was dragging the man
of the ring. He insisted upon returning.

"Look a-here, my friend," said Mr. Bill. "I don't know you, nor nobody
e don't seem to know you; but if I didn't have Rom and Reme——"

The fellow made another rush. Mr. Bill took hold of him, but receiving
rip he fell flat, and the stranger fell into the ring, rolling out of the track
lucky time. The ring-master seemed much embarrassed.

"Oh, give him a little ride, Captain!" cried out Colonel Grice. "If he falls,
s too drunk to git badly hurt."

"It's a shame, Mose!" remonstrated Miss Cash. "I didn't come here and
r my money to see people killed. Notwithstanding and nevertheless the poor

creeter's drunk, and not hardly fitten too live, he ought by good rights to h
some time to prepare for the awful change that——"

But by this time Mazeppa was mounted and dashing away; and, but t
Miss Cash had made up her mind not to be cheated out of any portion of
money, she would have shut her eyes, or veiled her face, as the madde
animal sped along, while the infatuated inebriate clung to his mane. An a
[374/375]ious time it was. Kind-hearted people were sorry they had come.
the struggle between life and death, the stranger seemed to be beginning
sober. Sooner than could have been expected, he raised himself from the hors
neck (Miss Cash twisting her mouth and screwing her neck as he reeled b
and forth from side to side), gathered up the reins, shook from his feet
thick shoes he was clad with, flung aside his old hat, brushed up his curly h
and before Miss Cash could utter a word, was on his feet. Then began t
prolonged metamorphosis which old Mr. Pate was never satisfied with recou
ing, whether to those who saw it or those who saw it not.

"Coat arfter coat, breeches arfter breeches, gallis arfter gallis, shirt arf
shirt, ontwell he shucked hisself nigh as clean as a ear o' corn."

When everybody saw that the stranger was one of the showmen, the f
rose to a height that delayed for full five minutes the next scene. As for Colo
Grice, his handkerchief was positively wet with the tears he shed. Even Mr.
forgot his own discomfiture in the universal glee.

"It's a shame, Mose," said Miss Cash, "to put such a trick on Bill Willia
and that right where his wife is. It would be a good thing if he could pu
back on you."

Even at this late day, a survivor of that period can scarcely recall with
some exaltation of feeling that young girl of eleven (who had been advertis
as "Mademoiselle Louise, the Most Celebrated Equestrienne in the World'
as she ran out with the daintiest of frocks, the pinkest of stockings,
goldenest of flounces, the bluest of belts, the curliest of hair, the peachiest
cheeks, kissed her hand to the audience, put one foot into the clown's hand, a
flew into the saddle. As she went around, dancing upon that horse in full gall
hopping over her whip and jumping through rings, and, when seated, smooth
down her skirt and waved her sleeveless arms—well, there was one boy (
name was Seaborn Byne) that declared he "would be dinged if it wasn't enou
to melt the hearts clean outen a statute."

In the interval before the last, named "The Wonderful Tooth-Drawi
Coffeepot-Fire-cracker Scene," an incident occurred that was not on the p

mme—an interlude, as it were, improvised by the exuberant spirits of both
ctators and showmen. Colonel Grice, deeply gratified at the success of what,
hout great stretch, might be called his own treat, was in the mood to receive
cial attention and compliment from any source. When the pretended in-
iate had been lifted upon Mazeppa, the clown took a bottle from his pocket,
ed it when he had gotten behind his master, smacked his lips, set it down
the middle pole, and, being detected in one of his resortings to it, was reached for not inviting some one to drink with him. They were on the portion
he ring next the main entrance.

"Why don't you invite Colonel Grice?" said Mr. Bill Williams, in a low
ce. "He expects it."

The master turned to notice from whom the suggestion proceeded, and,
ore he could determine, the clown, though with some hesitation, said:

"If Colonel Grice——"

"Stop it!" whispered the master.

But he was too late. The Colonel had already risen, and was carefully
cending.

"Is you goin' there, Mose, sure enough?" said Miss Cash. "It do look like
se is complete carried away with them circus people and hisself."

Having gotten safely over the intervening heads and shoulders, the
onel stepped with dignity into the ring, at the same time feeling somewhat
the embarrassment which will sometimes befall the very greatest warrior
en, without his weapons, he knows himself to be the object of the attention
a large number of civilians, both male and female. This embarrassment
dered his observation of the captain's winks, and the clown's pouring a
tion of the liquor upon the ground. He walked up rapidly and extended his
d. The clown, with an effort at mirthfulness, the more eager because he
s doubtful of perfect success, withdrew the bottle from his grasp, spread out
legs, squatted his body, and, applying the thumb of his disengaged hand to
nose, wriggled his fingers at the Colonel's face, winking frantically the
ile, hoping the latter would advance the joke by insistence.

In this he miscalculated. Persons who claimed to have seen Colonel Moses
ice, on previous occasions, what was called *mad,* said that that was mere
dish fretfulness compared with his present condition of mind, when, after
withdrawal of the bottle, the whole audience, Miss Cash louder than all,
ke into uproarious laughter. Fortunately the enraged chieftain had nor
rd, nor pistol, nor even walking-cane. His only weapon was his tongue.

[375/376] Stepping back a pace or two, and glaring upon the ludicr⟨
squatter, he shouted:

"You spotted-backed, striped-legged, streaked-faced, speckled-b-breast⟨
p'inted-hatted son-of-a-gun!"

With each ejaculation of these successive, uncommon appellations, ⟨
poor clown lifted himself somewhat, and, by the time their climax was reach⟨
was upright, and, dressed as he was, seemed most pitiful.

"My dear Colonel Grice——" he began.

"Shet up your old red mouth," broke in the Colonel. "I didn't *want* y⟨
whisky. I got better whisky at home than you know anything about. But as y⟨
asked me to drink, like, as I thought, one gentleman would ask another gent⟨
man, I didn't feel like refusing you. I give the whole of you your breakf⟨
your blasted varmints and all; I put at least twenty into your cussed old sh⟨
and arfter that——"

"My dear-est Colonel Grice!"

"Oh, you p'inted-hatted, streaked-fac-ed, speckled-b-breasted——" beg⟨
ning, as it were, a back-handed stroke by reversing the order of his epithets.

At this moment the ring-master, who had not been able thus far to get ⟨
a single word, said in a loud but calm tone:

"Colonel Grice, don't you see that it was a mere jest, and that the sugg⟨
tion came from one of your neighbors? The bottle contains nothing but wat⟨
We beg your pardon if you are offended; but I can but think that the abus⟨
words you have used already are quite enough."

"Come, Mose! come, Mose!" cried Miss Cash, who had just been able ⟨
stop her laughter. "Give and take, Mose. You put it on to Bill Williams, and ⟨
stood it; and he put it back on to you, and now you can't stand it, eh?" And ⟨
old lady again fairly screamed with laughter, while hundreds of others join⟨

The Colonel stood for a moment, hesitating. Then he suddenly turn⟨
and, remarking that this was no place for a gentleman, walked toward ⟨
entrance.

"You goin' to let 'em cheat you out of the balance of your money th⟨
way, Mose?" asked Miss Cash. He turned again. Finding himself wholly wi⟨
out support, and unwilling to lose the great scene of the "Tooth-Drawing," et⟨
he halted and stood until it was over. By that time, he was considerably m⟨
lified, and the manager approaching, apologized for himself, the clown, and ⟨
his *troupe,* begged that he would join in a glass of the genuine at Spout⟨
tavern.

How could the Colonel refuse? He could not, and he did not.

"Go with us, wont you, sir?" said the manager, addressing Mr. Williams. 'e had some little fun at your expense also; but I hope you bear us no malice, we never intend to hurt feelings."

"Sperrits," answered Mr. Bill, "is a thing I sildom takes—that is, I don't h it riglar; but I'll try a squirrel-load with you—jes' a moderate size squirrel-d."

At Spouter's all was cordially made up. Mr. Bill set Rom and Reme on counter, and the clown gave them a big lump of white sugar apiece.

"They seem to be nice, peaceable little fellows," said he. "Do they ever pute?"

"Oh, no great deal," answered Mr. Bill. "Sometimes Rom—that the bluest-d one—he wants to have all his feed before Reme gits any of his'n, and he ws at the spoon and Reme's nose. But when he does that, I jes' sets *him* right wn, and I makes him wait ontwell Reme's fed. I 'tends to raise 'em to be aceable, and to give and take, and to be friends as well as brothers, which is ghty fur from bein' always the case in families."

Mr. Bill knew that Colonel Grice and his younger brother Abram had not ken together for years.

"Right, Bill," said the Colonel. "Raise 'em right. Take keer o' them boys, l. Two at a time comes right hard on a fellow, though, don't it, Bill? pensive, eh?" and the Colonel winked pleasantly all around.

"Thank ye, Kurnel; I'll do the best I can. I shall raise 'em to give and take. , Kurnel, not so very hard. Fact, I wa'n't a-expectin' but one, yit, when me come, I thought jest as much o' him as I did o' Rom. No, Kurnel, it uldn't be my desire to be a married man and have nary ar—to leave what le prop'ty I got to. And now, sence I got two instid o' one, and them o' the ne size, I feel like I'd be sort o' awk'ard 'ithout both of 'em. You see, Kurnel, ey balances agin one another in my pockets. No, Kurnel, better two than nary e; and in that way you can larn 'em better to give and take. Come, Rom, me, Reme—git in; we must be a-travelin'." He backed up to the counter, and boys, shifting their sugar-lumps to suit, stepped aboard and away they went.

After that day Dukesborough thought she could see no reason why she ght not be named among the leading towns of Middle Georgia.   [end 376]

HISTORY OF EUROPEAN MORALS FROM
AUGUSTUS TO CHARLEMAGNE*

William Edward Hartpole Lecky

LECKY starts by distinguishing "two rival theories of morals," "known
by many names and . . . subdivided into many groups," with which it is to concerned:

> One of them is generally described as the stoical, the intuitive, the
> independent or the sentimental; the other as the epicurean, the in-
> ductive, the utilitarian, or the selfish. The moralists of the former
> school, to state their opinions in the broadest form, believe that we
> have a natural power of perceiving that some qualities, such as ben-
> evolence, chastity, or veracity, are better than others, and that we
> ought to cultivate them, and to repress their opposites. In other
> words, they contend, that by the constitution of our nature, the no-
> tion of right carries with it a feeling of obligation; that to say a
> course of conduct is our duty, is in itself, and apart from all con-
> sequences, an intelligible and sufficient reason for practising it; and
> that we derive the first principles of our duties from intuition. The
> moralist of the opposite school denies that we have any such natural
> perception. He maintains that we have by nature absolutely no
> knowledge of merit and demerit, of the comparative excellence of
> our feelings and actions, and that we derive these notions solely
> from an observation of the course of life which is conducive to
> human happiness. That which makes actions good is, that they in-
> crease the happiness or diminish the pains of mankind. That which
> constitutes their demerit is their opposite tendency. To procure 'the
> greatest happiness for the greatest number,' is therefore the highest
> aim of the moralist, the supreme type and expression of virtue.
>
> [I, p. 3]

Lecky favored the former group and wrote his history accordingly. Clemens
in his marginal comments, indicated that he tended to favor the second group

---

* (New York: D. Appleton and Company, 1869) pp. 60-65. The same plates used for the 1874 printing, which Clemens is known to have read and annotated.

Thus the Stoics were, among the ancients, admirable in Lecky's opinion, ause they supposed that man's end, in their belief, "is not to find peace either life or in death," but "to do his duty, and to tell the truth." [I, p. 197] h philosophers were superior to the populace which was governed by super- ution: "The Greek word for superstitition signifies literally 'fear of the ds,' or daemons, and the philosophers sometimes represent the vulgar as ddering at the thought of death through dread of certain endless sufferings which it will lead them." [I, p. 216] Clemens scored this passage, and when cky praised the early philosophers for opposing the emphasis of early Chris- ns upon fear of punishment, Clemens also indicated agreement in the margin. 'o agitate the minds of men with religious terrorism," wrote Lecky, "to fill : unknown world with hideous images of suffering, to govern the reason by rming the imagination, was in the eyes of the Pagan world one of the most inous of crimes." Clemens' comment: "It is an odious religion."

The following passage from Lecky's book deals with the operation of science:

This theory of the perfect coincidence of virtue and interest rightly understood, which has always been a common-place of moralists, and has been advocated by many who were far from wishing to resolve virtue into prudence, contains no doubt a certain amount of truth, but only of the most general kind. It does not apply to nations as wholes, for although luxurious and effeminate vices do undoubtedly corrode and enervate national character, the histories of ancient Rome and of not a few modern monarchies abundantly prove that a career of consistent rapacity, ambition, selfishness, and fraud may be eminently conducive to national prosperity.[1] It does not apply to imperfectly organised societies, where the restraints of public opinion are unfelt and where force is the one measure of right. It does not apply except in a very partial degree even to the most civilised of mankind. It is, indeed, easy to show that in a polished community a certain low standard of virtue is essential to prosperity, to paint the evils of unrestrained passions, and to prove that it is better to obey than to violate the laws of society. But if turning from the criminal or the drunkard we were to compare the man who simply falls in with or slightly surpasses the average morals of those about him, and indulges in a little vice which is neither injurious to his own health or to his reputation, with the man who earnestly and painfully adopts a much higher standard than that of his time or of his class, we should be driven to another conclusion. Honesty it is said is the best policy—a fact, however, which depends very much

p. 269. Mr. J. S. Mill in his *Utilitarianism* dwells much on the heroism which he thinks this view of morals may produce.

[1] See Lactantius, *Inst. Div.* vi. 9. Montesquieu, in his *Décadence de l'Empire romain*, has shown in detail the manner in which the crimes of Roman politicians contributed to the greatness of their nation. The history of Prussia forms a modern illustration of the same truth.

upon the condition of the police force, but heroic virtue must rest upon a different basis. If happiness in any of its forms be the supreme object of life, moderation is the most emphatic counsel of our being, but moderation is as opposed to heroism as to vice. There is no form of intellectual or moral excellence which has not a general tendency to produce happiness if cultivated in moderation. There are very few which if cultivated to great perfection have not a tendency directly the reverse. Thus a mind that is sufficiently enlarged to range abroad amid the pleasures of intellect has no doubt secured a fund of inexhaustible enjoyment; but he who inferred from this that the highest intellectual eminence was the condition most favourable to happiness would be lamentably deceived. The diseased nervous sensibility that accompanies intense mental exertion, the weary, wasting sense of ignorance and vanity, the disenchantment and disintegration that commonly follow a profound research, have filled literature with mournful echoes of the words of the royal sage, ' In much wisdom is much grief, and he that increaseth knowledge increaseth sorrow.' The lives of men of genius have been for the most part a conscious and deliberate realisation of the ancient myth—the tree of knowledge and the tree of life stood side by side, and they chose the tree of knowledge rather than the tree of life.

Nor is it otherwise in the realm of morals.[1] The virtue which is most conducive to happiness is plainly that which can be realised without much suffering, and sustained without much effort. Legal and physical

---

[1] 'That quick sensibility which is the groundwork of all advances towards perfection increases the pungency of pains and vexations.'—Tucker's *Light of Nature,* ii. 16, § 4.

penalties apply only to the grosser and more extreme forms of vice. Social penalties may strike the very highest forms of virtue.[1]   That very sentiment of unity with mankind which utilitarians assure us is one day to become so strong as to overpower all unsocial feelings, would make it more and more impossible for men consistently with their happiness to adopt any course, whether very virtuous or very vicious, that would place them out of harmony with the general sentiment of society.   It may be said that the tranquillity of a perfectly virtuous mind is the highest form of happiness, and may be reasonably preferred not only to material advantages, but also to the approbation of society; but no man can fully attain, and few can even approximate, to such a condition. When vicious passions and impulses are very strong, it is idle to tell the sufferer that he would be more happy if his nature were radically different from what it is.   If happiness be his object, he must regulate his course with a view to the actual condition of his being, and there can be little doubt that his peace would be most promoted by a compromise with vice.   The selfish theory of morals applies only to the virtues of temperament, and not to that much higher form of virtue which is sustained in defiance of temperament.[2]   We have no doubt a certain pleasure in cultivating our good tendencies, but we have by no means the same pleasure in repressing our bad ones.   There are men whose whole lives are spent in

---

[1] This position is forcibly illustrated by Mr. Maurice in his fourth lecture *On Conscience* (1868).   It is manifest that a tradesman resisting a dishonest or illegal trade custom, an Irish peasant in a disturbed district revolting against the agrarian conspiracy of his class, or a soldier in many countries conscientiously refusing in obedience to the law to fight a duel, would incur the full force of social penalties, because he failed to do that which was illegal or criminal.

[2] See Brown *On the Characteristics*, pp. 206–209.

willing one thing, and desiring the opposite. In such cases as these virtue clearly involves a sacrifice of happiness ; for the suffering caused by resisting natural tendencies is much greater than would ensue from their moderate gratification.

The plain truth is that no proposition can be more palpably and egregiously false than the assertion that, as far as this world is concerned, it is invariably conducive to the happiness of a man to pursue the most virtuous career. Circumstances and disposition will make one man find his highest happiness in the happiness, and another man in the misery, of his kind ; and if the second man acts according to his interest, the utilitarian, however much he may deplore the result, has no right to blame or condemn the agent. For that agent is acting according to his interest, and this, in the eyes of utilitarians, in one form or another, is the highest, or to speak more accurately, the only motive by which human nature can be actuated.

We may remark too that the disturbance or pain which does undoubtedly usually accompany what is evil, bears no kind of proportion to the enormity of the guilt. An irritability of temper, which is chiefly due to a derangement of the nervous system, or a habit of procrastination or indecision, will often cause more suffering than some of the worst vices that can corrupt the heart.[1]

But it may be said that calculation of pains and pleasures is defective through the omission of one element.

---

[1] 'A toothache produces more violent convulsions of pain than a phthisis or a dropsy. A gloomy disposition . . . may be found in very worthy characters, though it is sufficient alone to embitter life. . . . A selfish villain may possess a spring and alacrity of temper, which is indeed a good quality, but which is rewarded much beyond its merit, and when attended with good fortune, will compensate for the uneasiness and remorse arising from all the other vices.'—Hume's *Essays: The Sceptic.*

Although a man who had a very strong natural impulse towards some vice would appear more likely to promote the tranquillity of his nature by a moderate and circumspect gratification of that vice, than by endeavouring painfully to repress his natural tendencies, yet he possesses a conscience which adjudicates upon his conduct, and its sting or its approval constitutes a pain or pleasure so intense, as more than to redress the balance. Now of course, no intuitive moralist will deny, what for a long time his school may be almost said to have been alone in asserting, the reality of conscience, or the pleasures and pains it may afford. He simply denies, and he appeals to consciousness in attestation of his position, that those pains and pleasures are so powerful or so proportioned to our acts as to become an adequate basis for virtue. Conscience, whether we regard it as an original faculty, or as a product of the association of ideas, exercises two distinct functions. It points out a difference between right and wrong, and when its commands are violated, it inflicts a certain measure of suffering and disturbance. The first function it exercises persistently through life. The second it only exercises under certain special circumstances. It is scarcely conceivable that a man in the possession of his faculties should pass a life of gross depravity and crime without being conscious that he was doing wrong; but it is extremely possible for him to do so without this consciousness having any appreciable influence upon his tranquillity. The condition of their consciences, as Mr. Carlyle observes, has less influence on the happiness of men than the condition of their livers. Considered as a source of pain, conscience bears a striking resemblance to the feeling of disgust. Notwithstanding the assertion of Dr. Johnson, I venture to maintain that there are multitudes to whom the necessity of discharging the duties of a butcher would be so inexpressibly painful and revolting, that if they could obtain flesh diet on no other condition, they would relinquish it for ever. But to those who are inured to the trade, this repugnance has simply ceased. It has no place in their emotions or calculations. Nor can it be reasonably questioned that most men by an assiduous attendance at the slaughter-house could acquire a similar indifference. In like manner, the reproaches of conscience are doubtless a very real and important form of suffering to a sensitive, scrupulous, and virtuous girl who has committed some trivial act of levity or disobedience; but to an old and hardened criminal they are a matter of the most absolute indifference.

Now it is undoubtedly conceivable, that by an association of ideas men might acquire a feeling that would cause that which would naturally be painful to them to be pleasurable, and that which would naturally be pleasurable to be painful.[1] But the question will immediately arise, why should they respect this feeling? We have seen that, according to the inductive theory, there is no such

---

[1] At the same time, the following passage contains, I think, a great deal of wisdom and of a kind peculiarly needed in England at the present day :—' The nature of the subject furnishes the strongest presumption that no better system will ever, for the future, be invented, in order to account for the origin of the benevolent from the selfish affections, and reduce all the various emotions of the human mind to a perfect simplicity. The case is not the same in this species of philosophy as in physics. Many an hypothesis in nature, contrary to first appearances, has been found, on more accurate scrutiny, solid and satisfactory. . . . But the presumption always lies on the other side in all enquiries concerning the origin of our passions, and of the internal operations of the human mind. The simplest and most obvious cause which can there be assigned for any phenomenon, is probably the true one. . . . The affections are not susceptible of any impression from the refinements of reason or imagination; and it is always found that a vigorous exertion of the latter faculties, necessarily, from the narrow capacity of the human mind destroys all activity in the former.'—Hume's *Enquiry concerning Morals*, Append. II.

QUESTIONS

1. How does Mark Twain adapt De Quille's stories of Pike and of the Piut so as to make action borrowed from them characteristic of Jim?

2. (A) How are the march of the mob and its turning back by Sherbur like and unlike the march and retreat of Carlyle's mob? (B) How ma the changes be justified? (C) Professor Henry Nash Smith has notice the way Twain, in describing mobs in *Huckleberry Finn,* "likens them t animals in a herd." Could this procedure have been suggested by Carlyl and Dickens? Could any other stylistic procedure?

3. (A) How has Twain made Emmeline Grangerford resemble Julia A Moore? How differ from her? (B) Why is Emmeline a typical Granger ford? (C) Contrast Emmeline's account of the death of Stephen Dowlin Bots with Huck's account of his finding Buck. What value is there in th juxtaposition of these accounts?

4. (A) Discuss procedures used by Twain to center attention on the King at the camp meeting to a greater extent than Hooper centers attention or Simon Suggs in his similar adventure. (B) Bernard DeVoto criticize Twain for having the King tell a more improbable story than Simon does Can Twain be justified in any way?

5. Compare and contrast the reactions to the clown's apparent danger ir (A) *Huckleberry Finn,* (B) Johnston's story. Why are the reactions in the former more characteristic of the people of Bricksville?

6. List the ways Twain adds to the episodes borrowed from both Hooper and Johnston which enlarge his indictments of society.

7. (A) Compare Huck's struggles with his conscience in Chapters XVI and XXXI with Lecky's statement about the workings of conscience. (B) Lecky, it will be recalled, argues for the intuitive perception of what is right; Twain opposes him, arguing that there is no such thing as intuition—that heredity and environment shape men's decisions. What view of man is represented in the picturing of Huck in the novel? Of Jim? Of the shore folk?

8. Generalize about the use Twain makes of literary sources, illustrating your generalizations with specific instances.

Criticism

[BRANDER MATTHEWS]
LIONEL TRILLING
WILLIAM VAN O'CONNOR
FRANK BALDANZA
J. R. BOGGAN
SYDNEY J. KRAUSE
RICHARD BRIDGMAN
JAMES M. COX
JAY MARTIN
QUESTIONS

The nine critical selections printed here reflect the range of commen both chronologically and geographically, that *Huck Finn* has evoked. The st dent will find a bibliography of items concerned with *Huckleberry Finn* fro 1885 to 1959 in Walter Blair, *Mark Twain & Huck Finn,* pp. 424 to 427.

HUCKLEBERRY FINN*

<hr>

[Brander Matthews]

ᴛʜE BOY of to-day is fortunate indeed, and, of a truth, he is to be congratulated.
While the boy of yesterday had to stay his stomach with the unconscious
humour of *Sandford and Merton,* the boy of to-day may get his fill of fun and
romance and of adventure in *Treasure Island* and in *Tom Brown* and in
Tom Sawyer, and now in a sequel to *Tom Sawyer,* wherein Tom himself appears
in the very nick of time, like a young god from the machine. Sequels of stories
which have been widely popular are not a litttle risky. *Huckleberry Finn* is a
sharp exception to this general rule. Although it is a sequel, it is quite as worthy
of wide popularity as *Tom Sawyer.* An American critic once neatly declared
that the late G. P. R. James hit the bull's-eye of success with his first shot, and
that for ever thereafter he went on firing through the same hole. Now this is
just what Mark Twain has not done. *Huckleberry Finn* is not an attempt to do
Tom Sawyer over again. It is a story quite as unlike its predecessor as it is like.
Although Huck Finn appeared first in the earlier book, and although Tom
Sawyer reappears in the later, the scenes and the characters are otherwise wholly
different. Above all, the atmosphere of the story is different. *Tom Sawyer* was
a tale of boyish adventure in a village in Missouri, on the Mississippi river,
and it was told by the author. *Huckleberry Finn* is autobiographic; it is a tale
of boyish adventure along the Mississippi river told as it appeared to Huck
Finn. There is not in *Huckleberry Finn* any one scene quite as funny as those in
which Tom Sawyer gets his friends to whitewash the fence for him, and then
takes the spoils thereby acquired to attain the highest situation of the Sunday
school the next morning. Nor is there any distinction quite as thrilling as that
awful moment in the cave when the boy and the girl are lost in the darkness,
and when Tom Sawyer suddenly sees a human hand bearing a light, and then
finds that the hand is the hand of Indian Joe, his one mortal enemy; we have
always thought that the vision of the hand in the cave in *Tom Sawyer* is one

<hr>

* [Brander Matthews], unsigned review of *The Adventures of Huckleberry Finn
(Tom Sawyer's Comrade).* By Mark Twain, London: Chatto & Windus. *Saturday Review* (London), LIX (January 31, 1885), pp. 153-154.

THE ART OF HUCKLEBERRY FINN **495**

of the very finest things in the literature of adventure since Robinson Crus
first saw a single footprint in the sand of the seashore. But though *Huckleber*
Finn may not quite reach these two highest points of *Tom Sawyer,* we incli
to the opinion that the general level of the later story is perhaps higher th
that of the earlier. For one thing, the skill with which the character of Hu
Finn is maintained is marvellous. We see everything through his eyes—and th
are his eyes and not a pair of Mark Twain's spectacles. And the comments
what he sees are his comments—the comments of an ignorant, superstitiou
sharp, healthy boy, brought up as Huck Finn had been brought up; they a
not speeches put into his mouth by the author. One of the most artistic thin
in the book—and that Mark Twain is a literary artist of a very high order a
who have considered his later writings critically cannot but confess—one of tl
most artistic things in *Huckleberry Finn* is the sober self-restraint with whi
Mr. Clemens lets Huck Finn set down, without any comment at all, scen
which would have afforded the ordinary writer matter for endless moral a
political and sociological disquisition. We refer particularly to the account
the Grangerford-Shepherdson feud, and of the shooting of Boggs by Colon
Sherburn. Here are two incidents of the rough old life of the South-Weste
States, and of the Mississippi Valley forty or fifty years ago, of the old li
which is now rapidly passing away under the influence of advancing civiliz
tion and increasing commercial prosperity, but which has not wholly disa
peared even yet, although a slow revolution in public sentiment is taking plac
The Grangerford-Shepherdson feud is a vendetta as deadly as any Corsic
could wish, yet the parties to it were honest, brave, sincere, good Christia
people, probably people of deep religious sentiment. Not the less we see the
taking their guns to church, and, when occasion serves, joining in what
little better than a general massacre. The killing of Boggs by Colonel Sherbu
is told with equal sobriety and truth; and the later scene in which Colonel She
burn cows and lashes the mob which has set out to lynch him is one of tl
most vigorous bits of writing Mark Twain has done.

In *Tom Sawyer* we saw Huckleberry Finn from the outside; in the pre
ent volume we see him from the inside. He is almost as much a delight
any one who has been a boy as was Tom Sawyer. But only he or she who h
been a boy can truly enjoy this record of his adventures, and of his sentimen
and of his sayings. Old maids of either sex will wholly fail to understar
him or to like him, or to see his significance and his value. Like Tom Sawye
Huck Finn is a genuine boy; he is neither a girl in boy's clothes like mar
of the modern heroes of juvenile fiction, nor is he a "little man," a ful

own man cut down; he is a boy, just a boy, only a boy. And his ways and
odes of thought are boyish. As Mr. F. Anstey understands the English boy,
d especially the English boy of the middle classes, so Mark Twain under-
inds the American boy, and especially the American boy of the Mississippi
alley of forty or fifty years ago. The contrast between Tom Sawyer, who is the
ild of respectable parents, decently brought up, and Huckleberry Finn, who
the child of the town drunkard, not brought up at all, is made distinct by
hundred artistic touches, not the least natural of which is Huck's constant
ference to Tom as his ideal of what a boy should be. When Huck escapes
om the cabin where his drunken and worthless father had confined him,
refully manufacturing a mass of very circumstantial evidence to prove his
vn murder by robbers, he cannot help saying, "I did wish Tom Sawyer was
ere, I knowed he would take an interest in this kind of business, and throw
the fancy touches. Nobody could spread himself like Tom Sawyer in such
thing as [153-154] that." Both boys have their full share of boyish im-
ination; and Tom Sawyer, being given to books, lets his imagination run
robbers and pirates and genies, with a perfect understanding with himself
at, if you want to get fun out of this life, you must never hesitate to make
lieve very hard; and with Tom's youth and health, he never finds it hard
make believe and to be a pirate at will, or to summon an attendant spirit,
to rescue a prisoner from the deepest dungeon 'neath the castle moat. But
Huck this imagination has turned to superstition; he is a walking reposi-
ry of the juvenile folklore of the Mississippi Valley—a folklore partly
aditional among the white settlers, but largely influenced by intimate associa-
on with the negroes. When Huck was in his room at night all by himself
aiting for the signal Tom Sawyer was to give him at midnight, he felt so
nesome he wished he was dead:—

> The stars was shining and the leaves rustled in the woods ever
> so mournful; and I heard an owl, away off, who-whooing about
> somebody that was dead, and a whippowill and a dog crying about
> somebody that was going to die; and the wind was trying to whisper
> something to me, and I couldn't make out what it was, and so it
> made the cold shivers run over me. Then away out in the woods I
> heard that kind of a sound that a ghost makes when it wants to tell
> about something that's on its mind and can't make itself understood,
> and so can't rest easy in its grave, and has to go about that way
> every night grieving. I got so downhearted and scared I did wish I
> had some company. Pretty soon a spider went crawling up my

shoulders, and I flipped it off and it lit in the candle; and before I could budge it was all shrivelled up. I didn't need anybody to tell me that that was an awful bad sign and would fetch me some bad luck, so I was scared and most shook the clothes off me. I got up and turned around in my tracks three times and crossed my breast every time; and then I tied up a little lock of my hair with a thread to keep witches away. But I hadn't no confidence. You do that when you've lost a horse-shoe that you've found, instead of nailing it up over the door, but I hadn't ever heard anybody say it was any way to keep off bad luck when you'd killed a spider.

And, again, later in the story, not at night this time, but in broad daylight Huck walks along a road:—

When I got there it was all still and Sunday-like, and hot and sunshiny—the hands was gone to the fields; and there was them kind of faint dronings of bugs and flies in the air that makes it seem so lonesome and like everybody's dead and gone; and if a breeze fans along and quivers the leaves, it makes you feel mournful, because you feel like it's spirits whispering—spirits that's been dead ever so many years—and you always think they're talking about *you*. As a general thing it makes a body wish *he* was dead, too, and done with it all.

Now, none of these sentiments are appropriate to Tom Sawyer, who has none of the feeling for nature which Huck Finn had caught during his numberless days and nights in the open air. Nor could Tom Sawyer either have seen or set down this instantaneous photograph of a summer storm:—

It would get so dark that it looked all blue-black outside, and lovely; and the rain would thrash along by so thick that the trees off a little ways looked dim and spider-webby; and here would come a blast of wind that would bend the trees down and turn up the pale underside of the leaves; and then a perfect ripper of a gust would follow along and set the branches to tossing their arms as if they was just wild; and next, when it was just about the bluest and blackest—fst! it was as bright as glory, and you'd have a little glimpse of tree-tops a-plunging about, away off yonder in the storm, hundreds of yards further than you could see before; dark as sin again in a second, and now you'd hear the thunder let go with an awful crash, and then go rumbling, grumbling, tumbling down the sky towards the under side of the world, like rolling empty barrels down stairs, where it's long stairs and they bounce a good deal, you know.

The romantic side of Tom Sawyer is shown in most delightfully humor-s fashion in the account of his difficult devices to aid in the easy escape of n, a runaway negro. Jim is an admirably drawn character. There have been t a few fine and firm portraits of negroes in recent American fiction, of ich Mr. Cable's Bras-Coupé in the *Grandissimes* is perhaps the most vigor-s, and Mr. Harris's Mingo and Uncle Remus and Blue Dave are the most ntle. Jim is worthy to rank with these; and the essential simplicity and dliness and generosity of the Southern negro have never been better shown n here by Mark Twain. Nor are Tom Sawyer and Huck Finn and Jim e only fresh and original figures in Mr. Clemens's new book; on the con-ry, there is scarcely a character of the many introduced who does not im-ess the reader at once as true to life—and therefore as new, for life is so ried that a portrait from life is sure to be as good as new. That Mr. emens draws from life, and yet lifts his work from the domain of the otograph to the region of art, is evident to any one who will give his work e honest attention which it deserves. Mr. John T. Raymond, the American median, who performs the character of Colonel Sellers to perfection, is nt to say that there is scarcely a town in the West and South-West where me man did not claim to be the original of the character. And as Mark vain made Colonel Sellers, so has he made the chief players in the present ama of boyish adventure; they are taken from life, no doubt, but they are aptly chosen and so broadly drawn that they are quite as typical as they e actual. They have one great charm, all of them—they are not written about d about; they are not described and dissected and analysed; they appear d play their parts and disappear; and yet they leave a sharp impression of dubitable vitality and individuality. No one, we venture to say, who reads is book will readily forget the Duke and the King, a pair of as pleasant onfidence operators" as one may meet in a day's journey, who leave the ory in the most appropriate fashion, being clothed in tar and feathers and lden on a rail. Of the more broadly humorous passages—and they abound -we have not left ourselves space to speak; they are to the full as funny as any of Mark Twain's other books; and perhaps in no other book has the morist shown so much artistic restraint, for there is in *Huckleberry Finn*

THE ART OF HUCKLEBERRY FINN **499**

no mere "comic copy," no straining after effect; one might almost say th
there is no waste word in it. Nor have we left ourselves room to do mo
than say a good word for the illustrations, which, although slight and u
pretending, are far better than those to be found in most of Mark Twai
books. For one thing, they actually illustrate—and this is a rare quality
illustrations nowadays. They give the reader a distinct idea of the Duke a
the King, of Jim and of Colonel Sherburn, of the Shepherdsons and t
Grangerfords. They are all by one artist, Mr. E. W. Kemble, hitherto kno
to us only as the illustrator of the *Thompson Street Poker Club,* an amusi
romance of highly-coloured life in New York.   [end on 15

INTRODUCTION [TO *HUCKLEBERRY FINN*]*

Lionel Trilling

1876 Mark Twain published *The Adventures of Tom Sawyer* and in the
ne year began what he called "another boys' book." He set little store by
: new venture and said that he had undertaken it "more to be at work
ın anything else." His heart was not in it—"I like it only tolerably well
far as I have got," he said, "and may possibly pigeonhole or burn the MS
ıen it is done." He pigeonholed it long before it was done and for as much
four years. In 1880 he took it out and carried it forward a little, only to
andon it again. He had a theory of unconscious composition and believed
ıt a book must write itself; the book which he referred to as "Huck Finn's
ıtobiography" refused to do the job of its own creation and he would not
erce it.

But then in the summer of 1881 Mark Twain was possessed by a charge
literary energy which as he wrote to a friend was more intense than any
had experienced for many years. He worked all day and every day, and
riodically he so fatigued himself that he had to recruit his strength by a
y or two of smoking and reading in bed. It is impossible not to suppose
ıt this great creative drive was connected with—was perhaps the direct
ult of—the visit to the Mississippi he had made earlier in the year, the
p which forms the matter of the second part of *Life on the Mississippi.*
s boyhood and youth on the river he so profoundly loved had been at
ce the happiest and most significant part of Mark Twain's life; his return
it in middle age stirred vital memories which revived and refreshed the
ea of *Huckleberry Finn.* Now at last the book was not only ready but eager
write itself. But it was not to receive much conscious help from its author.
e was always full of second-rate literary schemes and now, in the early
eks of the summer, with *Huckleberry Finn* waiting to complete itself, he
rned his hot energy upon several of these sorry projects, the completion of

---

* Mark Twain, *The Adventures of Huckleberry Finn* (New York: Rinehart Edi-
ıns, 1948), pp. v-xviii.

which gave him as [v/vi] much sense of satisfying productivity as did
eventual absorption in *Huckleberry Finn*.

When at last *Huckleberry Finn* was completed and published and wid
loved, Mark Twain became somewhat aware of what he had accomplish
with this book that had been begun as journeywork and depreciated, po
poned, threatened with destruction. It is his masterpiece, and perhaps
learned to know that. But he could scarcely have estimated it for what it
one of the world's great books and one of the central documents of Ame
can culture.

2

Wherein does its greatness lie? Primarily in its power of telling
truth. An awareness of this quality as it exists in *Tom Sawyer* once led Ma
Twain to say of the earlier work that "it is *not* a boys' book at all. It w
be read only by adults. It is written only for adults." But this was only
manner of speaking, Mark Twain's way of asserting, with a discernible tou
of irritation, the degree of truth he had achieved. It does not represent
usual view either of boys' books or of boys. No one, as he well knew, s
a higher value on truth than a boy. Truth is the whole of a boy's consci
demand upon the world of adults. He is likely to believe that the adult wo
is in a conspiracy to lie to him, and it is this belief, by no means unfound
that arouses Tom and Huck and all boys to their moral sensitivity, th
everlasting concern with justice, which they call fairness. At the same ti
it often makes them skillful and profound liars in their own defense,
they do not tell the ultimate lie of adults: they do not lie to themselves. Th
is why Mark Twain felt that it was impossible to carry Tom Sawyer beyo
boyhood—in maturity "he would lie just like all the other one-horse men
literature and the reader would conceive a hearty contempt for him."

Certainly one element in the greatness of *Huckleberry Finn*—as also
the lesser greatness of *Tom Sawyer*—is that it succeeds first as a boy's boo
One can read it at ten and then annually ever after, and each year find th
it is as fresh as [vi/vii] the year before, that it has changed only in beco
ing somewhat larger. To read it young is like planting a tree young—ea
year adds a new growth-ring of meaning, and the book is as little likely
the tree to become dull. So, we may imagine, an Athenian boy grew up
gether with the *Odyssey*. There are few other books which we can know
young and love so long.

The truth of *Huckleberry Finn* is of a different kind from that of To

wyer. It is a more intense truth, fiercer and more complex. *Tom Sawyer*
s the truth of honesty—what it says about things and feelings is never
se and always both adequate and beautiful. *Huckleberry Finn* has this kind
truth, too, but it has also the truth of moral passion; it deals directly with
e virtue and depravity of man's heart.

Perhaps the best clue to the greatness of *Huckleberry Finn* has been
ven to us by a writer who is as different from Mark Twain as it is possible
r one Missourian to be from another. T. S. Eliot's poem, "The Dry Sal-
ges," the third of his *Four Quartets,* begins with a meditation on the Missis-
pi, which Mr. Eliot knew in his St. Louis boyhood. These are the opening
es:

I do not know much about gods; but I think that the river
Is a strong brown god . . .

d the meditation goes on to speak of the god as

almost forgotten
By the dwellers in cities—ever, however, implacable,
Keeping his seasons and rages, destroyer, reminder of
What men choose to forget. Unhonoured, unpropitiated
By worshippers of the machine, but waiting, watching and waiting.[1]

uckleberry Finn is a great book because it is about a god—about, that is,
power which seems to have a mind and will of its own, and which, to men
moral imagination, appears to embody a great moral idea.

Huck himself is the servant of the river-god, and he comes [vii/viii]
ry close to being aware of the divine nature of the being he serves. The
orld he inhabits is perfectly equipped to accommodate a deity, for it is full
presences and meanings which it conveys by natural signs and also by
eternatural omens and taboos: to look at the moon over the left shoulder,
shake the tablecloth after sundown, to handle a snakeskin, are ways of
fending the obscure and prevalent spirits. Huck is at odds, on moral and
sthetic grounds, with the only form of Christianity he knows, and his very
tense moral life may be said to derive from his love of the river. He lives
a perpetual adoration of the Mississippi's power and charm. Huck, of

---

[1] Copyright, 1943, by T. S. Eliot, reprinted [in Rinehart Editions] by permission
Harcourt, Brace and Company.

course, always expresses himself better than he can know, but nothing dra
upon his gift of speech like his response to his deity. After every sally i
the social life of the shore, he returns to the river with relief and than
giving; and at each return, regular and explicit as a chorus in a Greek tra
edy, there is a hynm of praise to the god's beauty, mystery, and streng
and to his noble grandeur in contrast with the pettiness of men.

Generally the god is benign, a being of long sunny days and spacic
nights. But, like any god, he is also dangerous and deceptive. He genera
fogs which bewilder, and he contrives echoes and false distances which cc
fuse. His sandbars can ground and his hidden snags can mortally wound
great steamboat. He can cut away the solid earth from under a man's feet a
take his house with it. The sense of the danger of the river is what saves t
book from any touch of the sentimentality and moral ineptitude of most wor
of the imagination which contrast the life of nature with the life of socie

The river itself is only divine; it is not ethical and good. But its natu
seems to foster the goodness of those who love it and try to fit themselves
its ways. And we must observe that we cannot make—that Mark Twain do
not make—an absolute opposition between the river and human society.
Huck much of the charm of the river life is human; it is the [viii/ix] r
and the wigwam and Jim. He has not run away from Miss Watson and t
Widow Douglas and his brutal father to a completely individualistic liber
for in Jim he finds his true father, very much as Stephen Dedalus in Jam
Joyce's *Ulysses* finds his true father in Leopold Bloom.[2] The boy and t
Negro slave form a family, a primitive community—and it is a commun
of saints.

Huck's intense and even complex moral quality may possibly not appe
on a first reading, for one may be caught and convinced by his own estima
of himself, by his brags about his lazy hedonism, his avowed preference f
being alone, his dislike of civilization. The fact is, of course, that he
involved in civilization up to his ears. His escape from society is but his w
of reaching what society ideally dreams of for itself. Responsibility is the ve
essence of his character, and it is perhaps to the point that the original
Huck, a boyhood companion of Mark Twain's named Tom Blenkenship, di

---

[2] In Joyce's *Finnegan's Wake* both Mark Twain and Huckleberry Finn appear f
quently. The theme of rivers is, of course, dominant in the book; and Huck's name su
Joyce's purpose, as so many names do, for Finn is one of the many names of his he
Mark Twain's love of and gift for the spoken language makes another reason for Joyc
interest in him.

e Huck, "light out for the Territory," only to become a justice of the peace Montana, "a good citizen and greatly respected."

Huck does indeed have all the capacities for simple happiness he says has, but circumstances and his own moral nature make him the least care- e of boys—he is always "in a sweat" over the predicament of someone else. e has a great sense of the sadness of human life, and although he likes to alone, the words "lonely" and "loneliness" are frequent with him. The te of his special sensibility is struck early in the story: "Well, when Tom d me got to the edge of the hilltop we looked away down into the village d could see three or four lights twinkling where there were sick folks, aybe; and the stars over us was sparkling ever so fine; and down by the lage was the river, a whole mile broad, and [ix/x] awful still and grand." ne identification of those three or four lonely lights as the lamps of sick- atches defines Huck's character.

His sympathy is quick and immediate. When the circus audience laughs the supposedly drunken man who tries to ride the horse, Huck is only serable; "It wasn't funny to me . . . ; I was all of a tremble to see his nger." When he imprisons the intending murderers on the wrecked steam- at, his first thought is of how to get someone to rescue them, for he con- ders "how dreadful it was, even for murderers, to be in such a fix. I says myself, there ain't no telling but I might come to be a murderer myself t, and then how would I like it." But his sympathy is never sentimental. hen at last he knows that the murderers are beyond help, he has no inclina- n to false pathos. "I felt a little bit heavy-hearted about the gang, but not ach, for I reckoned that if they could stand it I could." His will is genuinely od and therefore he has no need to torture himself with guilty second oughts.

Not the least remarkable thing about Huck's feeling for people is that s tenderness goes along with the assumption that his fellow men are likely be dangerous and wicked. He travels incognito, never telling the truth out himself and never twice telling the same lie, for he trusts no one and e lie comforts him even when it is not necessary. He instinctively knows at the best way to keep a party of men away from Jim on the raft is to g them to come aboard to help his family stricken with smallpox. And if had not already had the knowledge of human weakness and stupidity and wardice, he would soon have acquired it, for all his encounters forcibly ach it to him—the insensate feud of the Graingerfords and Shepherdsons, e invasion of the raft by the Duke and the King, the murder of Boggs, the

lynching party, and the speech of Colonel Sherburn. Yet his profound a
bitter knowledge of human depravity never prevents him from being a frie
to man.

No personal pride interferes with his well-doing. He knows what stat
is and on the whole he respects it—he is really a [x/xi] very *respectat*
person and inclines to like "quality folks"—but he himself is unaffected
it. He himself has never had status, he has always been the lowest of t
low, and the considerable fortune he had acquired in *The Adventures of To
Sawyer* is never real to him. When the Duke suggests that Huck and J
render him the personal service that accords with his rank, Huck's o
comment is, "Well, that was easy so we done it." He is injured in eve
possible way by the Duke and the King, used and exploited and manipulat
yet when he hears that they are in danger from a mob, his natural impu
is to warn them. And when he fails of his purpose and the two men a
tarred and feathered and ridden on a rail, his only thought is, "Well,
made me sick to see it; and I was sorry for them poor pitiful rascals,
seemed like I couldn't ever feel any hardness against them any more in t
world."

And if Huck and Jim on the raft do indeed make a community of sain
it is because they do not have an ounce of pride between them. Yet this
not perfectly true, for the one disagreement they ever have is over a matt
of pride. It is on the occasion when Jim and Huck have been separated by t
fog, Jim has mourned Huck as dead, and then, exhausted, has fallen aslee
When he awakes and finds that Huck has returned, he is overjoyed; but Hu
convinces him that he has only dreamed the incident, that there has been
fog, no separation, no chase, no reunion, and then allows him to make
elaborate "interpretation" of the dream he now believes he has had. Th
the joke is sprung, and in the growing light of the dawn Huck points to t
debris of leaves on the raft and the broken oar.

> Jim looked at the trash, and then looked at me, and back at
> the trash again. He had got the dream fixed so strong in his head
> that he couldn't seem to shake it loose and get the facts back into its
> place again right away. But when he did get the thing straightened
> around he looked at me steady without ever smiling, and says:
> [xi/xii]
> "What do dey stan' for? I'se gwyne to tell you. When I got
> all wore out wid work, en wid de callin' for you, en went to sleep,
> my heart wuz mos' broke bekase you wuz los', en I didn' k'yer no

mo' what became er me en de raf'. En when I wake up en fine you
back agin, all safe en soun', de tears come, en I could a got down
on my knees en kiss yo' foot, I's so thankful. En all you wuz
thinkin' 'bout wuz how you could make a fool uv ole Jim wid a lie.
Dat truck dah is *trash*; en trash is what people is dat puts dirt on
de head er dey fren's en makes 'em ashamed."

Then he got up slow and walked to the wigwam, and went in
there without saying anything but that.

The pride of human affection has been touched, one of the few prides
at has any true dignity. And at its utterance, Huck's one last dim vestige
pride of status, his sense of his position as a white man, wholly vanishes:
t was fifteen minutes before I could work myself up to go and humble
yself to a nigger; but I done it, and I warn't sorry for it afterwards either."

This incident is the beginning of the moral testing and development
hich a character so morally sensitive as Huck's must inevitably undergo.
nd it becomes an heroic character when, on the urging of affection, Huck
scards the moral code he has always taken for granted and resolves to help
m in his escape from slavery. The intensity of his struggle over the act
ggests how deeply he is involved in the society which he rejects. The satiric
illiance of the episode lies, of course, in Huck's solving the problem not by
)ing "right" but by doing "wrong." He has only to consult his conscience,
e conscience of a Southern boy in the middle of the last century, to know
at he ought to return Jim to slavery. And as soon as he makes the decision
cording to conscience and decides to inform on Jim, he has all the warmly
atifying emotions of conscious virtue. "Why, it was astonishing, the way
felt as light as a feather right straight off, and my troubles all gone . . . I
lt good and all washed clean of sin for the first time I had ever felt so in
y life, and I knowed I could pray [xii/xiii] now." And when at last he
nds that he cannot endure his decision but must change it and help Jim in
s escape, it is not because he has acquired any new ideas about slavery—he
elieves that he detests Abolitionists; he himself answers when he is asked
the explosion of a steamboat boiler had hurt anyone, "No'm, killed a
gger," and of course he finds nothing wrong in the responsive comment,
Well, it's lucky because sometimes people do get hurt." Ideas and ideals can
e of no help to him in his moral crisis. He no more condemns slavery than
ristram and Lancelot condemn marriage; he is as consciously *wicked* as any
licit lover of romance and he consents to be damned for a personal devo-
on, never questioning the justice of the punishment he has incurred.

Huckleberry Finn was once barred from certain libraries and schools f
its alleged subversion of morality. The authorities had in mind the bool
endemic lying, the petty thefts, the denigrations of respectability and religio
the bad language and the bad grammar. We smile at that excessive care, y
in point of fact *Huckleberry Finn* is indeed a subversive book—no one wl
reads thoughtfully the dialectic of Huck's great moral crisis will ever aga
be wholly able to accept without some question and some irony the assum
tions of the respectable morality by which he lives, nor will ever again
certain that what he considers the clear dictates of moral reason are not mere
the engrained customary beliefs of his time and place.

3

We are not likely to miss in *Huckleberry Finn* the subtle, implicit mor
meaning of the great river. But we are likely to understand these mor
implications as having to do only with personal and individual conduct. A
since the sum of individual pettiness is on the whole pretty constant, we a
likely to think of the book as applicable to mankind in general and at
times and in all places, and we praise it by calling it "universal." And
it is; but like many books to which that large adjective applies, it is also loc
and particular. It has a [xiii/xiv] particular moral reference to the Unit
States in the period after the Civil War. It was then when, in Mr. Elio
phrase, the river was forgotten, and precisely by the "dwellers in cities,"
the "worshippers of the machine."

The Civil War and the development of the railroads ended the gre
days when the river was the central artery of the nation. No contrast cou
be more moving than that between the hot, turbulent energy of the river li
of the first part of *Life on the Mississippi* and the melancholy reminiscen
of the second part. And the war that brought the end of the rich Mississip
days also marked a change in the quality of life in America which, to ma
men, consisted of a deterioration of American moral values. It is of course
human habit to look back on the past and to find it a better and more innoce
time than the present. Yet in this instance there seems to be an objective bas
for the judgment. We cannot disregard the testimony of men so diverse
Henry Adams, Walt Whitman, William Dean Howells, and Mark Twa
himself, to mention but a few of the many who were in agreement on th
point. All spoke of something that had gone out of American life after tl
war, some simplicity, some innocence, some peace. None of them was und
any illusion about the amount of ordinary human wickedness that existed

e old days, and Mark Twain certainly was not. The difference was in the blic attitude, in the things that were now accepted and made respectable in : national ideal. It was, they all felt, connected with new emotions about ney. As Mark Twain said, where formerly "the people had desired money," w they "fall down and worship it." The new gospel was, "Get money. Get quickly. Get it in abundance. Get it in prodigious abundance. Get it honestly if you can, honestly if you must."[3]

With the end of the Civil War capitalism had established itself. The axing influence of the frontier was coming to an end. Americans increasingly came "dwellers in cities" and "worshippers of the machine." Mark Twain nself [xiv/xv] became a notable part of this new dispensation. No one woripped the machine more than he did, or thought he did—he ruined himself his devotion to the Paige typesetting machine by which he hoped to make a rtune even greater than he had made by his writing, and he sang the praises the machine age in *A Connecticut Yankee in King Arthur's Court*. He sociated intimately with the dominant figures of American business enterise. Yet at the same time he hated the new way of life and kept bitter emoranda of his scorn, commenting on the low morality or the bad taste the smugness and dullness of the men who were shaping the national ideal d directing the destiny of the nation.

Mark Twain said of *Tom Sawyer* that it "is simply a hymn, put into ose form to give it a worldly air." He might have said the same, and with en more reason, of *Huckleberry Finn*, which is a hymn to an older America rever gone, an America which had its great national faults, which was full violence and even of cruelty, but which still maintained its sense of reality, r it was not yet enthralled by money, the father of ultimate illusion and lies. gainst the money-god stands the river-god, whose comments are silent— nlight, space, uncrowded time, stillness and danger. It was quickly forgotten ice its practical usefulness had passed, but, as Mr. Eliot's poem says, "The ver is within us. . . ."

4

In form and style *Huckleberry Finn* is an almost perfect work. Only one istake has ever been charged against it, that it concludes with Tom Sawyer's aborate, too elaborate, game of Jim's escape. Certainly this episode is too ng—in the original draft it was much longer—and certainly it is a falling-

---

[3] *Mark Twain in Eruption,* edited by Bernard DeVoto, p. 77.

off, as almost anything would have to be, from the incidents of the rive
Yet it has a certain formal aptness—like, say, that of the Turkish initiatic
which brings Molière's *Le Bourgeois Gentilhomme* to its close. It is a rath
mechanical development of an idea, and yet some device is needed to perm
Huck to return to his anonymity, to give up the role of hero, to fall in
[xv/xvi] the background which he prefers, for he is modest in all thin,
and could not well endure the attention and glamour which attend a hero
a book's end. For this purpose nothing could serve better than the mind
Tom Sawyer with its literary furnishings, its conscious romantic desire f
experience and the hero's part, and its ingenious schematization of life
achieve that aim.

The form of the book is based on the simplest of all novel-forms, th
so-called picaresque novel, or novel of the road, which strings its inciden
on the line of the hero's travels. But, as Pascal says, "rivers are roads th
move," and the movement of the road in its own mysterious life transmut
the primitive simplicity of the form: the road itself is the greatest charact
in this novel of the road, and the hero's departures from the river and h
returns to it compose a subtle and significant pattern. The linear simplici
of the picaresque novel is further modified by the story's having a cle
dramatic organization: it has a beginning, a middle and an end, and
mounting suspense of interest.

As for the style of the book, it is not less than definitive in America
literature. The prose of *Huckleberry Finn* established for written prose th
virtues of American colloquial speech. This has nothing to do with pronunci
tion or grammar. It has something to do with ease and freedom in the use
language. Most of all it has to do with the structure of the sentence, which
simple, direct, and fluent, maintaining the rhythm of the word-groups of spee
and the intonations of the speaking voice.

In the matter of language, American literature had a special probler
The young nation was inclined to think that the mark of the truly litera
product was a grandiosity and elegance not to be found in the commc
speech. It therefore encouraged a greater breach between its vernacular and i
literary language than, say, English literature of the same period ever allowe
This accounts for the hollow ring one now and then hears even in the wo
of our best writers in the first half of the last century. English writers
equal stature would [xvi/xvii] never have made the lapses into rhetoric
excess that are common in Cooper and Poe and that are to be found even i
Melville and Hawthorne.

510 THE ART OF HUCKLEBERRY FINN

Yet at the same time that the language of ambitious literature was high
d thus always in danger of falseness, the American reader was keenly
terested in the actualities of daily speech. No literature, indeed, was ever
 taken up with matters of speech as ours was. "Dialect," which attracted
en our serious writers, was the accepted common ground of our popular
amorous writing. Nothing in social life seemed so remarkable as the differ-
t forms which speech could take—the brogue of the immigrant Irish or the
ispronunciation of the German, the "affectation" of the English, the reputed
ecision of the Bostonian, the legendary twang of the Yankee farmer, and
e drawl of the Pike County man. Mark Twain, of course, was in the tradi-
on of humor that exploited this interest, and no one could play with it
early so well. Although today the carefully spelled-out dialects of nineteenth-
ntury American humor are likely to seem dull enough, the subtle variations
 speech of *Huckleberry Finn,* of which Mark Twain was justly proud, are
ill part of the liveliness and flavor of the book.

Out of his knowledge of the actual speech of America Mark Twain
rged a classic prose. The adjective may seem a strange one, yet it is apt.
orget the misspellings and the faults of grammar, and the prose will be seen
 move with the greatest simplicity, directness, lucidity, and grace. These
ialities are by no means accidental. Mark Twain, who read widely, was pas-
onately interested in the problems of style; the mark of the strictest literary
nsibility is everywhere to be found in the prose of *Huckleberry Finn.*

It is this prose that Ernest Hemingway had chiefly in mind when he said
at "all modern American literature comes from one book by Mark Twain
lled *Huckleberry Finn.*" Hemingway's own prose stems from it directly and
nsciously; so does the prose of the two modern writers who most influenced
emingway's early style, Gertrude Stein and [xvii/xviii] Sherwood Anderson
although neither of them could maintain the robust purity of their model) ;
, too, does the best of William Faulkner's prose, which, like Mark Twain's
vn, reinforces the colloquial tradition with the literary tradition. Indeed, it
ay be said that almost every contemporary writer who deals conscientiously
ith the problems and possibility of prose must feel, directly, or indirectly,
e influence of Mark Twain. He is the master of the style that escapes the
xity of the printed page, that sounds in our ears with the immediacy of the
eard voice, the very voice of unpretentious truth.   [end on xviii]

WHY *HUCKLEBERRY FINN* IS NOT THE GREAT AMERICAN NOVEL*

William Van O'Connor

FROM the late nineteenth century to World War I, and even after, there wa much discussion of the great American novel. Eventually the idea died, ap parently of its own inanity. But in recent years the idea, though not the phras has returned to life, for we are informed, from a variety of critical position that *The Adventures of Huckleberry Finn* is the truly American novel.

A novel wants to be circumscribed to live in its own terms, to fulfill it self imaginatively. On the other hand, it speaks to a people and to their be liefs about themselves. Huck is said to live for us somewhat as Roland liv for France or Arthur for England. If Huck is firmly enshrined in myth would be futile to try to dislodge him. But his place in an American myt would not of itself be assurance that *Huckleberry Finn* is a great novel.

The following observations maintain that the book owes much of it eminence to our mythologizing of the West and, further, that the claims mad for it as a source book for all later "American" fiction is not a valid claim. I making such observations it is helpful to refer to the introductions of *Huck leberry Finn* written by T. S. Eliot and Lionel Trilling. It is also necessar on occasion, to disagree with them. Mr. Eliot reads it—Twain's only maste piece he says—as the story of the Boy and the River, the former being the un conscious or all but unconscious critic of civilization, its pursuits, wickednes and vagaries, and the latter the symbol of time that is timeless and of huma affairs carried downstream, often capriciously. Lionel Trilling also writes o the unblinking honesty of the boy Huck, and of the river as a god. He find it a central American document and one of the world's great books.

Both Eliot and Trilling suggest that there is only one flaw, and this no a very serious one, to be charged against the structure of the book: the over elaborate scheme for Jim's escape engineered by Tom Sawyer in the closin section of the story. Trilling does say the episode is far too long but, lik

---

* *College English,* XVII (October, 1955), pp. 6-10.

iot, he justifies it as a way of returning the reader to civilization, and of eeing Huck, allowing him to disappear. The Tom Sawyer episode is cerinly *a* method for bringing off the dénouement, but involved with it is a rious anti-climax. Miss Watson's will had already freed Jim, and all the ghjinks and genuine danger have been merely to satisfy Tom's desire to ep things hopping. Tom is the Practical Joker of American literature and wain has a streak of it himself, which interferes with his true sense of medy.

I

The critical acumen of Eliot and Trilling notwithstanding, there are a mber of flaws in *Huckleberry Finn*, some of them attributable to Twain's fusal to respect the "work of art" and others attributable to his imperfect nse of tone. The downstream movement of the story (theme as well as acon) runs counter to Jim's effort to escape. Life on the raft may indeed be ad as implied criticism of civilization—but it doesn't get Jim any closer to eedom. One may also ask (it has been asked before) why it never occurred Jim, or to Huck, to strike out for the Illinois shore and freedom. It is posle that Twain felt Tom's highjinks were necessary not merely to prepare for e disappearance of Huck but to shift attention away from his conflicting emes.

For the downward movement of the novel, of course, the picaresque rm [6/7] serves its subject very well, allowing for innumerable and rapid ventures, afloat and ashore, and for the sort of ponderings that are peculiar Huck. The picaresque form is also a clue to the kind of unity the book es have, a melodramatic mixture of reality and unreality and of comedy and rror. It is frequently theatrical in a good sense of the word. But the unity pends on Huck's mind, and too often there are bits of action, dialogue, and servation which are not appropriate to him. There are two sorts of theatrility in the novel, melodrama and claptrap.

Huck's relationship with his father is melodrama. So is the shooting of oggs, or the tar and feathering of the Duke and King. A proof of their ing melodrama is the ease with which one moves from a scene of violence a humorous dialogue. For example, the encounter of Huck and Jim with e thieves and murderers aboard the *Walter Scott* is followed by the minstrel ow, end-men sort of humor of "Was Solomon Wise?" Verisimilitude offers problem when reality merges with unreality or horror dissolves innontly into comedy, but sometimes Twain's sense of proper distance, the de-

gree and nature of the stylization he is employing, fails him and the actic
becomes gruesomely real. An instance of this is Huck's telling of the murde
in "Why Harney Rode Away for His Hat." The starkness is too unrelieve
The scene does not respect the premises nor the general tone of the nove
and, even though it might work in another novel, it does not work here.

A good deal is made, quite justly, of Huck's affection for Jim, and th
example commonly given is Huck's apology to Jim after having tormente
him with a lie about there having been no storm. "It was fifteen minutes,
Huck says, "before I could work myself up to go and humble myself to
nigger, but I done it, and I warn't sorry for it afterwards neither." B
Twain sometimes loses sight of Huck's moral sensitivity. An instance is
Chapters XVII and XVIII.

Near the close of Chapter XVI the raft is run over by an upstrea
steamboat. In the darkness, after he and Jim have dived into the water, Hu
cannot see Jim and his calls go unanswered. Huck then strikes out for shor
The following chapter, "The Grangerfords Take Me In," is a humorous i
troduction to the Grangerford family. Huck stays with the Grangerfords f
many days, perhaps weeks, getting involved in their affairs, notably as couri
between the lovers Miss Sophia Grangerford and Harney Shepherdson. N
thought about Jim enters Huck's head! It doesn't occur to him to search fo
the old Negro. Jack, Huck's "nigger servant," finally invites him to see
"stack o' water-moccasins" in a swamp, a trick for leading him to the sp
where Jim is hiding. "I poked into the place a ways and come to a little ope
patch as big as a bedroom all hung round with vines, and found a man lyin
there asleep—and, by jingo, it was my old Jim!" There is not much indicatio
that Huck is greatly relieved or moved at finding Jim alive: "I waked hi
up, and I reckoned it was going to be a grand surprise to him to see me agai
. . . He nearly cried he was so glad. . . ." Huck says nothing about being gla
himself. Perhaps we are to read this passage ironically, as an instance of
boy's self-centeredness and believe that true affection lies beneath it. Th
might be so, but it doesn't explain away Huck's absence of grief over Jim
"death," or his failure to search for him if alive, or his general indifferenc
to Jim's fate.

Technically, too, the device for getting rid of Jim so that Huck can mov
into the Grangerford-Shepherdson world is awkward and unconvincing. Ji
tells Huck he had heard him call for him when they were swimming towar
shore but hadn't answered for fear of being detected. Presumably one rep

ould have quieted Huck and made detection much less likely. And if Huck
ad been allowed to help Jim hide, or even to maintain some awareness of
im, he would be the Huck known to us in "Fooling Old Jim." [7/8]

Huck's parody (Chapter XVII) of the activities of Emmeline Granger-
rd, poetess, is extremely amusing, but the "voice" is more nearly Twain's
an Huck's. Many other things are put into the mouth of the twelve or thir-
en year old Huck that, sometimes only weakly humorous themselves, are
wain himself speaking. This, for example, from a boy with almost no
hooling:

> Look at Henry the Eight; this 'n' a Sunday-school Superintendent
> to *him*. And look at Charles Second, and Louis Fourteen, and Louis
> Fifteen, and James Second, and Edward Second, and Richard Third,
> and forty more; besides all them Saxon heptarchies that used to rip
> around so in oldtimes and raise Cain. . . .

here are other witticisms about kings, a theme appropriate enough to *Huck-
berry Finn,* but Twain might have found some other way of introducing
em. In "An Arkansas Difficulty," where Twain is giving a sense of life in
small river-town, he makes Huck relate an observation on "chawing to-
cker" that one would expect to find as "filler" in a nineteenth-century news-
per or magazine. Most incongruous of all, perhaps, is Huck's account of the
uke's rendition of Hamlet's soliloquy.

A more self-conscious artist would not have allowed such discrepancies
mar the tone of his novel. The truth is that Twain, however gifted a
conteur, however much genius he had as an improviser, was not, even in
uckleberry Finn, a great novelist.

A glance at Twain's biography reveals attitudes that, if they were related
out another "major" writer, would appear highly damaging. In *My Mark
wain* William Dean Howells reported: "He once said to me, I suppose after
 had been reading some of my unsparing praise of [Jane Austen]: 'You
em to think that woman could write,' and he forbore withering me with his
orn. . . .'" Howells also wrote: "I fancy his pleasure in poetry was not
eat, and I do not believe he cared much for the conventionally accepted
asterpieces of literature." And of Henry James, whose *The Bostonians* was
rialized in the same magazine with *Huckleberry Finn,* Twain said, "I would
ther be damned to John Bunyan's heaven than read that."

II

Huckleberry Finn is involved with the mystique of America. The chi
symbols are the Boy and the River. Huck is the break not merely with Euro
but with civilization, the westward push. Self-sufficient and yet dependabl
he is the proper kind of individualist. He is also youth, a rugged Peter Pa
who lives eternally. Huck belongs also with Cooper's Leather-stocking at
Faulkner's Ike McCaslin, symbolic figures who reject the evils of civilizatio
(A weakness in all of them is that they do not acknowledge the virtues
civilization or try to live, as one must, inside it.) Huck is, finally, a sent
mental figure, not in himself, of course, since he is a boy, but in the min
of those who unduly admire his departure for the territory.

The River, as Eliot says, is time and timelessness, "a strong brown god
with his own thoughts about the machine, the hurry and fuss of cities, th
illusions and struggles that make us lie, steal, or cheat. But the River is al
the Mississippi as it borders the state of Missouri, the very heart of Americ
If Twain helped create a mythic river, the mythic river also helped Twa
find his place as a legendary writer. Having such a place, he is sometimes, l
sheer association, given more: he is made into the "Lincoln of America
literature."

My Mark Twain concludes with Howells' account of seeing Twain
his coffin, the face "patient with the patience I had often seen in it; somethin
of a puzzle, a great silent dignity, an assent to what must be from the deptl
of a nature whose tragical seriousness broke in the laughter which the univer
took for the whole of him." Howells then adds: "Emerson, Longfellow
Lowell, Holmes—I knew them all and all the rest [8/9] of our sages, poet
seers, critics, humorists; they were like one another and like other litera
men; but Clemens was sole, incomparable, the Lincoln of our literature." Stua
Pratt Sherman in the *Cambridge History of American Literature* also con
pares Twain with Lincoln: "In the retrospect he looms for us with Whitma
and Lincoln, recognizably his countrymen, out of the shadows of the Civil Wa
an unmistakable native son of an eager, westward moving people—unconve
tional, self-reliant, mirthful, profane, realistic, cynical, boisterous, popula
tender-hearted, touched with chivalry, and permeated to the marrow of h
bones with the sentiment of a democratic society and with loyalty to America
institutions."

The association of Lincoln and Twain may seem appropriate at fir
glance—but only at first glance. Presumably Howells meant that both me

scovered their need for comedy in the pathos and tragedy of the human
ndition, that both men were sons of a frontier society. To a degree, then,
e comparison holds. But to allow for a detailed comparison, Lincoln should
ve to have written novels, or Twain to have been a politician, statesman,
writer of speeches. Insofar as Lincoln the writer and Twain the writer can
compared, Lincoln is the greater. Lincoln's wit, also in a vernacular idiom,
frequently more subtle than Twain's and may be expected to be more lasting.
ncoln's ability in writing an analytical prose, flexible and closely reasoned,
d his ability in writing a serious and, when the occasion required, solemn
etoric were also greater than Twain's. The seriousness and solemnity in
wain are of innocence betrayed, as in the concluding paragraph of *The
ysterious Stranger*. Lincoln's seriousness is that of a man dealing with the
orld, in its own terms when forced to, but also above it, urging it to create
s destiny in ways that make for the fullest sense of achievement and dignity.
Lincoln had written novels, he would, without doubt, have been a greater
ovelist than Twain. His virtues include Twain's and surpass them.

III

It was in *The Green Hills of Africa* that Hemingway made his now
mous assertion that "All modern American literature comes from one book
 Mark Twain called *Huckleberry Finn*." The genealogy, as commonly
orked out, is as follows:

Huckle-	{	Crane	}	Hem-	Modern
berry →	{	Stein	} →	ing- →	American
Finn	{	Anderson	}	way	fiction

bviously there are other strands of American fiction. Writers like Willa
ather, Scott Fitzgerald, and Faulkner do not derive from Twain. Nor from
emingway. Again, an English reader could undoubtedly point out much in
e prose of Melville or Hawthorne or Poe that is "peculiarly American." In
her words, several semi-literate Missouri idioms are not exclusively "pure
merican language." Perhaps one can say that these idioms bear the same
lationship to general American English that the tall tale bears to American
ction as a whole. At any rate, the strand of language that Hemingway is
oncerned with is—though vigorous, vital, and concrete—unsuited to specula-
on or subtle distinctions.

It is interesting to compare Hemingway's prose[1] with Lincoln's in "Th Gettysburg Address." In the latter, one finds not merely the simplicity an repetition of the Hemingway prose but an ennobling rhetoric; Lincoln's pro both meets the Hemingway esthetic and transcends it.

Probably it is a time and a place, with a language appropriate to then that appeals to the followers of Twain. In a series of letters addressed to Va Wyck Brooks, Sherwood Anderson made many references to Twain, to th midwest, and to *the* book. In Brooks's introduction to the letters one read

[9/10

> I can remember how struck I was by his [Anderson's] fresh healthy mind and his true Whitmanian feeling for comradeship, his beautiful humility, his lovely generosity, and the 'proud conscious innocence' of his nature. This was his own phrase for Mark Twain's mind at the time he was writing *Huckleberry Finn;* and it goes for Sherwood also. He was the most natural of men, as innocent as any animal or flowering tree.

This passage, in language reminiscent of Anderson's own, of Hemingway too, but a little thin and nostalgic to have been Twain's, is obviously intende as wholly a compliment. If one wonders why an American quality, innocenc and superior writing go together, there is Anderson's reasoning on the matte "He [Twain] belonged out here in the Middle West and was only incidentall a writer." Presumably craftsmanship, wide experience, or even thought in an complexity inhibit a truly American writer. Innocence, that strange word i American life, helps to account for Twain's place, and the place of *Huckle berry Finn,* in the hierarchy of American literature.

Innocence, to pursue the subject a little further, also helps account fo the two writers who most clearly come in the wake of Twain—Anderson an Hemingway. The protagonists in Anderson's stories, as Trilling points ou are ensnared or caught: in poverty (*Marching Men*), in marriage (*Man Marriages*), by inhibitions (*Dark Laughter*). Anderson's message is that w must be "free," economically, emotionally, intellectually, but in his stories t be free is to escape. Anderson did not accept the conditions of human existenc and responsibility. The child, or the boy, is his chief protagonist, and th

---

[1] Perhaps the best summary of the style Hemingway admires and employs Gertrude Stein's "How Writing is Written." There are also good discussions of it Frederick Hoffman's *The Modern Novel in America* and in Philip Young's *Erne Hemingway.*

ader watches him confront and be offended by the adult world. In "I Want Know Why," the point of which Hemingway borrowed and improved on, Anderson has the young protagonist use one of Huck's phrases. "It ve me the fantods." In the context of Anderson's story the phrase sounds ted and ineffectual, but it may be a clue to what Anderson was attempting, live in the nineteenth century, or, better, in the boy's world which Huck mbolized for him.

Nick Adams, the protagonist in *In Our Time* (1925), suffers, as Philip oung points out, a trauma, or to use the more literary term, a wound, the sult of the anguish and evil he has experienced. He is the first of the emingway heroes. As Nick Adams this hero breaks with a pious and ghteous mother. As Jake Barnes in *The Sun Also Rises* he is an expatriate more senses than one. As Lt. Henry in *A Farewell to Arms* he makes a parate peace. As Harry Morgan in *To Have and Have Not* he is an outlaw. s Robert Jordan in *For Whom the Bell Tolls* he is a soldier adventurer. s Colonel Cantwell in *Across the River and into the Trees* he conducts a ivate war against stupid generals. As the old man in *The Old Man and e Sea* he fights his battle alone, except for a small boy admirer. The Hemgway hero, in addition to other characteristics, refuses the compromises l civilized people make. It is not fair to say he is Huck Finn grown up—but : is in part Huck Finn. Except for an occasional tribute to humanity as one, e Hemingway hero looks at civilization and says what Huck said: "I been ere before."

Beyond the Huck aspect in Hemingway is the irony that not even in the rritory is there peace. In the simplest of his phrases there is a suggestion f terror. His protagonists would like to find innocence, and in a way they earch for it, but they never expect to find it. And perhaps this suggests a asonable way of viewing *Huckleberry Finn*. It appeals to our desire for a ndition of innocence. The difficulty we have in conceiving what Huck ight be as an adult is an indication of the limited usefulness of Huck as symbol. If we refuse to over-value him as a symbol, we may be less inclined over-value the novel, or to over-value the language in which it is written.
[end on 10]

THE STRUCTURE OF *HUCKLEBERRY FINN**

Frank Baldanza

THE MUCH-VEXED question of the structure of *Huckleberry Finn* has receive
both distinguished and penetrating attention; T. S. Eliot and Lionel Trillin
have defended the plot as a whole in their introductions to editions of th
novel, and Leo Marx has ably replied to both.[1] James Cox and Philip Youn
have attempted symbolic and psychological interpretations which make pas
ing comments on the structure.[2] I should like to suggest, however, tha
both groups of critics, although they have made valuable exploratory searche
have neglected the one aspect of the structure which is perhaps the mo:
rewarding to investigate.

In the first place, as Edgar Goold points out in regard to Twain
theory of the novel:

> Concerning plot construction and related matters Clemens's contri-
> bution is of somewhat lesser significance for the writer of fiction
> than the uninitiated might expect. . . . His own temperament and
> training did not tend to develop in him the ability to plan carefully
> and practice the sustained concentration necessary for tight and ʻwell-
> developed plots.[3]

That this failure in planning out his plots had a temperamental basis i
corrobated, perhaps, by Twain's virulent antipathy to the total work of suc
a careful planner as Jane Austen. But many other critics, of whom I choos
James Cox as representative, argue that the structure of *Huckleberry Finn* i

---

* *American Literature,* XXVII (November, 1955), pp. 347-355.
[1] Leo Marx, "Mr. Eliot, Mr. Trilling, and *Huckleberry Finn*," *American Schola*
XXII, 423-440 (Autumn, 1953).
[2] James M. Cox, "Remarks on the Sad Initiation of Huckleberry Finn," *Sewane*
Review, LXII, 389-405 (Summer, 1954): Philip Young, *Ernest Hemingway* (Nev
York, 1952), pp. 181-212.
[3] "Mark Twain on the Writing of Fiction," *American Literature,* XXVI, 148-14
(May, 1954).

etermined by the interplay of sets of symbols—civilization and the fron-
er, gentility and barbarism, freedom and bondage, and the like. These
deas certainly play a major part in the development of the book because
ney are, in a certain sense, what the book is about; but the ques-[347/348]tion
ught to be in what way Twain uses these ideas. Bernard DeVoto, who assures
s that "Mark Twain was not a systematic thinker," finds him "as feeble a
ovice as ever ventured into [metaphysics]."[4] He goes on to say that

> . . . there is a type of mind, and the lovers of *Huckleberry Finn* be-
> long to it, which prefers experience to metaphysical abstractions and
> the thing to its symbol. Such minds think of *Huckleberry Finn* as
> the greatest work of nineteenth century fiction in America precisely
> because it is not a voyage in pursuit of a white whale but a voyage
> among feudists, mobbers, thieves, rogues, nigger-hunters, and mur-
> derers, precisely because Huck never encounters a symbol but always
> some actual human being working out an actual destiny.[5]

ut even if we overlook Twain's antisymbolic cast of mind (in which we
nould hardly be justified), we find that his own ambivalence blurs the
eatness of whatever categories we set up. Even though we interpret the
ook as a "sad initiation" into society, we are baffled by the final sentence
n which Huck lights out for the territory; if he has adamantly resisted the
ulture of the towns, then he is not in any sense "initiated." And if we try
o see the book as a progression toward Jim's liberation, we must ask why
ne Boggs episode, the Shepherdson-Grangerford feud, and the Wilks inter-
ude, which compose the bulk of the central portion, are so remarkably
relevant to the thesis. Even toward the close of the book, Huck is scandal-
zed by Tom's easy acquiescence in the escape plot, and invokes the wrath of
ociety on such behavior. The resolution of these dilemmas is perhaps to be
ound in Twain's own ambivalences, but an analysis of these leads us into
iography or psychology and inevitably away from *Huckleberry Finn*. Never-
neless, if we hold to any aesthetic standards at all, we hardly have the right
o make extravagant claims for a book which we must admit in the same
reath is negligible as a work of art.

Let us for a moment abandon the search for any plotted or symbolic or
sychological unity in the novel and return to what we know about Mark

---

[4] *Mark Twain at Work* (Cambridge, Mass., 1942), p. 99.
[5] *Ibid.,* p. 100.

Twain's temperament and about his habits of composition; in this way we can more easily make an inductive study of the kind of structure he put into the novel, rather than [348/349] impose from the outside some preconceived pattern. Bernard DeVoto, who gave an entire book to Twain's work habits, tells us that

> He wrote on impulse, and when impulse was in circuit with the deeper levels of his phantasy things went well, but when the circuit was broken he could only improvise. Improvisation was responsible for the worst and commonest blemishes in his books—and, because he could not long sustain it, for the breaking-off of many manuscripts. He had little ability to impose structure on his material; he could not think and feel it through to its own implicit form. He got 'ideas' for books, stories, or sketches and jotted them down in his notebooks where they survive by the hundred, promising or feeble but almost always undeveloped. He caught fire easily and when an 'idea' inflamed him, he attacked it with verve and enthusiasm, trusting to luck, providence, or his demon to make it good.[6]

We might say, as many have said, that the picaresque form would certainly be the ideal genre for such a talent, and that in the kind of episodic, spurting movement of such tales Twain would find his best vehicle; however, at the best, such an "explanation" of the structure of the book consists simply in the substitution of one word for another.

Let us rather try to see whether the very *élan* of his improvisation did not often carry him forward through a form which is implicit in his method. In Chapter VIII of his suggestive *Aspects of the Novel*, E. M. Forster remarks the same method as the fundamental source for the structure of Marcel Proust's *A la Recherche du Temps Perdu*. Like Twain's great river novel "the book is chaotic, ill constructed, it has and will have no external shape . . ." But Forster finds that "it hangs together because it is stitched internally, because it contains rhythms."[7] The parallel is enforced by what Forster tells us of Proust's work habits, because he attributes the quality of rhythm in the novel to a type of temperament that accords precisely with what we have already found in Goold's and DeVoto's descriptions of Mark Twain: "I doubt that it can be achieved by the writers who plan their books beforehand,

---

[6] *Ibid.*, p. 52.
[7] (New York, 1927), p. 236.

s to depend on a local impulse when the right interval is reached."[8] Local pulse and lack of planning, the two prime [349/350] characteristics of vain's genius, then, ought to produce in his novel effects parallel to those ythmic stitchings that Forster finds so exquisite in the work of the great ench novelist.

But before we turn to *Huckleberry Finn* itself, we ought to have a clearer ea of what Forster means by rhythm in the French novel. He selects as his ample the "little phrase" from the sonata by Vinteuil, later incorporated to a sextet: Proust employs this musical phrase, which recurs innumerable nes in the course of his narrative, in such a manner, says Forster, that in elf it has a "musical" function in the novel. Although most critics are ghtly chary about any such metaphorical applications of music to litera-re, we can see that Forster has a clear definition of what he means by a nusical" function. The use of "repetition plus variation" is the key to this nd of rhythm.[9] Simple repetition of a theme, such as Forster finds in eredith, is dead patterning; but repetition with variation and development, d especially with varying degrees of emphasis, is rhythm:

> . . . the little phrase has a life of its own, unconnected with the lives of its auditors, as with the life of the man who composed it. It is almost an actor, but not quite, and that "not quite" means that its power has gone towards stitching Proust's book together from the inside, and towards the establishment of beauty and the ravishing of the reader's memory. There are times when the little phrase —from its gloomy inception, through the sonata into the sextet— means everything to the reader. There are times when it means nothing and is forgotten, and this seems to me the function of rhythm in fiction; not to be there all the time like a pattern, but by its lovely waxing and waning to fill us with surprise and freshness and hope.[10]

I propose to show that without advanced planning, and spurred by omentary impulses, Mark Twain—in all probability unconsciously—con-

---

[8] *Ibid.*, p. 240. Forster precedes this analysis by one of James's *The Ambassadors* an example of "Pattern." Although he never states it overtly, Forster is simply monstrating, in his contrast between James and Proust (Pattern and Rhythm), the fference between conscious and unconscious intention.

[9] Mr. Cox uses these very terms in referring to *Tom Sawyer,* he does not indi- te, however, whether or not he draws them from Forster.

[10] Forster, *op. cit.*, p. 239.

structed whole passages of *Huckleberry Finn* on an aesthetic principle
repetition and variation. Because the process was unconscious, it does n
attain the regularity of Proust's employment of the Vinteuil theme, and v
must also remember that [350/351] Twain was working on a much small
scale than the seemingly inexhaustible French analyst. But to take one simp
example, we remember how Huck early in the book saws his way out of h
father's cabin undetected because he works behind a blanket that is stretch
over the wall; toward the end of the book, Jim's escape is managed through
hole dug beneath the cabin, again disguised by a hanging blanket. Regardless
how we justify the correspondence on other grounds, it remains as a repe
tion of an earlier incident with a variation: it is, as Forster remarks, the vari
tion which gives a sense of freshness and surprise, but it is the repetitic
that ravishes the memory, and, in its implicit assumption of order, it perha
gives hope too.[11]

If we survey the total bulk of such correspondences in the novel, v
find that they bear out our earlier assumption that they occur as unplanne
impulsive repetitions, sometimes seemingly enforcing a moral lesson, an
other times existing simply as abstract aesthetic flourishes. An example of t
latter is Tom's gratuitous insistence on having a rattlesnake to keep Ji
company in the Phelpses' cabin, which recalls, solely for the aesthetic pleasu
involved, the great to-do earlier in the book over the rattlesnake skin an
over Jim's being bitten in the heel.

The largest group of repetitions centers about the situations in whic
Huck encounters rogues on his side trips. Here we might distinguish sever
themes, all of which are involved with the self-defeating nature of evil,
exemplified in Chaucer's "Pardoner's Tale." We need not assume that Twai
chose such material for its profound moral significance, however; probab
it was simply what came to hand and what he knew would please his reader
For the first of these themes, we might use one of Twain's chapter heading
"Better let 'blame' well alone": if Huck and Jim had not boarded th
Walter Scott they would have been better off. In the same way, Bill an
Packard would have made a clean getaway if they had not returned fc
Turner's share of the money, thus giving Huck and Jim the chance to tak
their boat, and consequently abandoning them ironically to the fate they ha

---

[11] We can see the same principle at work in the material that Twain decided n
to use in the novel itself. Chapter III of *Life on the Mississippi*, for example, us
the device of Huck's overhearing conversations while hidden on a raft in the san
way that he overhears the discussion of Bill and Packard on the *Walter Scott*.

served [351/352] for Turner. This greedy lingering at the scene of the crime order to squeeze out every last cent is repeated subtly, and with a variation, when the Duke and the Dauphin, not content with the huge sum of gold, remain at the Wilks home in order to auction the goods and clean up the small change; it is repeated even more subtly, and with even wider variation, when Tom refuses to free Jim the easy way, but lingers in order to fulfil all the conditions of his rigorous code, and suffers a bullet wound because of his need for glory. This last example, too, shows how the aesthetic requirements of the novel dovetail with the meaning: most critics have been content with explaining the final passages of the novel solely in terms of Tom's romanticism, but with the need for rhythm in mind, we can see that Twain chose—again, probably unconsciously—to manage the incident so that it echoed the previous patterns of "better let 'blame' well alone."

A second major repetitive theme is that of desertion. Just as Bill and Packard lack even the honor of thieves in their plan to abandon Turner, so, the third night of the "Royal Nonesuch" performance, Huck and the Duke flee the theater before the performance; Huck thinks that they are abandoning the Dauphin to an angry crowd, but to his immense surprise, he finds the Dauphin asleep in the wigwam on the raft. Later in the book, when another angry mob has the three of them in tow in the graveyard at the end of the Wilks episode, Huck flees when he has the chance, and when the Duke and the Dauphin catch up with him at the opening of Chapter XXX, they make the same accusation that Turner might have made to his companions, and that the Dauphin might have made to Huck and the Duke after the Nonesuch flight. " 'Tryin' to give us the slip, was ye, you pup! Tired of our company, hey?' " The elaborate argument on who has a right to desert whom is a kind of climactic repetition of the whole theme in the book, although Twain reserves one more repetition, as a kind of coda, for the splitting up of Tom and Jim and Huck after their flight from the Phelpses.

To these two themes of lingering for spoils and abandoning companions we might add a third, which perhaps approaches patterning more nearly than any of the others—that of the crowd. But again, I think we can see that each individual treatment of a crowd [352/353] incident was impulsive on Twain's part, and that any pattern we find in the repetitions is either unconsciously or accidentally ordained. The first large crowd is that on the boat searching for Huck's body, a "good" crowd of friends (with the exception of Pap) bent on a mission of mercy: "Pap, and Judge Thatcher, and Bessie Thatcher, and Jo Harper, and Tom Sawyer, and his old Aunt Polly, and Sid and Mary,

and plenty more." Then the first nuance of possibly evil motivations on t
part of a crowd is indicated in Mr. Loftus's proposed search of the island
get the reward for Jim's capture. Later we descend to the cowardly violen
of the Sherburn lynching manqué, of the odoriferous Nonesuch mob, and
the stupid avengers of the Wilks family; after the tarring and feathering
the royal impostors, we return to the "good" crowd in the final chapte
where the farmers and their garrulous wives congregate to help Mr. Phelp
The variation in this employment of crowds is rich and inexhaustible; th
are all foiled, regardless of the quality of their motives, except the mob th
metes out justice to the Duke and the Dauphin; they are all impressionab
and stupid, and their little ruses, like the plan of the first Nonesuch crow
are all pitifully inadequate. The two "good" crowds which appear at t
opening and the closing of the book, do attain their ends, but in so indire
a fashion that they are rendered ridiculous: in the first case, Huck mus
that the bread filled with quicksilver *did* reach him, and that the widov
and the parson's prayers *were* answered after a fashion; and in the latter ca
the crowd *did* finally solve the mystery, but only by pure accident. At t
center of the problem, though, is the example of the Shepherdson-Grange
ford "crowd"; whether Twain intended it or not, this central incident in t
book embodies all the paradoxes of motivation that impelled the oth
crowds, because it is by a code of honor that these two groups defeat then
selves, even as the rogues defeated themselves by lack of a code.

And, in speaking of the gullibility of the crowd and the roguery of t
tricksters, we are reminded that before any of these examples of man's bas
ness occur in the book, Huck, in Chapter XV, gulls Jim himself, and
Huck's conscience-stricken reaction to Jim's eloquent rebuke, Twain sets th
pattern for our reaction to the complicated roguery of the vagabonds. [35
354]

These examples are perhaps sufficient to suggest the kind of rhythm th
pulses through the novel by repetition and variation; it remains to indica
that just as such repetitions were conceived unconsciously or accidentally o
the author's part, so their influence on the reader may be largely witho
his conscious attention to the means by which he is beguiled into finding th
book somehow ordered within his recollection, but by an order he cann
explain very clearly in terms of conventional plotting or symbols.

Thus it is unnecessary to survey in detail the abundantly burgeonin
variations on change of identity, on superstition and prophecy, and on lyin
which stitch one chapter to another in the reader's memory. One cou

ırly make a parlor game of searching out minor correspondences like ıck's dressing as a girl when he visits Mrs. Loftus, and Tom's later intence on Huck's assumption of the "yaller wench's frock" when he delivers : note to the Phelpses. The very proliferation of such repetitions, in fact, oves that Twain had no control over them and that they simply flowed from ; pen as exuberant impulse. What is more, it seems to me that this prinıle of repetition, as in the preceding example, gives some dignity and power what had heretofore been excused as the blemishes of a feverishly meloamatic imagination.

It remains to note that in at least one case the principle of repetition rays t to include unconscious recollection of culture tales as well as incidents ated earlier in the novel; this should not surprise us, because Blair and eVoto have shown how the Royal Nonesuch incident was derived from an scene frontier tale.[12] In the present case, we remember that the critics who nphasize the symbolic structure of the book are quick to point out that uck is "dead" throughout the book as far as the rest of his friends know. 'hen Jim sees him for the first time, he falls to his knees and entreats the ıost to leave him. The same reaction, with a significant variation, occurs to om when he sees Huck toward the end of the book in Chapter XXXIII:

> I says:
> 'I hain't come back—I hain't been *gone*'!
> When he heard my voice it rightened him up some, but he warn't quite satisfied yet. He says: [354/355]
> 'Don't you play nothing on me, because I wouldn't on you. Honest injun, you ain't a ghost?
> 'Honest injun, I ain't,' I says.[13]
> 'Well—I—I—well, that ought to settle it, of course; but I can't somehow seem to understand it no way. Looky here, warn't you ever murdered *at all?*'
> 'No. I warn't ever murdered at all—I played it on them. You come in here and feel of me if you don't believe me.'
> So he done it; and it satisfied him; and he was that glad to see me again he didn't know what to do.

om's doubts on the corporeality of Huck, besides recalling those of Jim, ıviously parallel those of his biblical namesake, and this Doubting Thomas

[12] DeVoto, *op. cit.,* pp. 67-68.

[13] It may be significant that the phrase "honest injun" occurs immediately following om's first interview with Huck too.

satisfies himself in the same way as his predecessor, by feeling of his bod
This is, too, an oblique recall of the previous references to Moses and Sol
mon and the biblical kings. There is no real need to see Huck as a Chri
figure, especially since he is Tom's disciple, rather than the reverse; we ne
only note the fact of Twain's repeating a situation already familiar to h
readers simply out of the exuberance of his aesthetic faculty.

If this explanation of the structure of *Huckleberry Finn* has any furth
recommendation, it is that in accepting it we completely exonerate ourselv
—as few other critics can claim to do—from the ominous threats that op
the novel: "Persons attempting to find a motive in this narrative will
prosecuted; persons attempting to find a moral in it will be banished; perso
attempting to find a plot in it will be shot."

THAT SLAP, HUCK, DID IT HURT?*

J. R. Boggan

number of commentators on *Huckleberry Finn* have stressed the importance
Huck's decision to go to hell rather than inform on nigger Jim. Lionel
rilling, for example, has said that Huck's character becomes "heroic"[1] when
decides to help Jim escape, and Leo Marx finds Huck's resolve to be the
limactic moment in the ripening of his self knowledge."[2] I would like to
ggest, however, that Huck's moment of decision ("to decide, forever, be-
ixt two things")[3] is not quite the emotional moment Twain wishes it to be,
d that this is because the reader has not been sufficiently prepared to believe
uck when he says that his thoughts and words ("All right, then, I'll *go* to
ll") are "awful" (180).

Despite Charles A. Allen's claim that Huck is "really convinced of his
ernal damnation,"[4] a view shared, perhaps, by Mr. Marx and Mr. Trilling,
d though Huck admittedly has a struggle with his conscience (between what
feels in his heart toward Jim and what he thinks, according to society, he
ght to feel toward him), Twain, I suggest, simply does not convince the
ader that Huck believes in or imagines in any way the terrible afterlife of
ffering which his decision supposedly entails—with the result that the oft-
oted line, "All right, then, I'll *go* to hell," is not as moving, not as forceful
convincing, as Twain surely wants it to be.

Huck's attitudes toward heaven and hell, toward Providence, are indi-
ted at the beginning of the novel, and may be traced up to and then past the
imactic moment when he decides to help Jim. If, though, as I intend to
ow, hell has no emotional meaning for Huck (outside the context of a few

---

* *English Language Notes,* I (March, 1964), pp. 212-215.
[1] "Huckleberry Finn," *The Liberal Imagination* (New York, 1951), p. 110.
[2] "Mr. Eliot, Mr. Trilling, and Huckleberry Finn," *American Scholar,* XXII
1953), 429.
[3] Mark Twain, *Adventures of Huckleberry Finn,* ed. Henry Nash Smith (Boston,
958), p. 180. All subsequent references to this edition will appear in the text.
[4] "Mark Twain and Conscience," *Literature and Psychology,* VII (1957), 17-21;
printed in *Mark Twain's Wound,* ed. Lewis Leary (New York, 1962), p. 259.

unrealistically contrived pages), the force of his exclamation is much dim[
ished, and the reader, though urged to think of a torment, a suffering, a t[
ture eternally sustained—of the kind, say, that Joyce's little Stephen was s[
jected to—will realize, perhaps, that he is being lured into a stock respon[
will realize that Twain's attempt to win an added Christian sympathy for [
good "bad boy" is unconvincing.

Huck is told about the "bad place" at the beginning of the novel but [
obviously unimpressed. "I wished I was there," he says to Miss Watson, a[
one has the feeling as he reads on that Huck is in no way being ironic. [
wants a change, wants to get away from Miss Watson and his uncomfortal[
situation at the widow Douglas's, and, being unable to visualize anythi[
about hell, and expressing often in his lonesomeness a wish he was " 'm[
dead," he would just as soon go there as anywhere. Indeed, it would seem [
rather comfortably concludes he *is* going there, for when he asks Miss Wats[
if Tom will go to heaven, and she says "not by a considerable sight," he [
relieved, since now he and Tom will be together (4). At this point, then, h[
clearly holds no horror for him.

What does frighten Huck, scare his imagination—and this despite [
the fun he has with the ignorant, superstitious niggers—are the ominous sig[
(like the snake-skin that brings Jim bad luck), the ghosts and witches [
thinks can affect his life in *this* world, for Huck lives for the here and n[
and not for the future. "I don't take no stock in dead people" (4), he sa[
and neither by inference does he take stock in where they go. Moreover, wh[
would Providence want with him, he thinks: of what benefit could he be [
Providence is more his line of reasoning than of what benefit Providence cou[
be to him (11-12). The widow or the parson might somehow get things fro[
Providence, might have some unexplainable interchange with God (33), b[
Providence for Huck is only an uncommunicative, generally unintrigui[
name. He does not think in terms of a Creator (in heaven or anywhere else[
for the stars just "happened"—unless the moon "laid" them (101). And [
though preachers might tell their congregations that "the door of heav[
stands open" if they repent of their sins, Huck senses that such phrases a[
but a standard part of the actors' repertoire (111).

The point I wish to make then is this: that not until the thirty-first cha[
ter does Huck suddenly get religion, fear God.

> And at last, when it hit me all of a sudden that here was the plain
> hand of Providence slapping me in the face and letting me know my

wickedness was being watched all the time from up there in heaven,
whilst I was stealing a poor old woman's nigger that hadn't ever done
me no harm, and now was showing me there's One that's always on
the lookout, and ain't agoing to allow no such miserable doings to
go only just so fur and no further, I most dropped in my tracks I
was so scared. (178)

He follows this by saying that had he gone to Sunday School he would
ve learned (meaning, that is, he had not learned until *now*) "that people
t acts as I'd been acting about that nigger goes to everlasting fire"—the
ught of which makes him "shiver."

And yet is all of this, after thirty chapters of disinterest and denial, be-
vable? Why, "all of a sudden," should Huck feel that an avenging Provi-
ace is slapping him in the face? Why, all of a sudden, should he feel that
less he informs on Jim he will be "lost" (179)? No reason, really, except
t Twain is trying to win a conventional, sympathetic reaction from his
der.

It was a close place. I took it up [the informing letter to Miss
Watson], and held it in my hand. I was a trembling because I'd got
to decide, forever, betwixt two things, and I knowed it. I studied a
minute, sort of holding my breath, and then says to myself:
"All right, then, I'll *go* to hell"—and tore it up. (179-180)

It is easy to see how Twain deliberately encourages a stock response.
ick, in a "close place," is "a trembling," holding his breath. The carefully
iced commas emphasize that his decision is irrevocable: he has to decide
w, "forever." (Why? Is he about to post this letter?) Moreover, the "two
ngs" remain artfully ambiguous. Not only must Huck send the letter or not
id it, tell on Jim now or never tell on him, but he must also either accept
: warning of Providence or never accept it and so suffer the consequences.
hat then will he do? Only one thing to do: he turns the other cheek.

Huck then says he is going to shove the "awful thoughts . . . the awful
rds" out of his head—and, sure enough, nothing to it, for the rest of the
vel he accepts without the shadow of a concern his eternal damnation. In
ct, he does something even more unbelievable than that. Only a few pages
er, he says:

I went right along, not fixing up any particular plan, but just trusting to Providence to put the right words in my mouth when the

time come; for I'd noticed that Providence always did put the right words in my mouth, if I left it alone. (184)

Quite clearly, despite the fact that his face ought still to be stingi from that slap he has just been given, it never enters his mind that Providen might not continue to favor him. And why is that? Because Huck is now ba in character, going right along, no longer conveniently believing in either avenging God or an eternal, excruciating place of physical and mental tormen

Twain, then, I suggest, has "used" Huck in this perhaps most famo passage of the novel, used him as much as he had momentarily used him b fore, when he had Huck describe his pap in Darwinian terms: "A bo would a thought he was Adam, he was just all mud" (24); and, because has used him so, Huck's resolve, though showing good-hearted emotion f Jim, is the less climactic, the less heroic, the less convincing.

HUCK'S FIRST MORAL CRISIS*

Sydney J. Krause

ere has been considerable discussion of Huck Finn's moral crises, but with
her little attention to how they have been specifically evolved, or to the in-
play of psychology and morality by which they have been motivated. I wish
consider these structural and motivational aspects of Huck's first moral cri-

The fog episode in chapter xv, where Huck fools "ole Jim wid a lie," is
t quite, as is normally assumed, the true beginning of Huck's moral aware-
ss of Jim.[1] Nor is it the first moral crisis in his relationship to Jim.[2] Rather,
what it is not, but seems to be, it clarifies the real moral crisis of the fol-
ving chapter, which unfolds excitingly, but with less fanfare and no dra-
tic profession of humility from Huck, who is doing his best to fend off
ve hunters and his own conscience. To realize that Huck's motivation in
king up with Jim is psychological (indeed, self-centered) and that his moti-
:ion in protecting him is radically moral is to appreciate the brilliantly de-
lopmental sequence that is staged in these two chapters.

I

It will be recalled that when Huck returns to the raft after their separa-
n and finds Jim asleep, he pretends to have been asleep himself, and leads
n to believe that the terrible time he had had in the fog was a dream. He
ows Jim to "paint it up considerable" and " 'terpret" it, before springing
: joke by asking him to explain the leaves and rubbish. Awakened, Jim
ks at Huck "steady without ever smiling" and the well known scene ensues
which Jim upbraids Huck.

> ". . . my heart wuz mos' broke bekase you wuz los', en I didn' k'yer
> no' mo' what become er me en de raf'. . . . En all you wuz thinkin'
> 'bout wuz how you could make a fool uv ole Jim wid a lie. Dat
> truck dah is *trash;* en trash is what people is dat puts dirt on de
> head er dey fren's en makes 'em ashamed."

---

* *The Mississippi Quarterly,* XVIII (Spring, 1965), pp. 69-73.
[1] See Lionel Trilling, "Introduction," *The Adventures of Huckleberry Finn* (New
rk, 1948), p. xii.
[2] See Frank Baldanza, *Mark Twain, An Introduction and Interpretation* (New York
51), p. 114.

Huck is properly remorseful,

> It was fifteen minutes before I could work myself up to go and
> humble myself to a nigger; but I done it, and I warn't ever sorry for
> it afterwards, neither. I didn't do him no more mean tricks, and I
> wouldn't done that one if I'd a knowed it would make him feel that
> way.[3]

Huck's statements that he wasn't sorry he had humbled himself to
nigger," and that he didn't play "no more mean tricks" on him may be tak
to indicate that he viewed this second trick as more reprehensible than t
earlier one, which had resulted in a snake bite and had well nigh done J
in. A big difference between the two, however, is that Jim did not compla
about the first one (Huck had kept mum), but did about the second. Th
were friends (the crucial term repeated by Jim in the next chapter), and J
felt himself morally entitled to speak out. In contrast, the motive behi
Huck's reaction was not so much moral as it was psychological. By humbli
himself he did more than assuage a hypersensitive conscience. Huck needed
do it *for himself*. For if Jim's feelings were hurt, Huck's were hurt even mc
by the utter righteousness of Jim's rebuke. The stigma of "trash" was not l
on Huck. His phrasing plainly discloses that he could not stand having
Negro slave think so poorly of him. It was intolerable ("it made me feel
mean"), and the reason he could almost bring himself to kiss Jim's foot w
"to get him to take it back." He would not have played the trick if, as
says, "I'd 'a' knowed it would make him feel that way." "That way" refers
Jim's being upset. In the context of Huck's feelings it also means how J
felt about him.

Because the *effect* of Huck's action seems moral, he gets credit for n
tives he has not really developed yet. That he should value Jim's good opini
of him is, of course, a first step towards Huck's recognizing him as a hum
being. However, Huck is only being readied for a change, and no more th
readied. Jim's formal bondage continues to inhibit his recognition of the bo
that has grown up between them. In fact, we have no reason to think th
Huck's views on "morality" have been materially altered since the revelatc
interchange between him and Miss Watson over "spiritual gifts," when pc
dering the upshot of them ("I must help others . . . and never think abc

---

[3] *The Adventures of Huckleberry Finn* (New York, 1899), Author's Natio
Edition, XIII, 122, 123. All subsequent page references are to this text.

self") Huck concludes, "I couldn't see no advantage about it—except for other people; so at last I . . . just let it go" (pp. 28f.). His efforts to help criminals on the *Walter Scott* and the help he had already given Jim (he promised on Jackson's Island "I ain't a-going to tell," p. 69) constitute ironic difference between saying and doing right. Others say without ng, Huck does without saying. That is what distinguishes the apology from protection scene. In the second of these Huck is forced to contend with h his own view of himself and society's view of him, not just with the mer. We might say he becomes more objective.

In relation to chapter xvi, chapter xv provides anticipation, contrast idst apparent similarity, and the basis for an escalation of Huck's problem m that of ego satisfaction to an assertion of character. Huck's humbling nself to Jim cannot be taken as a sign that his personal conscience has gun to overcome his social conscience, for, if it had, such a change would ve undercut the imperatives that make Huck fear Jim's talk of freedom in pter xvi—which would eliminate all possibility of a true moral crisis.

II

In chapter xvi Huck saves Jim by dint of courage and wit. A singular ture of the thinking which made him do it is that he thinks of others not much under pressure of wanting to be well thought of, but in terms of ir rights—Miss Watson's property rights and Jim's as a person and friend. ce these rights are incompatible, Huck could have gotten out of his di- nma quite easily by allowing the slave hunters to take Jim. If he might ul- iorly have felt himself compelled to protect Jim to save his own hide, it is nificant that neither by thought nor deed does Huck suggest anything of : kind. Also banished are his earliest psychological misgivings (p. 69) on kson's Island ("People would call me a low-down Abolitionist and despise : for keeping mum. . . ."). What consumes his spirit is the awesomeness of ral realities. Here is Jim so close to freedom and he is to blame. It would difficult to construct a more tenaciously moral analysis than Huck's. One is ecially impressed by his demolishing circumstantial and psychological ex- es.

It hadn't ever come home to me before, what this thing was that I was doing. But now it did; and it stayed with me, and scorched me more and more. I tried to make out to myself that *I* warn't to blame, because *I* didn't run Jim off from his rightful owner; but it warn't no use, conscience up and says, every time, "But you knowed he was running for his freedom, and you could 'a' paddled ashore and told somebody." That was so—I couldn't get around that no way. That was where it pinched. Conscience says to me, "What had poor Miss Watson done to you that you could see her nigger go off right under your eyes and never say one single word? What did that poor old woman do to you that you could treat her so mean? Why, she tried to learn you your book, she tried to learn you your manners, she tried to be good to you every way she knowed how. *That's* what she done." (p. 125)

Rather than seek personal alleviation from what Twain was to call "deformed conscience" (Had Miss Watson really been considerate of him Huck knows that in all moral consistency its pangs are deserved. His reaction properly to begin, as he says, "abusing myself to myself." What follows one of the most remarkable pieces of ironic counterpoint in the book. Hu fidgets up and down the raft, silently berating himself, while Jim, bursti with elation, paces up and down past him—until, as Jim rambles on ab freedom, vowing he will steal his children out of slavery if necessary, he livers Huck from his problem. Jim's intention to compound the wrong co pounds Huck's guilt. Jim must be turned in.

As Huck pushes off in the canoe to do his duty, Jim at first (p. 12 reinforces his resolve ("Pooty soon I'll be a-shout'n for joy, en I'll say it's on accounts o' Huck") and then withers it by applauding Huck's magnani ity in honoring the code of friendship ("Jim won't ever forget you, Hu you's de bes' fren' Jim's ever had; en you's de *only* fren' ole Jim got now. Huck cannot act without doing wrong, and he cannot fail to act. Howev faced with the actuality of betrayal—"Is your man black?"—Huck's soc conscience buckles. Previously intangible, the incubus of conscience is n bodied forth by men with guns, before whom Jim *must* be "white" (p. 12ξ

Psychology was assuredly a factor in Huck's putting the men off but like its use in the previous episode, it operates as means rather than moti Huck is in control of it and he controls others with it, instead of its contr ling him. Roguish wit is his psychological instrument. It enables him at t last moment to leap out of the jaws of disaster. His motive is moral revulsi at the thought of what he might have done. Moreover, the "form" of Huc act has an interesting ethic. At the height of the crisis, he noted that "hadn't the spunk of a rabbit." He was just that, a rabbit, in prevailing o the slave hunters. To all intents and purposes, he was recapitulating the r of the most famous underdog hero in Negro folk literature: Brer Rabbit.

III

While morality is usually helpless, the ingenious Huck uses helplessness
efeat one morality and achieve another. But he cannot let the matter rest
e. Stern moralist that he is, he feels "bad and low" after saving Jim, and
erplexed. He has done wrong and would have felt the same way had he
e right. His pragmatic resolution (p. 130) of the antinomy (hereafter he
't "bother" about right and wrong, but "always do whichever comes
diest at the time") is not to be taken at face value, though. In rationaliz-
his failure to uphold the social conscience, Huck is struck by the absurdity
: "learning to do right" (he says it twice) seems useless when it is so
ublesome to do right" (p. 130). He had already abrogated the social code
oo many instances to remain steadfast to it in this crucial one. Thus we see
: Huck's thinking lags behind his acting because none of his acquired
ughts is adequate to his actions. In fact, Twain goes out of his way to
w us that Huck's over-zealous sense of guilt is a throwback on pathological
vinism, the source of his *deformed* conscience. Huck is so insistent on tak-
the blame for everything that he blames himself for their missing Cairo
Jim is obliged to plead with him to stop blaming himself.

More important than Huck's pragmatism are his ethical objectivity and
first active criticism of the social conscience. For the time being he knows
at morally he must negate, and in his final moral crisis he will know what
ffirm: "I couldn't seem to strike no places to harden me against [Jim], but
y the other kind." He will also know how to act on the affirmation, for it
pecifically on recalling Jim's gratitude over being saved from the slave
ters that Huck gets the necessary impetus to tear up the letter to Miss
tson and decide to brave Hell itself to free Jim (pp. 278f.).

There are various theories as to why Twain set his MS aside at about the
ce where the steamboat smashed the raft, separating Huck and Jim. One
ig is relatively certain. He had come to the end of the most important epi-
e he had written to that point. The collision forms an appropriate symbol
the gradual dawning of moral consciousness. It took place when "the
ht got gray and ruther thick, which is the next meanest thing to fog" (p.
?). This reminds us of the progress Huck had made since he had fooled
e Jim" in the fog, when morality had been clouded by the need to salve a
unded ego. Also suggested by the emphatic ending of this phase of Huck's
rney is the moral distance he had traveled since the fog and had yet to
vel before he could come wholly out of it and surmount his social con-
nce.

Richard Bridgman

Mark Twain admitted that the literary experience was not essentially a c
structive one for him, but re-constructive. "Words realize nothing, vi
nothing to you," he wrote in *Connecticut Yankee*, "unless you have suffe
in your own person the thing which the words try to describe" (XIV, 27
In "That Day in Eden" he was even more emphatic about the experien
foundation of literary communication. "Things which are outside of our o
—our own particular world—things which by our constitution and equipm
we are unable to see, or feel, or otherwise experience—*cannot be made c
prehensible to us in words*."[1] To this extent then Mark Twain was ident
with Huck, and when Mark Twain decided to express his experience
Huck's voice, the American vernacular that had long been lapping at the
of the restraining dike surged over the quotation marks to flood his narra
with new and muddy life. What Huck sees and does is relived experience
Mark Twain in a way that fiction rarely is for Henry James, who even sh
away from hearing the end of an anecdote, lest it contradict his private ela
ration of its terms.

Oddly and yet appropriately enough, one of James's own stretches
theorizing helps to explain the success of Mark Twain's decision to speak
Huck. In his preface to *The Princess Casamassima*—a book published
1886, about a year after *Huckleberry Finn*—James noted that "clearness a
concreteness constantly depend, for any pictorial whole, on some *concentra
individual notation of them*." Referring to his novel specifically, he add
"That notation goes forward here in the mind of little Hyacinth, immens
quickened by the fact of its so mattering to his very life what he does m
of things."[2] That the perceptions of Huck and Hyacinth are different no c
could fail to agree, but it is equally certain that James's analysis goes a lc
way to explain the revelatory powers of Huck's idiom.

---

* *The Colloquial Style in America* (New York: Oxford University Press, 196
pp. 109-120 238-239. Footnotes renumbered.
[1] *Europe and Elsewhere*, XXIX, 341.
[2] *The Art of the Novel*, p. 69.

For it is Huck's concentrated observation of the world around him that ws him to express himself so acutely. Both his youth and his lack of sophistion contribute to his concentration. His immaturity and the necessary limions of his brief life make his perception of a material world vivid, unenbered, immediate. Huck does not normally see through a haze of acquired al attitudes, for as yet he has barely acquired any. When he does, as in his tradictory responses toward Jim, the purity of his inner light is still suffit to pierce the haze. Nor is Huck's vision blurred by preoccupation with fessional matters. He is still a free agent and can see a horse, for example, a horse, undistorted by the special interest of a farmer, a trader, a smith, or nner. In short, Huck is disengaged.

The second source of Huck's remarkable clarity lies in the fact that his ironment is his only business. In James's words, his vision is "immensely ckened by the fact of its so mattering to his very life what he does make of gs." Abroad in a hostile world of adults, unprepared by experience for at might happen next, but already sufficiently marked to be cautious and simistic, Huck lives in an almost unrelieved state of alert. His accounts ne to us with the laconic tautness of battlefield reports. He sees with the ensity of one threatened when the steamboat drives his raft under; of one rified in the Boggs episode; of one enraptured when the lady bareback ridperform. And it is to the particulars of his world that Huck pays the most ention. He is a brooder, a worrier, and an occasional talker, but he is not ably a thinker. His powers of generalization are almost nil. If these characistics seem to apply to Huck's creator almost as well as they do to Huck nself, then they suggest how closely Huck's mask fitted Mark Twain.

No less important than Huck's personality is the source of his diction l his syntactical rhythms, for both supplement and extend the clarity of his rrative. If Joseph Warren Beach can properly describe the diction of nes's characters as being without "any tincture of solecism, dialect or localn unless it be those of London," and add, "They speak, almost without ception . . . the purest of London drawingroom slang,"[3] then in contrast it n be said that Mark Twain's characters in *Huckleberry Finn* speak several riations of what we may take to be the purest of Missouri small-town slang, : which Huck provides the norm. In a sense, despite his insistence in the efatory note that he had "painstakingly" worked out seven varieties of dict, Mark Twain is open to the charge of having writ no language. After an

[3] *The Method of Henry James* (Philadelphia: Albert Saifer, 1954), pp. 76-7.

examination of Mark Twain's revisions of *Huckleberry Finn,* Sydney Kra
remarked, "In order that it might *count,* he had to use dialect judiciously,
the same was true of his colloquial diction at large and his illiterate gramm
Twain regularized his grammar almost as often as he changed from the st
dard to the illiterate forms."[4]

Mark Twain, of course, always mediated between whatever inner v
he could hear speaking as Huck and the written expression of it. Someti
he faltered—on the side of formality in "We shot a water-fowl now
then," or of strain in the parody of Shakespeare (chs. 12, 21). By and la
though, *Huckleberry Finn* maintains a consistent tone. The language is in
esting in itself and at the same time capable of vividly evoking the life of
novel. Reading the book, one is constantly moving between absorption in
action itself and pleasurable examination of the words that convey the sto

Mark Twain's conscious importation of words new to the literary c
text, his invention of dialectical oddities, his placement of familiar words
unfamiliar situations, his isolation of words through strings of co-ordinat
conjunctions, his high-spirited word-play, his repetitions of sounds, his cho
(if it can be called that) of words through apparently unconscious associat
—all these stylistic activities inevitably stressed the individual verbal u
whether a phrase, a single word, or a part of one.

The opening of the king's speech at Peter Wilks's house furnishes
example. The king's words are florid, full of spurious rhetoric in the beg
ning, and tinged with illiterate usage. As such they successfully represent
fraudulent confidenceman at work.

> "Friends all, my poor brother that lays yonder, has done
> generous by them that's left behind in the vale of sorrers. He has
> done generous by these-'yer poor little lambs that he loved and shel-
> tered, and that's left fatherless and motherless." (ch. 25)

As the king grows absorbed in his task following these opening lines,
lapses into rich linguistic barbarities, but considering his first words alone,
find that only one important word has been spelled phonetically—sorrers, tl
is, sorrows. The malformation usefully suggests dialect, but there is more to
than that. In context "sorrers" appears among references to friends, brothe

---

[4] "Twain's Method and Theory of Composition," *Modern Philology,* LVI, No
(February, 1959), 176.

ers, and mothers. The inevitable connotation then is to "sister," or "soror." e situation fully supports this apparently gratuitous suggestion, for now y three mourning sisters are left in the Wilks house, Mary Jane, Susan, l Joanna. This house is indeed "a vale of sorrers." Corroborating evidence Mark Twain's interest at this time in etymology occurs a few paragraphs er as the king develops an elaborate etymological explanation of his refer-e to funeral "orgies" rather than "obsequies." "Orgies is better, because it ans the thing you're after, more exact. It's a word that's made up out'n the eek *orgo*, outside, open, abroad; and the Hebrew *jeesum*, to plant, cover ; hence in*ter*. So, you see, funeral orgies is an open er public funeral."[5]

One cannot insist too much on the verbal quality of *Huckleberry Finn.* ten Huck concludes his story by saying,

> But I reckon I got to light out for the Territory ahead of the rest,
> because Aunt Sally she's going to adopt me and sivilize me and
> I can't stand it. I been there before.[6]

ick has of course been in that situation before: not only in deed, but in rds as well. On the first page Huck had told us that

> The Widow Douglas, she took me for her son, and allowed she
> would sivilize me; but it was rough living in the house all the
> time, considering how dismal regular and decent the widow was in
> all her ways; and so when I couldn't stand it no longer, I lit out.

iree terms appear in both passages: "sivilize," "can't stand it," and "light t." Although some of the efforts to make *Huckleberry Finn* a unified book ms strained, here is evidence of significant verbal repetition at the two ex-mes of the book. Such verbal echoes sound repeatedly throughout, crossing d reviving, so that one is always faintly aware of the book's music.[7]

Mark Twain contrived his verbal resonance in a variety of ways. One of

---

[5] Ch. 25. Knowing Twain's propensity for concealed bawdiness, one may easily ke something out of the American slang term "jism" meaning "semen"—see the *ctionary of American Slang,* ed. Harold Wentworth and Stuart B. Flexner (New York, 50). Then there is the joining of the king's two words: *orgojeesum.*

[6] Ch. 43. The title of Wright Morris's book of criticism, *The Territory Ahead,* torts the phrase, making "ahead" qualify "territory" rather than "light out."

[7] Frank Baldanza has suggested that similar thematic and episodic repetitions give ickleberry Finn its coherence. See "The Structure of *Huckleberry Finn,*" *American erature,* XXVII (November, 1955), 347-55.

the simplest has already been indicated: the use of dialectical variati
of familiar words, as in the duet between Huck and Jim. This needs little
pansion, except to point out instances where dialect enlarges a word's pot
tial for multiple meaning. For example, when Jim describes the face of
dead man in the floating house as "gashly," there is an addition to meaning
this dialectal version of "ghastly" (ch. 9). A more extended, virtually surre
istic version of this kind of thing occurs in Mrs. Hotchkiss's monologue
chapter 41. It is based on the observation that the colloquial voice moves
means of partial recapitulation. Repetitions, like kennings, afford the mi
time to work up verbal extensions and variations of the central idea. In t
monologue Mark Twain produces a spasmodic speech which at the same ti
moves the reader through a whirlwind of changes played upon two word
"nigger" (again) and "crazy," plus various aspects of the verbal notation,
says."·

> Well, Sister Phelps, I've ransacked that-air cabin over an' I
> b'lieve the NIGGER was CRAZY. I SAYS so to Sister Damrell—didn't I,
> Sister Damrell?—s'I, he's CRAZY, s'I—them's the very words I SAID.
> You all hearn me; he's CRAZY, s'I; everything shows it, s'I. Look at
> that-air grind-stone, s'I; want to tell *me*'t any cretur 'ts in his right
> mind's agoin' to scrabble all them CRAZY things onto a grindstone, s'I?
> Here sich 'n' sich a person busted his heart; 'n' here so'n' so pegged
> along for thirty-seven years, 'n' all that—natcherl son o' Louis some-
> body, 'n' sich everlast'n rubbage. He's plumb CRAZY, s'I; it's what
> I SAYS in the fust place, it's what I SAYS in the middle, 'n' it's what
> I SAYS last 'n' all the time—the NIGGER'S CRAZY—CRAZY's Nebokood-
> neezer, s'I. (capitals added)

In this amazing verbal display Mrs. Hotchkiss, Huck, and Mark Twain are
very much aware that it is a *said* piece, as the weird repetitions of "s'I," t
claim "them's the very words I said," and near the end the tripartite ins
tence that she, the speaker, has never ceased saying the same thing at any tir
all indicate. Isolated by dashes, Mrs. Hotchkiss's original judgment is triu
phantly reasserted finally—"the nigger's crazy"—and then comes a comic e
plosion of sound, "Nebokoodneezer." This is verbal inventiveness of a ve
high order, for it holds carefully to a realistic line while at the same time
builds, shapes, and orders the words to draw from them their strongest effe
Orthographical distortion was not, as we have seen, original with Ma

ain; he worked out of an established American tradition. But as Bernard
Voto remarked, "The orthography of humor . . . must be distinguished
m the American language. In the misspellings of Artemus Ward and Josh
llings, for instance, there is no attempt to render speech, still less to record
habit or personality of thought, but only to produce the laughter of incon-
iity."[8] Mark Twain is more inventive than that. Nothing could be more
propriate than that a lady of the Bible Belt should call up Nebuchadnezzar,
Babylonian infidel, as a comparison for Jim. Even her mistaken pronuncia-
n has realistic integrity, for "Nebo" was the mountain from which Moses
w the Promised Land, and Mrs. Hotchkiss's confusion of the two Levantine
mes is altogether believable.

This passage also indicates yet another way in *Huckleberry Finn* in
ich the reader's attention was brought to the individual word, its composi-
n, and its relation to the words in company. When one of the criteria for
erary composition is realistic accuracy, then each word is subject to scrutiny
d tested mentally. The good writer, however, tries not to abuse the reader's
ention by forcing it into incessant surface activity, as in the Uncle Remus
ries, whose orthography may be an excellent guide to oral reading, but
ich makes silent reading arduous. He chooses the moments when he will
dge the reader. As Mark Twain well knew, such selectivity generates more
wer than does an overwhelming reproduction of verbal effects.

Again and again we are struck by terms that have an imaginative life of
eir own off the page: "if I could tip her the wink," "now for the grand
lge," "I let go all holts then," "don't you deffersit *me* no more deffersits,
ıg's *you* live," "I knowed better than to move another peg," "we had a long
bble," and "I found him roosting on the bitts, forward" (chs. 29, 39, 33,
, 16, 30, 13). These figurative expressions are like streaks of brilliant color
the narrative stream and they call for our appreciation as well as interpreta-
n.

If emphasis upon the individual word results when dialectically distorted
ords are placed in a familiar context, so does it when familiar words are
ed for unconventional purposes. Slang expressions sometimes work this way,
when Huck says that after the Royal Nonesuch performance he expects that
e audience will give the king "a gaudy time of it" (ch. 23). More often it
Huck's stimulated imagination that produces unexpected and, from a pur-
's point of view, unwarranted combinations of words. Their high imagina-
e order, however, is warrant enough. Running from the graveyard in a

---

[8] *Mark Twain at Work* (Cambridge: Harvard University Press, 1942), p. 93.

thunderstorm, Huck says the lightning occurs in "now-and-then glares" (
29). Or as he is being quizzed by the harelipped girl at the Wilks hou
Huck is asked a particularly pointed question, and remarks, "I see I was u
stump. I had to let on to get choked with a chicken-bone, so as to get time
think how to get down again." After he has painfully worked his way "out
the woods again," he is trapped once more. Then a truncated metaph
emerges, which, although consonant with past remarks, makes an odd a
very distinctive clause: "I see I was up a stump again, so I played anoth
chicken-bone and got another think" (ch. 26). This fanciful verbal structu
gives "think" substance and uses the chicken-bone as if it were a card i
poker game—aptly, since Huck is at this moment gambling.

Mark Twain is usually prepared to invest words with new meanin
Tom Sawyer's description of the coat-of-arms he proposes for Jim is exe
plary. Mark Twain takes words from the terminology of heraldry that ha
only the thinnest patina of meaning for most readers and then lays irreleva
yet pertinent connotations over them. His most successful improvisation
"Crest, a runaway nigger, *sable,* with his bundle over his shoulder on a b
sinister; and a couple of gules for supporters, which is you and me" (ch. 38
Even "gules" (mispronounced) has a phonetic accuracy for the kind of be
who introduce snakes, spiders, and rats into Jim's cabin-prison.

And only acknowledgment of Mark Twain's conscious verbal adroitn
can explain the inventive delirium of Huck's description of where he is
stay while at the Wilks house. There is no strain to it, the diction is co
pletely natural, and yet the combination achieved has a flourish of nonsen
"Up garret," says Huck in a curious initial abbreviation, "was a little cub
with a pallet in it. The king said the cubby would do for his valley—meani
me" (ch. 26).

Mark Twain sets up such play when he can, but he always builds out
his characters' normal diction. The surface of his prose is littered with qu
ore quarried from Huck's mine. A melodeum is "pretty skreeky," a watchm
refuses to be bribed by "spondulicks," Huck "smouches" a spoon, he h
"clayey" clothes, and he notices "shackly" houses; he speaks of an underta
er's "softy soothering ways," and to him a thunder clap is a "sockdolage
Colonel Grangerford is said to have no "frivolishness" about him; and anoth
man has a "startlish" way; after the duke "hove a sigh," the king inquir
what he was "alassing about"; and when an imaginary horse-ferry bump
real steamboat wreck, Huck describes the action by saying it "saddlebaggse
on the wreck; he guts a catfish by "haggling" it open with a saw; and fina

says that a certain surprise would make "most anybody sqush," by which
means "squshed down like a bluff bank that the river has cut under" (chs.
13, 37, 2, 21, 27, 20, 18, 13, 19, 13, 8, 29).

The effect of these words—dialect, nonce, slang—is that of poetry. Car-
ıg expository meaning, they flash out with a light unique for prose. They
employed less to build an effect cumulatively, more to make an effect
nediately. And they contribute to the gradually accumulating feeling in
ıerican literature for the importance of the single word, for verbal indepen-
ce.

Huck's grammatical mistakes also serve to re-enforce potentially flat
ements. The melodious jar of incorrect grammar catches the reader in "I
n there before," and "There set pap—his own self!" (chs. 43, 4). Both
significantly the last words of chapters. The formulation of the past tense
a present base increases the sense of immediacy. "We catched a little sec-
ı of a lumber-raft," and "I'd got to decide, forever, betwixt two things,
l I knowed it" (chs. 9, 31). Mark Twain augmented the life that he de-
:d from fresh diction by means of syntactical manipulation not very differ-
in kind from James's. Mark Twain's initial desire was, as always, to ap-
ximate the accents of the speaking voice in prose. He then refined the con-
.tions he had established, especially when they heightened a dramatic point.
ıile Huck's pap is sleeping off an attack of delirium tremens, Huck sits
vn with a gun "to wait for him to stir." With that tableau the chapter ends
he father (who has already tried to kill his son with a clasp-knife) resting
he can finish the job; the boy watching, with a loaded gun pointed at his
ıer. Huck's comment finishes the chapter: "And how slow and still the
e did drag along" (ch. 6). The ticking one-syllable units of this sentence,
h its periphrastic verb maintaining the rhythm, mark the heavy pulse beat
Huck's shocked sensibility. At the same time the monotony of the iambic
thm expresses Huck's growing fatigue, and when the next chapter begins
" 'Git up! What you 'bout!' "—Huck is discovered asleep.

Earlier I pointed out that by using radical punctuation Henry James died his sentence into a series of spasmodic units. I suggested that this tech-
ue was derived from an attempt to reproduce the way a mind thinks.
ıes's concern for psychological imitation determined the punctuation of
; typical sentence: "With time, actually—for the impression but deepened
his sense of the contrast, to the advantage of Merton Densher, became a
se of relief, and that, in turn, a sense of escape" (ch. 30). A similar divi-
eness or fragmenting tendency appears in Mark Twain. His prose atten-

tively marks each block of perception rather than blending them all int‹
fluid, synthetic compound. Huck's vision, that is, is direct and linear. Unl‹
say, Dos Passos' impressionistically flooded Camera Eye, Huck moves delil
ately from object to object and detail to detail and his report of what he s
is rarely impeded by reflective considerations. The objects are enumerated
lists, lists not punctuated solely by the discreet turn of a comma at the base
the line, but by a chain of co-ordinating conjunctions. Huck's images, lik
series of slides thrown upon a screen, come into focus in a succession of ‹
lated moments. He observes, for example, that the gardens of Arkansas
pear to contain only

> jimpsom weeds, and sunflowers, and ash-piles, and old curled-
> up boots and shoes, and pieces of bottles, and rags, and played-out
> tin-ware. (ch. 21)

The peculiar vividness of these objects, these *words,* is due in part to w‹
they are and in part to how they are presented. They follow one another, ‹
disturbed by commentary, indignation, uplift, or disgust. Without the med
tion of "and" such lists would create a more confused and jumbled impressi‹

> jimpsom weeds, sunflowers, ash-piles, old curled-up boots and
> shoes, pieces of bottles, rags, and played-out tin-ware.

That has the frenetic sound of a Dickens catalogue. With the "ands" in pla
each object emerges clearly as if Huck were again contemplating them one
a time. True, Mark Twain the writer makes an implicit judgment of the ‹
kansas householders when he enumerates the contents of their gardens, ‹
Huck only sees. He is one kind of a camera.

THE ENDING OF *HUCKLEBERRY FINN**

James M. Cox

begin with, the ending is, to use Huck's term, uncomfortable. The prob-
m is to define the source of this discomfort. Without question, there is a
ange when Tom Sawyer reappears. The narrative movement changes from
e of adventure to burlesque—a burlesque which, in place of Huck's sincere
t helpless involvement in freeing a real slave, puts Tom Sawyer's relatively
el yet successful lark of freeing a slave already free. It is not Mark Twain's
lure to distinguish between the two actions which jeopardizes his book;
her, it is his ironic exposure of Tom's action which threatens the humor of
e book and produces the inharmonious burlesque De Voto regrets. Tom ap-
ars in such an unfortunate light in the closing pages that many readers of
uckleberry Finn can never again read *Tom Sawyer* without in one way or
other holding Tom responsible for motives he had not had in the earlier
ok.

Tom's play seems unpardonable because he already knows that Jim is
e. Yet this knowledge—which Tom withholds from Huck—finally clears up
r Huck the mystery of Tom's behavior toward him. Upon at last discovering
e knowledge Tom has withheld from him, Huck, who has been troubled by
om's "badness," at last understands why his respectable companion has been
le to commit such a crime. His only remaining problem is to find out why
om spent so much effort "setting a free nigger free." This, too, is cleared up
en Tom explains to the long-suffering Aunt Sally that he made his elabo-
te and vexing arrangements purely for "adventure."

Tom's adventures are a unique cruelty in a book which depicts so much
uelty. All the other cruelties are committed for some "reason"—for honor,
oney, or power. But Tom's cruelty has a purity all its own—it is done solely
r the sake of adventure. After facing Tom's long play, it is possible to see
uck's famous remark about the King and the Duke in a larger perspective.
Human beings can be awful cruel to each other," Huck had said upon seeing
e scoundrels ridden out of town on a rail. This statement not only points

---

* *Mark Twain: The Fate of Humor* (Princeton: Princeton University Press, 1966),
. 174-184. Footnotes renumbered.

backward to the episodes with the King and the Duke, but serves as a gatew
leading from the King and the Duke's departure to Tom Sawyer's perf
mance. For Tom's pure play runs directly counter to a wish the journey |
generated. That is the frustration of the ending—the inversion. Having |
Huck's slow discovery of Jim's humanity, the reader perforce deplores To
casual ignorance and unawareness.

Yet the judgment which the last ten chapters render upon Tom is sur
the judgment rendered upon the moral sentiment on which the book has r
den. If the reader sees in Tom's performance a rather shabby and safe bit
play, he is seeing no more than the exposure of the approval with which
watched Huck operate. For if Tom is rather contemptibly setting a free sla
free, what after all is the reader doing, who begins the book after the *fact*
the Civil War? This is the "joke" of the book—the moment when, in out
geous burlesque, it attacks the sentiment which its style has at once evok
and exploited. To see that Tom is doing at the ending what we have be
doing throughout the book is essential to understanding what the book |
meant to us. For when Tom proclaims to the assembled throng who have w
nessed his performance that Jim "is as free as any cretur that walks t
earth," he is an exposed embodiment of the complacent moral sentiment
which the reader has relied throughout the book. And to the extent the read
has indulged the complacency he will be disturbed by the ending.

To be frustrated by the ending is to begin to discover the meaning
this journey, which evokes so much indulgence and moral approval that |
censor is put to sleep. Beneath the sleeping censor, the real rebellion of *Hu
leberry Finn* is enacted. For there must be a real rebellion—a rebellion whi
cannot so easily be afforded—else Mark Twain is guilty of a failure |
greater than the ending. If the "incorrect" vernacular of *Huckleberry Finn*
to be more than décor, it must enact an equally "incorrect" vision. Otherwi
the style becomes merely a way of saying rather than a way of being. It is r
simply the "poetry" or "beauty" or "rhythm" of Huck's vernacular whi
makes his language work, but the presence of a commensurate vernacular
sion. The reason that imitators of *Huckleberry Finn* fail—the reason that Ma
Twain himself later failed—is that they lack the vision to match their sty
and thus their language is merely décor. One has but to read Edgar Lee M
ters' *Mitch Miller*—which is a "modern" attempt to show what the childho
of Huck and Tom was really like—to know how sentimental such langua
can be unless it is sustained by a genuinely radical vision. Even Sherwood A
derson's "I Want to Know Why," in many ways the finest example of verna

r vision directly derivative from *Huckleberry Finn,* falls far short of Mark
ain, because its end, though finely climactic, is unfortunately sentimental.
e young boy's anguished appeal upon discovering the Jockey with the
ore is, after all, just the same old truth we knew all the time.

What then *is* the rebellion of *Huckleberry Finn?* What is it but an at-
k upon the conscience? The conscience, after all is said and done, is the
l tyrant in the book. It is the relentless force which pursues Huckleberry
n; it is the tyrant from which he seeks freedom. And it is not only the
ial conscience which threatens Huck, but *any* conscience. The social con-
nce, represented in the book by the slaveholding society of the Old South,
easily seen and exposed. It is the false conscience. But what of the true
science which the reader wishes to project upon Huck and which Huck
nself is at last on the threshold of accepting? It, too, is finally false. Al-
ugh the book plays upon the notion that all conscience is finally social, it
es not stand on that line; for the action is not defining the conscience so
ach as rejecting it. Whether the conscience is "lower" social conscience or
"higher" inner conscience, it remains the tyrant which drives its victims
o the absurd corners from which they cannot escape. Thus on the one hand,
re is the "law" or "right" of slavery from which Jim is trying to escape
d against which Huck finds himself in helpless rebellion. But there are then
"inner" codes which appear as equally absurd distortions. There is Pap's
lief in freedom; there is the code of the feud which the Grangerfords and
epherdsons hold to; there is the "honor" of Colonel Sherburn; and finally
re is the "principle" of Tom Sawyer who rises proudly to the defense of
n because he "is as free as any cretur that walks this earth." In every case
conscience, whether it comes from society or from some apparent inner
lm, is an agent of aggression—aggression against the self or against an-
er. Either the means or the excuse by which pain is inflicted, the conscience
both law and duty, erasing the possibility of choice and thereby constrain-
g its victims to a necessary and irrevocable course of action.

From the "Southern" conscience, Huck first attempts to flee. But even in
ght from it, borne southward on the great river, his "Northern" conscience
gins to awaken. This is the apparently internal conscience—the Civil War
finds himself engaged in on the raft as it glides deeper and deeper into the
rritory of slavery, not of freedom. Our moral sentiment approves his flight
om his Southern conscience, but with the approval comes the hope that he
ll discover his Northern conscience. But it is just here that Huck will not
cept the invitation. For chapter after chapter he remains the fugitive—in

flight from the old conscience and evading the development of a new one.

And the reason he evades it is clear—the conscience is *uncomfortab* Indeed, comfort and satisfaction are the value terms in *Huckleberry Fir* Freedom for Huck is not realized in terms of political liberty but in terms pleasure. Thus his famous pronouncement about life on the raft: "Otl places do seem so cramped and smothery, but a raft don't. You feel migl free and easy and comfortable on a raft."[1] And later, when the King and t Duke threaten to break the peace, Huck determines not to take a stand agaii them, observing, "What you want above all things, on a raft, is for everybo to be satisfied, and feel right and kind toward the others."[2] In almost eve instance Huck projects the good life in terms of ease, satisfaction, comfort. satirist would see it in terms of justice; a moralist would have it as a place righteousness. But a humorist envisions it as a place of good feeling, whe no pain or discomfort can enter. This is why Huck does not see clothes, whi figure so prominently as the garments of civilization, as veils to hide the boc or as the false dress whereby a fiction of status is maintained. This would the satiric vision. As far as Huck is concerned, clothes and civilization itse are undesirable because they are essentially *uncomfortable*. "But I reckon got to light out for the territory," he says as he departs, "because Aunt Sa. she's going to adopt me and sivilize me, and I can't stand it."[3] When Hu says he "can't stand it," he is literally referring to the cramped discomfort submitting to the clothes and quarters of civilization. To be sure, the phra suggests a vastly wider range of significances, but significances that are inexc ably rooted in a logic of feeling, comfort, and bodily satisfaction. The sign. icances are *our* discoveries, which are at once made possible by and anchor to the concrete image of the raft, the boy, and the Negro. The good feelin comfort, and ease dominating this journey which makes its way through a s ciety of meanness, cowardice, and cruelty are perfectly embodied by the ra adrift upon the river.

This logic of pleasure at the heart of the book must also be at the hea of any "positive" value we may wish to ascribe to the experience of readi it. Most criticism of *Huckleberry Finn*, however, retreats from the pleasu

---

[1] *Writings*, XIII, 162. The conscience, on the other hand, is the source of discomfo As Huck says, ". . . it don't make no difference whether you do right or wrong, a po son's conscience ain't got no sense, and just goes for him *anyway*. If I had a yeller d that didn't know no more than a person's conscience does I would pison him" (*Writing* XIII, 321).

[2] *Ibid.*, p. 174.

[3] *Ibid.*, p. 405.

rinciple toward the relative safety of "moral issues" and the imperatives of
ṭe Northern conscience. This flight is made because of the uncomfortable
ẹeling relating to Huck's "evasion," his "escape," and finally his "rejection"
f civilization. What Huck is rejecting is, of course, the conscience—which
Ḷark Twain was later to rail at under the name of the "Moral Sense." The
ọnscience, the trap of adult civilization which lies in wait for Huck through-
ụt the novel, is what he is at such pains to evade. It is his successful evasion
·hich we as readers cannot finally face. The reader who rejects the paradox
ṣually does so on the grounds that the book is "just" a humorous book. The
ṇe who detects and is disturbed by it is more likely to follow William Van
)'Connor's pronouncements about the "dangers" of innocence and the "fail-
ṛe" of moral vision. A weakness in Huck—pontificates O'Connor in his at-
ẹmpt to prove that the book is *not* a great American novel—is that he does
ọt "acknowledge the virtues of civilization and live, as one must, inside it."[4]
Ḷuck does acknowledge the virtues, of course, and upbraids himself for being
ncomfortable with them.

But far from relying upon such cozy affirmations as O'Connor longs for,
ḥe book moves *down* the river into the deeper repressions of slavery, enact-
ṇg at every moment a conversion of morality into pleasure. Extending the
ạnge of humor through the ills, the agonies, and the cruelties of civilization,
t shows how much the conscience—whether Northern or Southern—is the
ṇegative force leading to acts of violence upon the self or upon another.
Ḷuck's "escape" is of course an escape from violence, a rejection of cruelty
—his instinct is neither to give nor to receive pain if he can avoid it.

The prime danger to his identity comes at the moment he chooses the
ḍeveloping inner or Northern conscience. This moment, when Huck says
·All right, then, I'll *go* to hell," is characteristically the moment we fatally
ụpprove, and approve *morally*. But it is with equal fatality the moment at
·hich Huck's identity is most precariously threatened. In the very act of
ċhoosing to go to hell he has surrendered to the notion of a *principle* of right
ạnd wrong. He has forsaken the world of pleasure to make a moral choice.
Ṛrecisely here is where Huck is about to negate himself—where, with an act
ọf positive virtue, he actually commits himself to play the role of Tom Sawyer
·hich he *has* to assume in the closing section of the book. To commit oneself
ṭo the idea, the *morality* of freeing Jim, is to become Tom Sawyer. Here again

---

[4] William Van O'Connor, "Why *Huckleberry Finn* Is Not The Great American
Novel," *College English*, XVII (October, 1955), p. 8.

is the irony of the book, and the ending, far from evading the consequence of Huck's act of rebellion, realizes those consequences.

Mark Twain's real problem—his real dilemma—was not at all his inability to "face" the issues of slavery; certainly it was not a fear of the society or a failure of moral and political courage which brought Mark Twain to the tight place where Huck had to decide forever and ever. Rather, it was the necessities of his humorous form. For in order to achieve expression of the deep wish which *Huckleberry Finn* embodies—the wish for freedom from any conscience—Mark Twain had to intensify the moral sentiment. The moment there is any real moral doubt about Huck's action, the wish will be threatened. Yet when Huck makes his moral affirmation, he fatally negates the wish for freedom from the conscience; for if his affirmation frees him from the Southern conscience, it binds him to his Northern conscience. No longer an outcast, he can be welcomed into the society to play the role of Tom Sawyer, which is precisely what happens. When he submits to Tom's role, we are the ones who become uncomfortable. The entire burlesque ending is a revenge upon the moral sentiment which, though it shielded the humor, ultimately threatened Huck's identity.

This is the larger reality of the ending—what we may call the necessity of the form. That it was a cost which the form exacted no one would deny. But to call it a failure, a piece of moral cowardice, is to miss the true rebellion of the book, for the disturbance of the ending is nothing less than our and Mark Twain's recognition of the full meaning of *Huckleberry Finn*. If the reader is pushed to the limits of his humor, Mark Twain had reached the limits of his—he had seen through to the end. The disillusion begins not when Tom returns to the stage, but when Huck says "All right, then, I'll go to hell"—when our applause and approval reach their zenith. At that moment, which anyone would agree is Mark Twain's highest achievement, Huck has internalized the image of Jim; and that image, whose reality he has enjoyed during the fatal drift downstream, becomes the scourge which shames him out of his evasion. The whole process is disclosed in the lyric utterance leading to his decision. Having written the note to Miss Watson telling where Jim is, Huck feels cleansed and at last able to pray:

> But I didn't do it straight off, but laid the paper down and set there thinking—thinking how good it was all this happened so, and how near I come to being lost and going to hell. And went on thinking. And got to thinking over our trip down the river; and I

see Jim before me all the time: in the day and in the night-time, sometimes moonlight, sometimes storms, and we a-floating along, talking and singing and laughing. But somehow I couldn't seem to strike no places to harden me against him, but only the other kind. I'd see him standing my watch on top of his'n, 'stead of calling me, so I could go on sleeping; and see him how glad he was when I come back out of the fog; and when I come to him again in the swamp, up there where the feud was; and such-like times; and would always call me honey, and pet me, and do everything he could think of for me, and how good he always was; and at last I struck the time I saved him by telling the men we had smallpox aboard, and he was so grateful, and said I was the best friend old Jim ever had in the world, and the *only* one he's got now; and then I happened to look around and see that paper.

It was a close place.[5]

This lyrical rehearsal of the journey is also the journey's end. And the decision which ends it is cast in the positive locution of Tom Sawyer, not in Huck's essentially negative vernacular.[6] When Huck says he will go to hell, in five minutes of reading time he is there. For in this novel, which constantly plays against superstitious hereafters, there is no fire-and-brimstone hell but only civilization—which is precisely where Huck finds himself as a consequence of his own determination.

This dilemma and disillusion are what Mark Twain would not shrink from, but carried through, though it cost him almost everything—which is saying it cost him his good humor. In the burlesque chapters, he understandably though precariously turned upon his invention, upon his reader, and upon himself. Yet even here he did not entirely abandon the pleasure principle, but left his "serious" readers pleased with themselves instead of the book, their moral complacency ruffled by nothing more than comfortable indignation at the evasions of humor.

As for Mark Twain, he had seen through to the end, and it almost

---

[5] *Writings,* XIII, 296-97. Although Huck's language constantly describes his feelings and thoughts, they are so directly wedded to external action and dependent on it that he seems to have no independent "thought." This passage is the only extended narrative of such an inner life. Once the decision is made, he hardly reflects upon his past. If he remembers, he keeps it to himself.

[6] Huck's most characteristic errors of grammar are, significantly enough, his constant use of the double negative and his persistent confusion of verb tense.

killed him. He never would have so good a humor again. His despair, havin
set in at the moment of Huckleberry Finn's affirmation, never really let u
The only way he could survive was to try to swallow the joke which becam
more and more sour the rest of his embattled way. Having seen the limits o
his humor, he turned upon them and railed at the conscience and the need fo
self-approval, the twin human characteristics which seemed to make th
human race utterly ridiculous and damned.

And what of Huck? As Nick Carraway said of Gatsby, he came out a
right. He went to the territory because he was true to himself and to his crea
tor. He didn't go there to lead civilization either, but to play outside it. Refus
ing to grow up and tell the lie of the conscience, he left behind him a nove
for all time. It was truly a novel of reconstruction. First, it had brought int
fiction not the Old South but an entirely new one which the northern con
science could welcome back into the Union. And in the process of its humo
it reconstructed the psyche, following the pleasure principle as far as it woul
go to discover in the southern reaches of the Great River the tyranny of th
conscience which keeps the adult in chains and makes his pleasure the enact
ment of greater and greater cruelty. He had not reached childhood's end, bu
had disclosed the lie of the adult world. In his last moment he said, "so ther
ain't nothing more to write about, and I am rotten glad of it, because if I'
'a'knowed what a trouble it was to make a book I wouldn't 'a'tackled it, an
ain't a-going to no more." We of course constantly lecture Mark Twain abou
having turned away from his true vein of ore. The fact is, however, that h
could not turn away but kept trying to do just what we want of him. He kep
trying to call Huck back to tell another story. But Huck, though he came doc
ilely, could never tell the truth. He had told all the truth he had to tell in on
glorious lie.

FROM *HARVESTS OF CHANGE:*
*AMERICAN LITERATURE 1865-1914**

Jay Martin

'oward the end of *Life on the Mississippi* Twain found in Hannibal a strik-
ag symbol of the simultaneity of past and present. "I woke up every morn-
ag," he writes, "with the impression that I was a boy—for in my dreams the
aces were all young again, and looked as they had looked in the old times."
timulated momentarily into a blissful dream of youth—and so declaring the
ontinued possibility of a free existence—he daily watched his dream dissolve
a reality. "But I went to bed," he immediately adds, "a hundred years old,
very night—for meantime I had been seeing those faces as they are now." In
Iannibal he found realized his own diverse allegiances: to youth and adult-
iood, to nature and technocracy, to the free creature as well as to the astute
iusinessman, to the loving husband and father and to the professional scrib-
ler of books—to the Huck Finn that he admired and to the Tom Sawyer
whom he resembled.

The hero of *The Adventures of Huckleberry Finn* (1885) shares with
Twain his richly ambiguous personality, even in name. While Huck's surname
vas derived, appropriately, from the actual Hannibal town drunkard, Jimmy
Finn, "Huckleberry" is the name of a fruit strictly New England in origin,
one Twain had not seen in the West.[1] Like Twain himself, Huck is both the
inarchical Westerner and the conservative New Englander. In the fictive time
which elapsed between *Tom Sawyer* and this novel, Huck's character has
shifted. Under the supervision of the widow Douglas and Miss Watson, he
1as begun to absorb and assume the conventions of his society. He has become
1is own Tom Sawyer. No longer "conscience-free," he finds, in the course of
:he novel, that his conscience follows him like a "yaller dog," as theirs had
earlier pursued Tom and Joe. Drawn into acquisitive society by his accidental

---

* *Harvests of Change: American Literature 1865-1914* (Englewood Cliffs, Prentice-
Hall, Inc., 1967), pp. 190-193.
[1] Rose Terry Cooke, who was intimate with the Twichell family and whose stories—
particularly "Freedom Wheeler's Controversy with Providence"—Twain admired, named
her last collection of tales *Huckleberries: Gathered from New England Hills,* explaining:
"I have called this latest collection of New England stories by the name of a wild berry
that has always seemed to me typical of the New England character."

acquisition of wealth at the end of *Tom Sawyer,* his problem is how to r achieve and retain his earlier Adamic state.

In this novel, then, the pressure of society is all the more imperativ Huck learns both Presbyterian and Methodist versions of Heaven and Hell; i a slaveholding house he absorbs the assumptions of slavery. In school h learns to spell, read, and write; he wears new clothes and sleeps in a bed. I short, after three or four months, Huck finds that although

> I liked the old ways best, . . . I was getting so I liked the new
> ones, too, a little bit. The widow said I was coming along slow but
> sure, and doing very satisfactory. She said she wasn't ashamed of
> me.

Tom, too—now even more obsessed than earlier with chivalric fancies—initi ates Huck into the rituals of romance. As slavishly as others follow the forma rules of Christian culture, Tom relies upon his "pirate books . . . and robbe books" for their unimpeachable (though frequently incomprehensible) code of behavior. Still being shaped by this environment, Huck begins to be af fected by both Christianity and romance: on the one hand he prays; on th other, he attempts to raise a genie by rubbing an old tin lamp. But when shortly, Pap arrives and forces Huck to live with him, he soon reverts, ostensi bly, to his conscience-free existence.

Nevertheless, the impressions exerted on him by culture, howeve briefly, have altered the state of his mind. Now that he is no longer the inno cent his only alternative to social acquiescence, we are made to realize, is to become bestial and brutal like Pap. Unless he is innocent he cannot escape society without degradation. His father, for instance, although alienated from society, a vagrant and a hopeless drunk, still carries with him a guilt-ridden conscience and a full measure of social prejudices. His delirious hallucination of the Angel of Death and his disquisition on the free Negro able to vote show him to be, in his ignorance, not free from society, but merely the lowest, most vicious form of it. Now tainted with convention like Pap, and invested with a conscience, Huck, the innocent of *Tom Sawyer,* threatens to sink into barbarianism in *Huckleberry Finn.* In *Roughing It* and *Following the Equator* Twain described how, touched by the knowledge of good and evil—the civi- lizing effect of Christian missionaries—the noble Hawaiian islanders soon dis- integrated into a shiftless, diseased, ignoble, rapidly dying race. Huck stands perilously on the edge of a similar transformation.

His salvation comes, of course, through Jim. A slave, and therefore ever a part of the dominant conventional society, Jim revives in Huck an immediacy of response to nature—a response outer and inner—undistorted by stereotyped social patterns of belief or action. Terrorized in slavery by the vagaries of the white society over which he has no control—his ultimate terror of being sold down the river—Jim is, in society, merely the grotesque darky who tells tall tales for psychic self-protection. But when he is free upon the river, Jim becomes, as Daniel G. Hoffman has written, "a magus, . . . a magician in sympathetic converse with the spirits that govern—often by malice or caprice—the world of things and men."[2] Helplessly impotent as magician and prophet in the slave huts, he becomes an infallible guide in the natural world. For the brutal, half-civilized father Huck has lost, he is given a surrogate in Jim. (It is Jim, significantly, who finds and conceals Pap's body.) Continuing the theme of initiation from the first part of *Life On the Mississippi,* in his novel Twain removed all traces of the technology that threatened joyous life in the second part of that book by substituting, in this new fable, a raft for the steamboat, Jim for the river-wise pilot, and Huck for the cub who has run away from home. The child and savage drive through the adult, civilized mask. By the conclusion of the novel Twain has understood society through Huck and Jim in ways that he could not understand it in his own person in *Life on the Mississippi.* And in this respect *Huckleberry Finn* is a more nearly perfect *Life on the Mississippi.*

But their river remains an Eden infested with serpents. Ever touched and invaded by the life of the shore, it provides only moments of true freedom. Tricked by nature, Huck and Jim drift past Cairo, Illinois, in a fog and so lose their opportunity to mount the Ohio to freedom. Once their chance for freedom is lost, they are immediately beset by the serpents of civilization. The troublesome conscience which Huck has acquired now asserts itself. At Jim's joy over the likelihood of literal freedom, Huck meditates:

> He *was* most free—and who was to blame for it? Why, *me*. I couldn't get that out of my conscience, no how nor no way. . . . It hadn't ever come home to me before, what this thing was that I was doing. But now it did; and it staid with me, and scorched me more and more. I tried to make out to myself *I* warn't to blame . . . but it warn't no use.

---

[2] *Form and Fable in American Fiction* (New York, 1961), p. 332.

THE ART OF HUCKLEBERRY FINN **557**

Driven by conscience, Huck prepares to betray Jim by paddling ashore. F
fails because, he says significantly, "I warn't man enough." Rather, he is chi
enough to follow his natural impulses.

Immediately thereafter civilization reenters upon the river even mo
ominously: a steamboat runs over their raft and drives Huck to shore. Th
Shepherdson-Grangerford feud that Huck witnesses there and, later, Colon
Sherburne's murder of Boggs and the deception of the Wilks girls presei
Huck with testaments concerning the essential brutality of a society that pr
tends to be chivalric, law-abiding, and Christian. Jim, shaman of nature,
subjugated and replaced by the Duke and Dauphin, who, assuming a sequenc
of disguises, duping an ignorant and degraded populace, are the magicians c
civilization. Pretending to be exiled royalty, repeating the chivalric formula
playing heroic scenes from Shakespeare, disguising Jim as an Arab, or playin
a multiplicity of other fantastic roles, these two are adult versions of Tor
Sawyer, refashioning his romantic fantasies as devices in their confidenc
game.

Huck, too, assumes disguises, chiefly of a protective variety, the natura
expression of his fear of discovery by society. Nowhere are his psychic fear
better demonstrated than in the roles he spontaneously assumes. In all of h
deceptions he imagines his isolation. As "Sarah Williams" ("my father an
mother was dead, and the law had bound me out to a mean old farmer, . . . so
. . . cleared out"); in his tale of the shipwreck and disaster of the *Walte
Scott* to the ferryboatman; in the account of his family tragedy to the Grang
erfords ("my sister Mary Ann run off and got married and never was hear
of no more, and Bill went to hunt them and he warn't heard of no more, an
Tom and Mort died, and then there warn't nobody but just me and Pap lefi
and he was just trimmed down to nothing . . . so when he died I took wha
there was left, . . . started up the river, . . . and fell overboard, and that wa
how I come to be here"); with the King and the Duke ("my folks was livin
in Pike County, in Missouri, . . . and they all died off but me and pa and m
brother")—in all of these he naturally hints, in the kind of masks he assumes
at his fears about his own alienation and death. Unlike the deceptions of th
confidence men, these guises are the spontaneous, unconscious expression o
his essential being. Of the tales he tells, he himself says: "I went right along
. . . just trusting to Providence [i.e., intuition] to put the right words in m
mouth, . . . for I'd noticed that Providence always did put the right words in
my mouth, if I let it alone."

Thus conceiving of himself as a spy in society, he can pierce the ultimate ɹise of conventional society itself—the notion of slavery and the mask of ɔlor that veneer Jim's essential manhood. Thus he can learn that Jim is white inside." Surrendering only for a moment to his social conscience in his ɹtimate moral self-confrontation, Huck finally decides: "All right, then, I'll ɔ to hell," and sets out to free Jim. Heroically accepting the alienation from ɔciety that he so deeply fears, he resolves to follow the impulses of intuition. J. H. Auden well calls this a pure act of "moral improvisation."[3] But in turning to the shore Huck is once more immersed in social convention. Alɹough he has resolved to be an outlaw in a literal sense, he is mistaken by ɹunt Sally, in the book's sternest irony, for Tom Sawyer. True to his final ɹentity, he plays out the mannered "Evasion" of setting Jim free according to ɹe conventional plot of romantic escape. He identifies as wholly with his new ɹle as with his earlier ones, and reassumes the mores of the shore. Explaining ɹ Aunt Sally why he is late, for instance, he says:

> ". . . We blowed out a cylinder-head."
> "Good gracious! Anybody hurt?"
> "No'm. Killed a nigger."
> "Well, it's lucky; because sometimes people do get hurt."

ɹp to the end of the book he remains Tom Sawyer. Only at the very end, ith the Evasion concluded happily within social convention, is he free from ɹis role and able to "light out for the territory ahead of the rest," where he ɔpes thenceforth to be free from civilization. On the river or in the territory, ɹe know, Huck can never return into the Eden of innocence; even if the Tom ɹawyers of the world did not pursue him, he carries his sense of them within ɹim. It is appropriate, then, that the numbers of *The Century* that serialized *ʻuckleberry Finn* also carried Thomas Nelson Page's idealization of the slaveɔlding Old Dominion, "Marse Chan."

---

[3] "Huck and Oliver" in *Mark Twain: A Collection of Critical Essays,* ed. Henry ʻash Smith (Englewood Cliffs, N.J., 1963), pp. 113-114.

QUESTIONS

||||||||||||||||||||||||||||||||||||||||||||||||||||||||||||||||||||||||||||||||||||||||||||||||||||||||||||||||||||||||||||||||||||||||||||||||||||||||||||

1. (A) What are Brander Matthews' criteria for excellence in fiction, ar
   how does Twain's novel measure up to them? (B) Are the criteria goo
   ones? Why or why not?

2. (A) Is Trilling interested in the form of the novel only, in the conter
   of the novel only, or in both? Cite support for your answer in his discu
   sion. (B) Part 3 of Trilling's essay deals chiefly with *Huckleberry Fin*
   in relation to "the American Myth." Using other source materials [a goo
   start might be F. I. Carpenter, " 'The American Myth': Paradise (to be
   Regained," *Publications of the Modern Language Association,* LXXI
   (December, 1959), pp. 599-606], expand and elaborate Trilling's ideas.

3. (A) O'Connor complains (paragraph 7) about the alternation of seriou
   and comic episodes in *Huckleberry Finn.* What is his assumption concern
   ing a great novel? Attack or support this assumption. (B) What othe
   adverse criticisms does O'Connor offer? Attack or support these, citin
   relevent passages in the novel. (C) Does O'Connor find any excellence
   in the book?

4. (A) Baldanza believes that Mark Twain gave *Huck* its rhythmic structur
   "without advance planning, and spurred by momentary impulses." See i
   the library *Mark Twain to Mrs. Fairbanks,* pp. 226-227, and *The Lov*
   Letters of Mark Twain, pp. 165-166, for evidence that the structuring ma
   have been conscious. If these statements by the author are relevant, wh
   values did Twain ascribe to the repetitions with variations? Was he co
   rect? (B) What values does Baldanza believe they have? Is he correct

5. (A) What does Boggan claim is Huck's attitude toward orthodox Christ
   anity? Support or counter his argument by discussing relevant passages. (B
   (1) Relate Boggan's concern about Huck's shifting attitudes toward He
   to Baldanza's theory about repetitions and variations in structure. (2) R
   late Boggan's statement that when Huck decides to go to Hell the reade
   "is being lured into a stock response" to Cox's claim that the Evasion s
   quence is a joke on the reader (Question 8 below). (C) Although Bogga
   and Martin quote the identical passage about "Providence," one assume
   that Providence is God and the other that it is "instinct." Which critic
   correct? Why?

6. (A) How does Sydney J. Krause argue that a "brilliantly developmental s

quence . . . is staged" in Chapters XV and XVI? (B) Why does Krause believe that Huck's struggle and decision in Chapter XXXI mark the youth's additional progress? (C) Compare and contrast Krause's interpretation with those of Boggan and Martin, and argue for your preference among these three.

(A) How do Richard Bridgman's concerns and methods of studying *Huckleberry Finn* differ from those of other critics whom you have read? (B) Discuss the comparative merits of his procedures and those of other critics. (C) If Bridgman's claims are correct, passages in the novel other than those which he cites might be used to support them. Can such passages be found? If so, demonstrate; if not, indicate why not.

(A) Cox states that "Huck projects the good life in terms of ease, satisfaction, comfort. A satirist would see it in terms of justice; a moralist would have it as a place of righteousness. But a humorist envisions it as a place of good feeling, where no pain or discomfort can enter" (p. 550). Using the entire novel, argue for or against the thesis that Mark Twain's purpose was satiric or moralistic rather than humorous, in the terms of this quotation. (B) Cox discusses the Evasion sequence as a "joke" upon the reader (p. 548). Formulate a lengthier statement, either attacking or supporting this theory, on the basis of your own response to the main sections of the novel.

(A) Using Martin's summary of the events of *Huckleberry Finn* as a starting point, discuss Huck's personality as it is evidenced in (1) his idea of himself as a "child," (2) his use of disguises, and (3) his "notion of slavery." (B) Compare and contrast Cox's and Martin's interpretations of the significance of Huck's "conscience."

B BLANK   =   2
lims i-01'   =   6
T PP   = 566   INCLUDES 5 BLANKS AT BACK
NUMBERED PP   =   2
EN PP 22 + 23   _____
                         576   TOTAL PAGES